Our Final Warning

Six Degrees of Climate Emergency

Mark Lynas

4th ESTATE • London

4th Estate
An imprint of HarperCollins*Publishers*
1 London Bridge Street
London SE1 9GF

www.4thEstate.co.uk

First published in Great Britain in 2020 by 4th Estate

1

A catalogue record for this book is
available from the British Library

ISBN 978-0-00-830855-1 (hardback)
ISBN 978-0-00-830856-8 (trade paperback)

Set in Minion Pro
Printed and bound in Great Britain by
CPI Group (UK) Ltd, Croydon

MIX
Paper from
responsible sources
FSC™ C007454
www.fsc.org

This book is produced from independently certified FSC™ paper
to ensure responsible forest management.

For more information visit: www.harpercollins.co.uk/green

IN MEMORIAM

Paul and Joan Rimmer
Together again

Contents

Foreword

When I started writing this book I thought that we could probably survive climate change. Now I am not so sure. As you will read in these pages, we are already living in a world one degree warmer than that inhabited by our parents and grandparents. Two degrees Celsius, which will stress human societies and destroy many natural ecosystems such as rainforests and coral reefs, looms on the near horizon. At three degrees I now believe that the stability of human civilisation will be seriously imperilled, while at four degrees a full-scale global collapse of human societies is probable, accompanied by a mass extinction of the biosphere that will be the worst on Earth for tens or even hundreds of millions of years. By five degrees we will see massive positive feedbacks coming into play, driving further warming and climate impacts so extreme that they will leave most of the globe biologically uninhabitable, with humans reduced to a precarious existence in small refuges. At six degrees we risk triggering a runaway warming process that could render the biosphere completely extinct and for ever destroy the capacity of this planet to support life.

In the UN Paris Agreement signed in 2015, world leaders vowed to hold global temperature rise at 1.5°C, or, failing that, 2°C. So far they have entirely failed to keep their promises. To meet the 1.5°C target we would have had to cut global emissions by nearly half within a decade, and reach net zero by mid-century. Instead, emissions have reached a new record-setting high every year since the agreement.

Many countries have offered their 'Paris pledges', but even if these were to be fully complied with, their combined effect on emissions is so trivial that they would still take us headlong into the four-degree world. That is why I wanted to write a completely new, fully updated version of *Six Degrees*, my book that was first published in 2007, because while the world's scientists have done an amazing job in conducting research and writing papers over the last two decades, somehow the full import of the science has failed to register on our political system. Each chapter of this book makes abundantly clear what every successive degree-by-degree rise in temperature will mean for human society and the planet's natural systems. The situation has become desperately urgent, and nobody who reads this will be able to say they didn't know what was coming.

Even as I was writing this book, I could see the climate emergency continuing to escalate. When I began, Australia was still a normal country. Following the devastating wildfires of January 2020, which themselves followed record-breaking high temperatures that seared a drought-stricken nation, it no longer is. Millions of Australians endured weeks of living under a pall of smoke, as 12 million hectares of bush and farmland were incinerated in catastrophic mega-fires. The human death toll, currently standing at 33, is tragic enough. But spare a thought for the estimated billion wild animals that have also lost their lives. And remember too that there can be no return to normal. Normal has gone, for ever.

I can't tell you with any precision when the globe will reach different temperature levels in the future. This is not so much because the science is uncertain – although to an extent it is – but because the rapidity of warming this century will depend on decisions yet to be made about how far and fast carbon emissions continue to rise. If we stay on the current business-as-usual trajectory, we could see two degrees as soon as the early 2030s, three degrees around mid-century, and four degrees by 2075 or so. If we're unlucky with positive feedbacks (more on them later in this book) from thawing permafrost in the Arctic or collapsing tropical rainforests, then we could be in for five or even six degrees by the century's end. On the other hand, if politicians make serious and determined efforts to implement the Paris targets, with the United States coming back into the fold as part of that effort, we can still hold off two degrees until the latter part of the century, and stop three degrees or higher temperature rises from ever happening at all.

As to which of these two outcomes is more likely, I am sorry to say that I am now substantially more pessimistic about the future than I was when *Six Degrees* was first published. Back then I believed that if only enough people could be better informed about the reality of climate change, then surely the world would be moved to act. While there have been positive shifts, such as declining coal use in some countries and cheaper renewable energy, these are dwarfed both by rising emissions and an alarming trend towards denialism. By this I don't just mean the overt climate denial of some US politicians stupid enough to call global warming a 'hoax' on Twitter. Nor am I simply referring to the populist backlash that seriously threatens liberal democratic values and has brought the political far right back into international ascendancy for the first time since the defeat of Hitler. (2007 already seems a much gentler world.) I'm talking, in addition, about the kind of denial that we all practise, the 'implicatory denial' of climate change that allows us to keep on living our lives as usual despite the obvious implications of what climate scientists are telling us. It's as if we don't really believe them.

After all, it's still possible – just – to pretend that the world isn't warming, or that the rate of change is nothing exceptional, or that the warming we see could be the result of 'natural cycles' or some such. Even the UN's Intergovernmental Panel on Climate Change (IPCC) admits this. In its 2014 report, IPCC experts stated that rising greenhouse gas concentrations in the atmosphere due to human activity are only 'extremely likely' to have been the dominant cause of observed warming since the mid-20th century. In

IPCC-speak, 'extremely likely' translates to a precise numerically quantified meaning of 95–100% probability. So yes, that does allow for a 5% probability that climate change is either natural or inexplicable with current knowledge. However, in 2019 a team of scientists re-evaluated these probabilities. Looking at three datasets of observed atmospheric temperatures combined with climate model outputs, they concluded that there is only a 1 in 3.5 million chance that current global warming is natural. That translates into about a 0.00003% chance that the US Republican Party is right. As the scientists wistfully conclude: 'Humanity cannot afford to ignore such clear signals.'

I agree, and the task I set myself in writing this book was to make the science so clear that nobody will have any excuse for ignoring it. I have spent years combing through long-forgotten issues of obscure glaciological journals. I have spent whole days lost in the small print of the citations in IPCC reports. In the process I have read hundreds upon hundreds of scientific papers – all so that you don't have to. So if you want to know the truth about climate change, here it is. I offer this not with optimism, for there is little enough cause for that, but with hope. Even when all else seems lost, hope remains. I can see it now, lighting a way to the future.

1º

Headline of the century

It happened in 2015. The event made the news, although only for a day or two, before normal service – terrorism, politics, sport, celebrity gossip – resumed. You could therefore be almost forgiven for not having noticed what might be considered the most important news story of the entire century so far.

To its credit, the Met Office (the UK's meteorological service) did put out a press release. This noted that, 'for the first time, global mean temperature at the Earth's surface is set to reach 1°C above pre-industrial levels' ('pre-industrial' was defined by the Met Office as 1850–1900). Human activities had, the scientists pointed out, now managed to cause a degree of global warming over and above what would have been the planet's natural temperature otherwise. There was no mystery about the main driver: look no further than the two *trillion* tonnes of carbon dioxide gas (henceforth CO_2) that have been poured into the Earth's atmosphere mainly through the combustion of fossil fuels since the start of the Industrial Revolution.

With one degree already in the bag, some historical comparisons are in order. In just over a century of unbridled fossil fuel use, humanity has returned atmospheric CO_2 concentrations to levels last seen in the Pliocene, around three to five million years ago. As a result, global surface temperatures can be expected to go on rising for a long time yet, but the thermal inertia of the planet – the centuries to millennia it takes to warm the abyssal depths of the oceans and melt the colossal bulk of the Greenland and Antarctic ice sheets – means that the temperature rise lags some way behind the 'forcing' effect of increased greenhouse gases. As we will see, there is much more still to come.

Most of the global warming has gone into increasing the heat content of the oceans. The latest estimates published in 2019 by the IPCC are that about 6 zettajoules of additional energy are accumulating in the upper oceans every year. A zetta is a big number: 6^{21} is a 6 followed by 21 zeroes, or 6,000,000,000,000,000,000,000 joules. For comparison, humans use about half a zettajoule per year in our total global energy consumption. A better visualisation might be to quantify all this extra energy in a more evocative unit: the heat released by the Hiroshima atomic bomb. Six zettajoules of energy equates to the same amount of heat as three Hiroshima atomic bombs exploding in the oceans every second. Count them: 3, 6, 9, 12, 15, 18 …

In late November 2018 the World Meteorological Organization (WMO) confirmed the UK Met Office's preliminary diagnosis. Based on five independently maintained global temperature data sets, the WMO in its annual State of the Climate report revealed that the global average temperature between 2014 and 2018 was 1.04°C above pre-industrial levels. In other words, we are now definitively living in the one-degree world. For me, seeing this announcement was a particularly significant moment, because when I wrote the original *Six Degrees* book nearly a decade and a half ago this one-degree world still lay in the future. For the purposes of this book it is as if we have moved forward a chapter: what was once the future is now the present. If we don't succeed in cutting back carbon emissions in time, the increasingly terrifying impacts detailed in later chapters – of two, three, four degrees and even higher – will also one day become our present. This really is our final warning.

The view from Mauna Loa

Mauna Loa, the gigantic shield volcano that sits at the centre of the Big Island of Hawai'i, is so tall that its summit protrudes above most of the island's active weather. On the east side of the mountain, as the trade winds hit and are forced to climb the slopes, they cool, form clouds and drop torrents of tropical rainfall. This makes Hilo, the island's biggest town, one of the wettest settlements in the United States. Drive through the glassy lava flows on the long haul up the flanks of the volcano, however, and you will quickly leave the rain clouds far below you. Conditions close to the summit are sub-Arctic, with only an inch or two of precipitation each year, much of that in the form of snow.

The paved road ends at the 3,200-metre contour line, where a group of antiquated buildings scattered across the volcanic debris together comprise the Mauna Loa Observatory. The Observatory is not as high as the solar telescopes that cluster atop the 4,207-metre summit of Mauna Kea, visible seemingly floating above the cloud layer 40 kilometres to the north. It is, however, arguably more historic, certainly from an earthly perspective. It was here that atmospheric chemist Charles Keeling first began collecting samples of airborne CO_2 in 1958, seemingly on a whim and with little official support, using pioneering monitoring equipment that he designed himself.

Keeling had found that measuring CO_2 lower down in the atmosphere was pointless, because the levels fluctuated constantly as a result of emissions from car exhausts, industrial chimneys, vegetation growth and so on. Thanks to its elevation, Mauna Loa rose above all that day-to-day noise, and Keeling's measurements were the first in the world to show that CO_2 mixed at high altitudes through the whole global atmosphere was increasing, in a sawtooth upwards seasonal pattern now known as the 'Keeling Curve' (probably the most famous global warming-related graph of all time). Charles Keeling died in 2005, but appropriately his efforts have been continued by his son

Ralph, also an atmospheric chemist. Ralph Keeling has made his own subsequent discoveries, such as that the oxygen content of the air is decreasing commensurately with our consumption of fossil fuels, as airborne O_2 is combined with carbon extracted from underground to form the gas CO_2.

When Charles Keeling began his measurements in 1958, the rarefied air atop the lava fields of Mauna Loa contained CO_2 at a ratio of 315 parts per million (ppm), already substantially higher than the pre-industrial concentration of about 278 ppm. On 10 May 2013 the Scripps Institution for Oceanography, which maintains the Observatory, made a landmark announcement. For the first time ever in human history, CO_2 levels had briefly touched the 400 ppm threshold. 'There's no stopping CO_2 from [permanently] reaching 400 ppm,' commented Ralph Keeling sadly. 'That's now a done deal. But what happens from here on still matters to climate, and it's still under our control. It mainly comes down to how much we continue to rely on fossil fuels for energy.' Perhaps no one was listening, because at the time of writing the atmospheric concentration of CO_2 has hit 408 ppm. This figure will already be out of date by the time you read this book. You can follow the relentless upwards progress of the Keeling Curve in real time on Twitter, via @Keeling_curve.

The Keeling Curve is a useful reality check, one that cuts through all the noise and confusion of the climate and energy debates. Unlike the slopes of the huge volcano on which it is measured, the initially gentle upward curve gets steeper the higher you go. That means that the rate of CO_2 accumulation in the atmosphere is steadily increasing, from roughly 1 ppm in the early years to about 2 ppm annually today. There is no visible slowdown, no sudden downwards blip, to mark the implementation of the Kyoto Protocol, still less 2009's Copenhagen 'two degrees' commitment or the landmark Paris Agreement of 2015. All those smiling heads of state shaking hands, the diplomats hugging on the podium after marathon sessions of all-night negotiating – none of that actually made any identifiable difference to the Keeling

Curve, which is the only thing that actually matters to the planet's temperature. All our solar panels, wind turbines, electric cars, lithium-ion batteries, LED lightbulbs, nuclear plants, biogas digesters, press conferences, declarations, pieces of paper; all our shouting and arguing, weeping and marching, reporting and ignoring, decrying and denying; all our speeches, movies, websites, lectures and books; our announcements, carbon-neutral targets, moments of joy and despair; none of these to date have so much as made the slightest dent in the steepening upward slope of the Keeling Curve.

This does not make us powerless prisoners of fortune. No trend continues for ever, and just because recent history has been all one way does not mean the future must necessarily follow suit. These emissions are not extra-terrestrial – they come from our everyday activities. Indeed they are an inescapable part of modern civilisation itself. We can get a sense of the sources, and the magnitudes, from the annual Global Carbon Project report. On average, every year over the last decade we humans transferred 35 billion tonnes of CO_2 from the geological reservoirs (that's coal, oil and gas) into the atmosphere. This was augmented by 6 billion tonnes of CO_2 from 'land-use change' (that's deforestation, ploughing up new farmland and so on). About 9 billion tonnes of this new CO_2 dissolved in the oceans, and 12 billion tonnes was taken up on land by vegetation and soils. That left a remainder of about 18 billion tonnes to accumulate in the atmosphere and drive the relentless upward climb of the Keeling Curve. (The imbalance of 2 billion tonnes is due to uncertainties.)

There are small changes in the carbon budget year on year, which sometimes cause great excitement. In 2014, 2015 and 2016, for example, there was little to no annual growth in fossil fuel emissions, which seemed to have stabilised for the first time. Cue some premature celebrations. But had the world reached an early peak in emissions? No. In 2017 growth resumed again, reaching a new high of 36.8 billion tonnes despite a record installation of 161 gigawatts of renewable generating capacity in 2016 alone. In 2018 emissions continued to accelerate, however, increasing nearly 3% on the previous year and pushing CO_2 levels to a new historic high. In 2019 growth slowed somewhat, to 0.6% above 2018, thanks to a reduction in coal use in Europe and the US. But what we need is carbon cuts, not slower growth – urgently.

So what's going wrong? Well, it's a matter of scale. The world is hungry for new energy: primary energy demand keeps on increasing, and 80% of that increase is supplied by new fossil fuels. Overall, renewables (not including hydro) in 2019 accounted for only 4% of global primary energy, still much too small a proportion to have any discernible effect on the upward trend in overall emissions. This is why solar and wind have so far not measurably dented the Keeling Curve. According to recent estimates, the installation rate for clean energy sources would have to increase tenfold to arrest the annual growth in fossil fuels.

Meanwhile, as the measurements conducted in the Observatory buildings continue to show relentlessly rising CO_2, Mauna Loa itself is experiencing the effects of the resulting climate warming. Temperatures are gradually rising, and night frosts are rarer than they were when Charles Keeling first began to keep records with his home-made equipment. Mauna Loa may sit above most weather, but no part of the world can entirely escape global heating. Snowfall is less frequent – and the snow melts earlier in springtime – while plant life on the slopes of the mountain is changing with every year that passes. In 1958 Charles Keeling had to design complex and sensitive equipment to discern subtle changes to the Earth's environment. Now these changes are plain for all to see.

Back to the future

With its official average temperature just over one degree above pre-industrial levels, 2015 was the warmest year on record. But what about much longer ago, before humans invented thermometers and started taking measurements? You have probably heard of the Little Ice Age spanning the 17th to 19th centuries, when frost fairs were held on the frozen River Thames in London, or the Medieval Warm Period, when the Vikings colonised Greenland. These are sometimes cited by climate sceptics as evidence of previous variations in the climate, with the accompanying assertion that today's high temperatures are therefore not caused by humans (a logical fallacy: whatever changed climate in the past is not necessarily what is changing it today) and are nothing to worry about.

However, a 2019 *Nature* paper using temperature records from corals, lake sediments, glacier ice, sea shells and trees, collected across the globe from Antarctica to Australia and from Canada to Chile, demonstrates convincingly that these earlier temperature fluctuations were regional phenomena and not globally coherent. So while it is a historical fact that frost fairs were held on the Thames from the 1600s to the early 1800s (our romantic myth of the ideal white Christmas dates from this period), colder European winters at the time were balanced out by simultaneous warmer temperatures in the western half of North America that no one now remembers. This was not a global cooling event, just as the Viking occupation of Greenland or the Romans growing grapes in Britain is not evidence of pre-historic global warming. In fact, according to these multiple data sources, today's global high temperatures are unprecedented for at least 2,000 years.

That's just two millennia, however. What about even longer ago? One study, combining data from 73 different sources around the world, concluded that the early Holocene, from 10,000 to 5,000 years ago, was just over half a degree warmer than the pre-industrial era. Given that temperatures since 2015 have been one whole degree higher than then, it is reasonable to conclude that the globe is now almost certainly warmer than at any point since the end of the last ice age, 18,000 years ago. Indeed, to find an analogue for today's anomalous warmth, you have to look beyond the last ice age to a period of time between 116,000 to 129,000 years ago often referred to by scientists as the Eemian.

In the first *Six Degrees*, I included studies about the climate of the Eemian in my second chapter, corresponding roughly with two degrees of warming. But more recent studies suggest that the Eemian was only about one degree warmer than the pre-industrial Holocene. In other words, it was roughly equivalent to global temperatures we are already experiencing now. Yet the Eemian world was radically different: the Arctic tree line was much further north and hippopotamuses bathed in rivers in southern England. The Eemian isn't a perfect match with today, because with humans still confined to cave dwelling, atmospheric CO_2 remained at pre-industrial levels of about 270 ppm. Why was it then so warm? Probably because slight variations in the Earth's orbit changed the distribution of incoming solar energy, warming the higher latitudes but leaving the tropics little changed or even slightly cooler than now. Studies of preserved dead midges in lake sediments have found that local summer temperatures in parts of Greenland were somewhere between 5°C and 8°C higher than today, but it seems that there was still plenty of sea ice in the Arctic Ocean.

Perhaps the most ominous lesson from the Eemian is that even with CO_2 at around 135 ppm *lower* than today, and worldwide temperatures about the same as modern averages, sea levels were six to ten metres higher than at present. Evidence from the Eemian suggests that about five metres of this sea level rise originated from the partial melting of the Greenland ice sheet, which shrank down to a largish remnant in the north-east of the landmass. The implication is pretty clear: it suggests that today's temperatures are already high enough to eventually melt the majority of the Greenland ice sheet and deliver a multi-metre rise in sea levels. This seems hard to believe, until you travel to Greenland and witness what was once a frozen wasteland currently undergoing rapid, epochal change.

Greenland's lakes

Greenland is turning blue. Hundreds of thousands of iridescent blue lakes now dot the fringes of the rapidly melting ice sheet throughout the summer months, and the melt area has been creeping steadily upwards and inwards towards the interior as global heating bites. The direct impacts of this increased thaw can be dramatic – in late July 2012 so much meltwater was sluicing off the south-western portion of the ice sheet that a bridge was washed away on the Watson River, which empties into a fjord just to the south of the town of Kangerlussuaq. Footage shared on YouTube shows a grey-brown torrent resembling a tsunami washing away a tractor and tearing through the bridge and the road leading up to it in just a matter of minutes.

This episode is more than just a revealing anecdote. Meltwater flows in the Watson River have been steadily rising in recent years, and on average are now nearly 50% higher than they were in the 1950s. The tattered, debris-covered edge of the giant ice sheet lies just a few kilometres up the valley from Kangerlussuaq, and most of the hundreds of blue lakes that pepper its surface in summer drain into the Watson River, which is fed by a 12,000-square kilometre catchment across the south-western portion of Greenland. In terms of annual averages, the three largest discharge years on record are 2010, 2012 and 2016, with the largest single discharge peak coming in July 2012, explaining why it was then that the bridge over the Watson at Kangerlussuaq succumbed to the dramatic flood.

The timing of this glacial torrent was no great mystery either. For the first time in living memory unprecedented melting had penetrated right up to the summit of the giant ice sheet, located at 3,216 m in altitude. Summit is classed as a polar desert, an inhospitable place of frigid thin air and snow as dry as dust. On 12 July 2012, however, temperatures edged above freezing at the summit for the first time in recorded history, and the automated weather instruments permanently located there were surrounded by slush. Lower down, on the western side of the ice sheet, climate researchers were forced to rebuild their camp when snow and ice supports melted away. Things were no better in North Greenland where Danish scientists logged six consecutive days of above-freezing temperatures at the surface between 10 and 15 July. It even rained on 11 and 13 July, with melt and rainwater percolating down into what had previously been permanent snow.

When the first satellite data came in about the July 2012 melt event, scientists analysing it thought their instruments must have malfunctioned. Later visuals showed the entire ice sheet coloured deep red, indicating pervasive melt conditions. When the scientists checked their data with output from other satellites, they found that on 8 July the temperature of about 40% of the ice sheet surface was above freezing. On 12 July the figure was 98.6%. Virtually the whole of Greenland was in the melt zone, the first time any of the scientists studying the colossal ice sheet had seen such a thing.

Longer-term data show that all-Greenland melt events are extraordinarily rare. A December 2018 paper concluded that the 2012 melt rates were exceptional and 'likely also to be unprecedented over the last 6,800–7,800 years'. The same paper stated that there has been a 500% increase in melt intensity at the ice core site in just the past 20 years. The latest data show that the fastest-expanding melt zones are now in the northern portion of Greenland, in what should be the coldest area closest to the North Pole.

Once the domain almost exclusively of ice and snow, Greenland has begun to see more rain, even in the depths of winter. While fresh snow is brilliant white, reflecting most of the sun's radiation back out to space, thawing slush is less reflective, and the bare ice sheet with snow removed is darker still. All around Greenland the snowline has retreated uphill, exposing more uncovered ice to the full heat of the summer sun. As the fringes of the ice sheet gradually shrink inland, bare rock and glacial debris are revealed, leading to an increase in dust storms. Plants have begun to colonise new areas, and are now coming into leaf a week or two earlier as spring temperatures rise.

It has long been clear from ice core records that the climate in Greenland can do sudden and strange things. About 11,700 years ago, at the end of a colder period called the Younger Dryas, temperatures shot up by 15°C over a few decades. A similarly dramatic warming, of 9°C in less than 70 years, took place 14,760 years ago during the last ice age. Scientists fear that Greenland may currently be crossing a similar threshold of rapid climate change, one that could lead to the eventual loss over centuries of the entire ice sheet. Mean annual air temperatures are already 3°C higher than they were a few decades ago. But these shifts did not happen gradually: they came about in sudden jumps, of 2°C in 1994 and a further 1.1°C in 2006. This is a rate of change that, if sustained over decades, easily matches the major climate tipping points of the distant past.

And 2019 was another epochal year. Temperatures across Greenland soared to 12°C above the late July average, and the summit of the ice sheet saw another thaw between 30 and 31 July 2019. This time temperatures at the highest point topped the record set in 2012, and stayed above freezing for longer over a two-day period. In response to these rapid changes, some scientists have begun to warn that the projections for 21st-century sea level rise may need to be revised upwards. According to one researcher, the current melt rates weren't supposed to happen until 2070. In the first *Six Degrees* I reported that Greenland's contribution to sea level rise was about 0.3 mm per year. In 2019, according to preliminary estimates, the melt rate may have been as high as 1.5 mm, a fivefold increase. If that's not a tipping point, I don't know what is.

Arctic on thin ice

Signs of increasingly rapid global warming are now evident through-out the Arctic, where temperatures are rising at a rate two to three times the global average. In late December 2015 at the North Pole itself temperatures rose close to freezing. Under normal circum-stances, air temperatures at the pole would be averaging around -30°C during the frigid polar nights of late December. On this occasion temperatures shot up by 25°C in just one day as a deep low-pressure system wafted in sub-tropical air from the south. Although no one was there to witness it directly, it seems likely that it was even raining at the North Pole for a brief period at the height of the Arctic winter.

This extreme Arctic warming event lasted for 40 days between 29 December 2015 and 6 February 2016, during which the entire polar Arctic above 66°N saw temperatures 4–6°C above average. Scientists studying the event called it 'unheard of' and 'super-extreme' – but the following December it happened again. 'A weather buoy about 90 miles south of the North Pole registered a temperature at the melting point of 0 Celsius early Thursday,' reported the *Washington Post*, adding: 'Santa may need water skis instead of a sleigh this year.' Temperatures throughout a broad area of the Arctic were 20°C or more above normal in November and December. At a time when the Arctic sea ice should have been regrowing due to winter cold, it actu-ally shed another 50,000 square kilometres (19,300 square miles), an event unprecedented during the entire satellite period. The high Arctic temperatures of October and November were 'off the charts', said baffled experts.

To test whether the event could have been caused by chance, scien-tists at the World Weather Attribution network plugged the temper-ature data into climate models and compared the results with 'natural' conditions without global warming. None of them showed Arctic events as hot as 2016 in the simulated world without human carbon emissions.

So what's going on? Part of the answer comes from the long-term trend in declining Arctic sea ice, which has been shrinking in area by 13% a decade (in its minimum summertime extent) since satellites began measuring it in 1978. That means half the entire Arctic's stock of sea ice has disappeared since the late 1970s, and what remains has become about 85% thinner. In fact the thinning trend has become so extreme that scientists now struggle to find thick enough ice floes on which to deploy their measuring instruments. All this new open water has transformed the atmospheric dynamics of the Arctic region, allowing warm, moist winds – whose energy would previously have been dissipated by ice – to penetrate right up to the pole itself.

Other researchers have confirmed that the extreme polar heat of 2016 would not have been possible without the extensive disappearance of Arctic sea ice. While 2018's Arctic ice minimum was only the sixth lowest in the satellite record, the overall trend continues irrevocably downwards, equating to 82,300 km^2 lost on average every year, an area four times the size of Wales. Cumulatively this adds up to a vast total: the extent of Arctic summer sea ice lost since the 1980s would be sufficient to cover 40% of the contiguous United States. And the 2019 September sea ice area, at 4.15 million square kilometres, was the second-lowest since the beginning of the satellite era in 1979. *Nature* reported that 13 of the lowest Arctic sea-ice extents have been recorded in the last 13 years.

Because there is now dark-coloured open water during the summer rather than highly reflective snow and ice, solar heat absorption has increased fivefold since the 1980s in the once-frozen seas north of Alaska and Canada, introducing vast quantities of additional energy into the Arctic system. I wrote about the Arctic albedo feedback in the first *Six Degrees*: 'While bright white, snow-covered ice reflects more than 80% of the sun's heat that falls on it, the darker open ocean can absorb up to 95% of incoming solar radiation. Once sea ice begins to melt, in other words, the process quickly becomes self-reinforcing:

more ocean surface is revealed, absorbing solar heat, raising temperatures and making it more difficult for the ice to re-form during the next winter.' This change in albedo (how much sunshine gets absorbed by darker coloured surface versus how much gets reflected from brighter surfaces) has now been measured directly by satellites, and its impact is dramatic. Averaged globally, the heating effect is equivalent to pumping another 200 billion tonnes of CO_2 into the atmosphere.

Global warming makes us all responsible for this dramatic ongoing transformation of the Arctic, and in a surprisingly direct way. Scientists have found a linear relationship between cumulative CO_2 emissions and the September sea ice minimum. It turns out that every metric tonne of CO_2 implies a sustained loss of 3 m² of Arctic ice. Given the disparities in emissions between countries, that means that every American is on average responsible for the loss of nearly 50 square metres of ice each year, while a British person is responsible for just under 20 m² of annual ice loss. This compares to 22 m² of disappeared ice for each Chinese, 5 m² of loss for each Indian but under 1 square metre each for the low fossil fuel-consuming inhabitants of east Africa. For Antarctica the equivalent figures are even more dramatic: each kilogram of released CO_2 is responsible for melting two metric tonnes from the much larger ice cap over the South Pole.

This transformation of the Arctic is also having serious effects on the wildlife of the polar region. That most emblematic symbol of global warming – the polar bear – is facing population declines because it depends on the sea ice on which to hunt seals. Less ice means fewer seals can be caught, which translates to fewer cubs able to survive into adulthood, and more hungry, skinny adult bears scavenging on ice-free coastlines during the summer. Body-fat samples recovered from polar bears shot by Inuit hunters – who together typically harvest a couple of hundred bears per year across Canada – show a strong seasonal correlation between the availability of sea ice and the condition of the polar bears. 'We're restructuring a whole ecosystem,' says polar bear ecologist Andrew Derocher. 'Sea ice is to the Arctic what soil is to the forest. Without sea ice we'll still have an ecosystem but it won't include polar bears and many other species.'

It's not yet too late to save the polar bear. Scientists have determined that dramatic emissions reductions and the stabilisation of CO_2 at 450 ppm could still retain enough summer sea ice to prevent the polar bear becoming extinct in the wild. Polar bears are not the only species highly dependent on sea ice; walrus, bearded and ringed seals, bowhead whales, beluga and narwhal all need ice for part or all of their life cycles. And the changing Arctic ecosystem brings other new threats. Those marine mammals that survive the loss of ice face being chopped up by boat propellers thanks to the increase in shipping traversing the newly open Northern Passage. The rapid warming affects the oceans too, with Arctic fish species retreating north towards the pole as Atlantic and Pacific migratory fish move in.

These ecological shifts can have tragic effects. For example, the summer sea ice edge has retreated 400 km further away from the nesting grounds of the black guillemot on Cooper Island, off the north coast of Alaska. The guillemots' primary prey species, Arctic cod, has retreated with the ice, and the majority of chicks now starve to death. Seabird die-offs have also been recorded thanks to low ice conditions in the Bering Sea. With more moisture in a warmer atmosphere, heavy snow can also be an issue – in the summer of 2018 so much snow was left lying across the high Arctic that scientists documented a near-total collapse in the food web of north-east Greenland. Plants failed to flower until late in the season, while migratory shorebirds had only a few eggs hatching. Those nestlings that did fledge would not have had enough time to grow to full size in time to survive the return southward migration. Some shorebirds even starved to death. There were no Arctic fox cubs, and almost no muskox calves. This was the 'most complete reproductive failure encountered in the terrestrial ecosystem during more than two decades of monitoring', scientists reported.

The ongoing reorganisation of the Arctic system is also beginning to have ricochet effects on weather patterns across the Northern Hemisphere. Record-breaking wildfires in California, for example, have been linked to changes in atmospheric circulation possibly triggered by the disappearance of Arctic sea ice. These changes are one of the factors behind the devastating multi-year drought that has parched much of the south-western United States, making the area tinder-dry and extremely prone to wildfire outbreaks. This drought has also led to declining yields of crops in the United States, thereby fingering faraway Arctic sea ice as a factor in falling food production thousands of kilometres away. One study published in May 2019 suggests an additional relationship between reductions in sea ice in the Hudson Bay and more frequent heatwaves across the southern Plains of the United States. Another points to a 'regime shift' towards ice-free conditions taking place in the Barents Sea in 2005 that may have subsequently 'contributed to the increasingly frequent extreme weather events experienced over Europe in the past decade or so'.

Several studies have also suggested a possible Arctic amplification fingerprint in 'planetary waves' – large-scale wave-like meanders in the Northern Hemisphere jet stream that can remain nearly stationary for long periods of time and cause devastating weather extremes, from summer heatwaves to floods or even winter cold events. Although some experts urge caution in assigning blame, multiple studies have linked these waves to events as diverse as the 2003 European heatwave, the Russian heatwave and Pakistan floods of 2010, the 2011 Texas drought and the persistent lack of rainfall in California, evidence that is now supported by climate models. These 'blocked' weather patterns have also contributed to record cold extremes in the Eurasian and North American continents in recent years. Warming of the Arctic Ocean may have helped weaken and shift the 'Polar Vortex' of extremely cold, high-pressure air, bringing intense winter conditions across Eurasia and North America. The evidence linking this shift with the changing Arctic is increasingly strong: one study showed a clear link between anomalous warmth in the newly ice-free Barents–Kara Sea region of the Arctic Ocean and severe winters in East Asia, and also linked extreme cold in North America to extra heat in the Chukchi Sea north of Alaska. Another group of meteorologists assessed the record-breaking cold and blizzards that hit parts of North America in the winter of 2014/15, and found that reduced Arctic sea ice might have helped drive the 'anomalous meander of the jet stream' which led to the extreme cold.

Teasing out the relative contributions of the different factors is incredibly complex, but one thing is clear: the Arctic circulation that has been established for millennia is breaking down, and this must be having impacts further afield as well. As Chris Rapley, professor of climate science at University College London, told the *Guardian*:

> What happens in the Arctic doesn't stay in the Arctic. By upsetting the energy balance of the planet we are changing the temperature gradient between the equator and the pole. This in turn sets in motion major reorganisations of the flow patterns of the atmosphere and ocean. The consequences are emerging and they are disruptive, and likely to become even more profoundly so.

In the summer of 2019 the Arctic even began to burn. In mid-June more than a hundred wildfires were burning above the Arctic Circle across Alaska, Siberia and Canada. Even Greenland saw wildfires erupting on fenlands scorched by unusual summer heat. But most importantly of all, the Russian wildfires were not just burning trees. They were also smouldering in dried-out peat, much of it formerly immobilised in permafrost. By the end of July it was estimated that the blazes had released more than 120 million tonnes of CO_2 – an all-time record, and more than the total annual emissions of Belgium.

All this extra carbon can only do one thing: accumulate in the atmosphere and cause more warming. These weren't just wildfires, they were positive feedbacks, showing that the heating of the Arctic is threatening to run out of control.

Gulf Stream collapse

The winter blizzards of recent years were as nothing compared with the icy onslaught that hit Europe about 12,000 years ago during the Younger Dryas. During this brief return to near ice age conditions, thawing glaciers in the British Isles and other parts of northern Europe suddenly re-advanced. The remains can be seen all around the peaks of Britain's now ice-free hills, such as the Lake District, the Scottish Highlands and Snowdonia, where tell-tale hummocks of grassed-over moraines testify to the final extent of these long-disappeared small glaciers. The cause of the sudden cold snap is still disputed, but the driver may have been a shift in the strength of the critically important Atlantic current popularly known as the Gulf Stream. Even longer ago, during the depths of the last ice age, abrupt periods of extreme cold – during which armadas of icebergs were launched across the North Atlantic – have also been blamed on fluctuations of this gigantic ocean current.

Today, the 'Atlantic Meridional Overturning Circulation' (AMOC, of which the true Gulf Steam is but a small component) continues to have an outsized impact on Europe's climate. It is thanks to the AMOC that north-western Europe is roughly 6°C warmer than equivalent maritime latitudes on the Pacific coast of North America. This mighty current carries sub-tropical surface water equivalent in volume to the flow of all the world's rivers north via the Gulf Stream to the British Isles and Scandinavia. The AMOC is so big that it even has its own unit, the Sverdrup (Sv), equivalent to one million cubic metres of water moving at one metre per second. The AMOC has an average strength of around 17 Sv in the North Atlantic; compare this with the flow of the Amazon – the world's biggest river – at a paltry 0.2 Sv. It transports oceanic heat of 0.9 petawatts, equivalent to the output of half a million or so nuclear power stations from the tropics to the higher latitudes. For this reason alone, the Northern Hemisphere as a whole is warmer than the Southern Hemisphere, because ocean heat is transported from the south across the equator and into the North Atlantic. A fictionalised AMOC shutdown was the scenario depicted in the 2004 film *The Day After Tomorrow*; while the giant tsunami hitting New York might have been stretching things a little, it is widely agreed that a total AMOC collapse has the potential to plunge Europe back into decades of sub-zero winters and destabilise weather across the globe.

Whether the AMOC is beginning to weaken – and if so, whether human global warming is to blame – is currently the focus of intense debate. The driving forces behind the AMOC are the areas of very salty, colder water that form offshore from Greenland, Iceland, Scandinavia and Arctic Canada during the winter. This water has a higher density than warmer, fresher surface water and consequently sinks to the ocean floor, where it begins a long journey south to restart the process, like a gigantic heat conveyor belt. Although there is substantial variability year to year, recent data from ocean sensors shows that the strength of the AMOC has already slowed by 15% since the mid-20th century, making it weaker now than probably at any point in the last 1,500 years.

Studies based on data gathered by ocean arrays found that the AMOC's strength declined by 0.6 Sv per year – that's three River Amazons'-worth – between 2007 to 2011, and that this weaker state still persists today. It is possible that this is just part of a longer natural fluctuation, as one later study suggests. However, concerns have been growing that the weakening of the AMOC current is linked with the huge quantities of fresh water that are now sluicing off the thawing Greenland ice sheet every summer. This meltwater, combined with increased rainfall, is diluting the waters of the north Atlantic, reducing its salinity. Less saline water is less dense and heavy, and therefore does not sink into the depths and drive the movement of the current.

Climate models also disagree about whether and how the AMOC will collapse, making this issue one of the classic 'known unknowns' in the climate debate, a potential shift that could have huge impacts through global weather destabilisation. Whether the current weakening trend will continue is highly uncertain. But one thing we do know: AMOC collapse has happened before, and it had drastic impacts on the climate of the entire Northern Hemisphere. Any prolonged shutdown would have equally disastrous effects today.

Antarctic icebergs

They called it B-46. This was not a code name for a new bomber or some other piece of military hardware, but something potentially much more significant. B-46 was huge, 300 km² in area – a gigantic iceberg spawned in November 2018 by one of Antarctica's biggest glaciers, Pine Island Glacier (PIG). And B-46 was not even a record, being substantially smaller than the more than 500 km² monster that floated away from the same Antarctic glacier in 2015. PIG, the mothership for these mega-bergs, is one of the largest ice streams draining the West Antarctic Ice Sheet (WAIS) and has consequently been the focus of intense study in recent years. Something big is happening to PIG: from 1974 to 2010 it accelerated by 75% to a forward speed of 4 km per year. At this speed an observer standing on land at the edge of the glacier would almost be able to see the massive stream of ice grind by with the naked eye. Its rate of annual ice loss in the same period increased from 6 billion tonnes per year to 46 billion tonnes, an increase of a whopping 750%. The accelerating rate of melt now makes PIG the largest single glaciological contributor to sea level rise in the world. This one glacier now adds a tenth of a millimetre each year to the height of the global oceans.

Although the front of the glacier is floating on the ocean, its grounding line – where the glacier's base is attached to the seabed – has retreated by 30 kilometres inland since 1992, and herein lies the problem. Like its neighbour, the even bigger Thwaites Glacier, the bed of PIG slopes downhill towards the centre of the West Antarctic Ice Sheet, where it is anchored over 1,500 metres below sea level. Many scientists fear that a process of irreversible collapse has already been triggered, with a positive feedback seeing warming waters penetrating further and further towards the centre of the vulnerable ice sheet in a process of unstoppable melt that will continue for centuries to come.

All-told, the WAIS has enough ice to raise global sea levels by more than three metres. However, this massive meltwater pulse would not be released overnight. Currently the whole WAIS is adding about 0.3 mm per year to global sea levels, but this rate is increasing as the massive glaciers that drain into the warming ocean shed more and more mass. In May 2019 Antarctic scientists published their latest data; this showed that both Thwaites and Pine Island glaciers have thinned by up to 122 metres in places and that rates of ice loss have increased fivefold since surveys began in 1992. They concluded that nearly a quarter of the entire West Antarctic Ice Sheet is now in 'structural imbalance'. Scientists fear that a 'wave of thinning' is spreading rapidly across some of Antarctica's most vulnerable glaciers, driving up sea levels around the planet.

Rapid changes are taking place elsewhere in Antarctica too. A huge 100-metre waterfall of meltwater now pours off the edge of the Nansen Ice Shelf into the ocean during the Austral summer. Although melting on Antarctica is not new – streams and ponds were also documented by early explorers – researchers now envisage a gradual transformation towards a melt regime closer to that of Greenland. Indeed, in September 2019 researchers reported having spotted more than 65,000 lakes all around the margins of the East Antarctic, many in areas previously thought too cold to allow substantial summertime thawing. One of the new lakes was more than 60 kilometres long, and meltwater pools were spotted as far as 500 km into the interior of the vast ice sheet and as high as 1,500 metres in elevation.

In March 2015 the tip of the Antarctic Peninsula registered the highest ever temperature recorded on continental Antarctica, a balmy 17.5°C, an event classed as an 'extreme Antarctic heatwave' and which helped trigger yet more melting across nearby ice shelves. Some ice shelves have been suffering periods of intense melt even in the dead of the Antarctic winter. Ocean waves now reach exposed glacier fronts that were previously protected by sea ice, promoting rapid disintegration. The Larsen C shelf may in fact be the next to disintegrate, following on the heels of the collapse of Larsen A in 1995, Larsen B in 2002 and Wilkins in 2009. Larsen C reduced in size in 2017 by 10% following the calving of a single colossal iceberg of 5,000 km² in area, larger than the US state of Rhode Island and ten times bigger than anything that PIG could produce.

Overall, the latest survey – published in the journal *PNAS* in 2019 – shows that the rate of ice loss from the continent has increased *sixfold* over the last four decades, from an estimated 40 billion tonnes to 252 billion tonnes per year. Although the majority of the melt comes from the more immediately vulnerable West Antarctic ice sheet, East Antarctica is now a 'major participant in the mass loss'. This is noteworthy both because East Antarctica contains the vast majority of the continent's ice, and because it was previously thought too cold to lose significant mass. This melt has added about 14 mm to global sea levels since 1979, an amount that would have been even higher were it not for the fact that rising temperatures are increasing snowfall and accumulation rates in the interior of the frigid continent. 'I don't want to be alarmist,' Eric Rignot, lead author of the 2019 *PNAS* paper and an Earth-systems scientist for the University of California at Irvine and NASA, told the *Washington Post*, '[but] the places undergoing changes in Antarctica are not limited to just a couple of places. They seem to be more extensive than what we thought. That, to me, seems to be reason for concern.'

The current melting in Antarctica may sound huge, Rignot added, but actually it is 'just the tip of the iceberg, so to speak'. The future is a much greater concern. 'As the Antarctic ice sheet continues to melt away, we expect multi-metre sea level rise from Antarctica in the coming centuries.' All round the continent, grounding lines where glaciers meet the ocean are retreating, as experts have long feared. Although the ice-sheet models project relatively slow melt rates, recent evidence suggests that glaciers in contact with the warming oceans may thaw much more rapidly than expected. This would not just be two or three times faster, either. 'The observed melt rates are up to two orders of magnitude greater than predicted by theory,' the experts reported. If Antarctic tidewater glaciers all increase their melting rate a hundredfold over what has so far been predicted, expect much quicker impacts on the world's coastlines.

Melting mountains

'*El Nevado Pastoruri estuvo aquí en 2015*,' announces the sign ('The Pastoruri Glacier was here in 2015'). All around are rocks, and the front of the receding mass of ice is now hundreds of metres away. Welcome to Peru's famous Ruta del Cambio Climático – Climate Change Route – that winds its way up to the rapidly thawing snows of the Cordillera Blanca in Huascarán National Park. Once famous for its ice caves, this easily accessible glacier has split in two and now mostly turned into a lake. Tourists are requested not to climb on the ice or break pieces off; where once Peruvian high-school students used to slide down on plastic bags, most of the glacier is now roped off to protect it from further damage.

The ice-clad peaks of the Cordillera Blanca are sacred places for me. A chapter in my first book detailed my journey to a remote glacier on the eastern side of the range above the small town of Huari, retracing the footsteps of my father's team of geological surveyors, who made the trek back in 1980. When I visited in 2002, the glacier

I was looking for – a huge wedge of ice that tumbled down a precipice and calved icebergs into a lake – had disappeared. I haven't been back since, but Google Earth shows that the parent glacier has receded well back from the top of the slope, and will now be out of sight of my 2002 vantage point at the lakeside below. One of my favourite photos from this expedition was of our bivouac site high on the ridge to the north, on a lovely round tongue of snow that protruded from the upper-level glacier. That seems to have gone now too; indeed the whole ridge looks denuded and bare.

The ice on these peaks has more than just sentimental value for climbers like me mourning its loss. The high mountains are sacred to local people as an abode of the Incan spirits and for their very practical value as a source of freshwater. Most communities in the area depend on glacial runoff for much of their water, and this diminishing resource is beginning to spark conflicts between settlements. Huaraz, the main town in the province and a climbers' mecca within sight of Peru's highest peak, depends on glacial runoff for 90% of its water during months of drought. The water from glaciers on the western side of the Cordillera runs off into rivers that then enter the Pacific via an intensely arid coastal plain (water on the eastern slopes ends up in the Amazon). Without this freshwater for irrigation, the majority of Peru's agricultural production – not to mention its hydropower – would disappear. The sprawling capital city Lima is also dependent on mountain runoff for its fresh water, part of which originates from glacial melt. In neighbouring Bolivia, the high-altitude capital La Paz gets about 15% of its annual average water supply from surrounding mountain glaciers, but this rises to as much as 85% during dry months.

Peru's glaciers are now critically endangered. The Cordillera Blanca has lost a third of its area in recent decades, and other Peruvian glaciated mountain ranges are suffering similar losses, as are those elsewhere in the Andes. Overall, the South American Andes have shed nearly 23 billion tonnes of ice since the year 2000, contributing more to sea level rise than even the Himalayas. The melt rate on mountain glaciers around the world is now so rapid that, combined, they now add nearly as much to sea level rise each year as the whole Greenland ice sheet, totalling an estimated 335 billion tonnes of melted ice.

Glaciologists do not tend to communicate in overly emotive language, but the latest publications suggest that even they are beginning to panic. 'Rates of early 21st-century mass loss are without precedent on a global scale, at least for the time period observed and probably also for recorded history,' wrote a team of authors from the World Glacier Monitoring Service recently in the *Journal of Glaciology*. With a few short-term regional exceptions, every major mountain range in the world is rapidly losing glacial mass.

It is not just glacier ice that is disappearing; snow cover is vanishing too. California, the most populous state in the US, with the world's sixth-largest economy and producing a quarter of all the country's agricultural produce, depends for 30% of its freshwater on the Sierra Nevada winter snowpack. This is because most of the state's precipitation comes in the winter, accumulating in the high mountains as deep snow cover. This snowpack then gradually melts during the dry spring and summer months, keeping the rivers flowing and irrigating the vegetable and fruit crops that flourish in the state's Mediterranean climate. However, with more winter precipitation now coming in the form of rain, less and less snow is accumulating to keep the rivers flowing during the summer dry season. On 1 April 2015, for example, after four years of record-setting drought, scientists calculated that the Sierra Nevada snowpack was at only 5% of its historical average, a low that they declared 'unprecedented in the context of the past 500 years'.

Other mountain ranges have also suffered from strange wintertime climate shifts. In the European Alps sudden warming events have become increasingly common. In December 2015 an unprecedented 'winter heatwave' hit the eastern Alps, with temperatures rising above freezing even as high as 2,500 metres in altitude, removing lying snow and even melting the glacier ice underneath – something previously unknown in winter. In January 2018 high temperatures – again in the Alps – brought heavy rain that melted lying snow, causing landslides and debris flows in French and Swiss alpine valleys. Higher up the slopes more than five metres of snow fell, adding to the risk of huge avalanches hitting roads and villages, and leaving tourists stranded in major ski resorts.

In lowland areas across Europe, meanwhile, snow cover is now 'dramatically decreasing', in the words of one 2018 study published in the journal *Geophysical Research Letters*. The authors found that the average snow depth in Europe had decreased by more than 12% per decade since the 1950s, and that this trend had accelerated after the 1980s. Memorable cold extremes can obscure these longer-term trends; where I am based in the UK, the winter of 2017–18 saw heavy snowfalls and prolonged freezing temperatures during an Arctic blast dubbed the 'Beast from the East'. The following winter, temperatures hit an all-time high, reaching 20°C in mid-February. This latter event – much more unusual in a historical context than a couple of weeks of blizzards – was quickly lost to memory.

The heatwave that came in the summer of 2019 won't be so easily forgotten. France set a new all-time temperature record, with daytime highs of a sort normally seen in North Africa rather than Europe. Up in the French Alps, the high temperatures melted out a new glacial lake below the spectacular summit of the Dent du Géant in the Mont Blanc massif. Alpinist Bryan Mestre's Instagram photo of a turquoise-blue pond entirely surrounded by ice, 3,500 metres up the mountain, quickly went viral. The climber himself was perturbed: 'I have been up there a fair amount of times, in June, July and even August, and I have never seen liquid water up there.' Mestre might have compared his photo with similar ones from melting mountain ranges around the world, from the Himalayas to the Andes – even perhaps to tourist photos taken in Peru's Cordillera Blanca, where at the end of the Ruta de Cambio Climático an even bigger lake is steadily replacing what is left of the once-famed Pastoruri Glacier.

Fickle floods

Not all climate impacts in our one-degree world are as clear-cut as the melting glaciers in the Alps and Andes. So it is with the vexed issue of floods. The IPCC's most recent summary is a masterpiece of studious equivocation. After reviewing a number of sources, it concludes: 'In summary, streamflow trends since 1950 are not statistically significant in most of the world's largest rivers, while flood frequency and extreme streamflow have increased in some regions.' In 2012 the IPCC released a special report on extreme events, which looked at how climate disasters were impacting society and how those impacts could be mitigated. It acknowledged that while there have been increases in heavy rainfall events, there was 'low confidence' in any resulting changes in flooding. A year later, in 2013, the IPCC's Fifth Assessment Report assessed the situation similarly, admitting that confidence remained 'low' about any potential increases in flooding.

The IPCC's caution was well justified. The most comprehensive recent review of river-flow trends at the global scale, published in 2016, investigated 50 years of changes on the world's largest 200 rivers. Out of these rivers, those exhibiting negative trends in flow rate (totalling 29) slightly outnumbered those showing positive trends (26). All the largest rivers – the Amazon, Congo, Orinoco, Chang Jiang, Brahmaputra, Mississippi, Yenisei, Parana, Lena, Mekong, Tocantins and the Ob – showed peaks and troughs over the period, as might be expected from natural climate variability. But there were no obvious upward trends in any of them that might indicate increased runoff or more severe flooding. Indeed, for the vast majority, 145 out of 200, any long-term (1948–2012) trends were statistically insignificant. A second study, published in 2017 and investigating changes in water flows at 9,213 river-monitoring stations, found 'more stations with significant decreasing trends than significant increasing trends', confirming the 2016 analysis.

This situation might seem perplexing because of frequent media reports about flood disasters around the world, which are often attributed to the changing climate. Plus, as all these reports acknowledge, there is unambiguous evidence that global warming is leading to heavier and more frequent intense precipitation events across much of the globe. This observed increase in precipitation intensity fully accords with climate physics. Warmer air can hold more water so as climate change accelerates, there is potentially more vapour available in a warmer atmosphere to be condensed into clouds and fall as rain, hail or snow.

For heavy precipitation, therefore, the IPCC offers no equivocation. 'The observed record suggests that increases in precipitation extremes can be identified for annual maximum 1-day precipitation and consecutive 5-day precipitation [events],' it stated in 2018. In other words, short-term cloud bursts and long-term deluges have both got worse. According to one recent assessment, a quarter of the land mass on Earth has experienced a definitive increase in heavy rainfall events. Extreme precipitation has been found to be increasing far faster than the average, and the number of record-breaking rainfall events is also clearly increasing.

Evidence is now stacking up from around the world. A 2019 study found an intensification of storm rainfall totals in the south-western United States, while a 2017 *Nature Communications* paper reported a 'threefold increase in widespread extreme rain events over central India during 1950–2015'. Perhaps counter-intuitively, arid areas are just as affected as wet regions by this increase in extreme rainfall. For example, a recent study found a tripling in the frequency of extreme storms in the dry Sahel region of West Africa since the 1980s. Flash flooding is often followed by 'flash droughts', sudden and intense dry periods combined with extreme heat; such events have tripled in incidence in southern Africa over the last 60 years.

Researchers also found that the extreme rains that hit Wuhan, China, in June and July 2016 are now ten times more likely in the one-degree world. These storms dropped over a metre of rainfall, causing severe flooding, the loss of 237 lives and $22 billion in economic damage, making them the second-most expensive weather-related disaster in China's history. In the United States, the strongest type of large-scale storm – the 'mesoscale convective systems' that often generate destructive tornados and large hailstones – are becoming more frequent and lasting longer. When it comes to heavier rainfall, therefore, the jury is no longer out.

So why has this not translated into clearly observed increases in flooding? A 2018 study examining this question acknowledged that there is a clear 'dichotomy' between the trend towards heavier rainfall events and the 'lack of corresponding increases in floods'. The truth is that there are many confounding factors influencing whether increased frequency of heavy rainfall translates into worsening floods. In many parts of the world, for example, snowmelt is an important part of river basin hydrology, and a warming climate means less snow accumulating during the winter and suddenly melting in spring – hence, less early-season flooding. Many rivers are also now interrupted by dams, which means that flows are directly controlled by human managers. Others have been dredged, channelled, diverted or otherwise altered in recent decades, while runoff has also been affected by changes in land use, urbanisation and forest cover. In addition, large amounts of water are withdrawn into reservoirs or pumped out of the ground for irrigation and direct human use. Some rivers – such as the Colorado and the Yellow rivers – have so much water abstracted for farming and industry that they sometimes fail to reach the sea at all. An increase in their annual flows, whatever the changing climate, is therefore unlikely to be registered over recent decades.

There is one type of extreme event, however, where the magnitude of rainfall changes is becoming so enormous that its effects on flooding are much more evident. The immediate impacts include the submergence of whole areas, resulting in disastrous economic damage and tragic loss of life. These storms form over warm ocean water, and strike fear into the hearts of people living close to the sea throughout the tropics and sub-tropics. I am talking, of course, about hurricanes.

Houston's hurricane

'GET OUT OR DIE!'

As a warning message, written in all caps, it was unsubtle but effective. So was the message that preceded it, also written by Tyler County judge Jacques Blanchette as Hurricane Harvey loomed over Texas on 29 August 2017: 'Anyone who chooses to not heed this directive cannot expect to be rescued and should write their social security numbers in permanent marker on their arm so their bodies can be identified,' wrote Blanchette. 'The loss of life and property is certain.'

The judge's warning was no exaggeration. As the floodwaters eventually receded after nearly a week of torrential deluge, the bodies of six family members – including four children – were pulled from a van that had been swept off a Houston bridge into a bayou. During the disaster itself, a shivering three-year-old girl was found clinging to the submerged body of her drowned mother. In all, at least 68 people died from the effects of Hurricane Harvey, the largest number of direct deaths from a tropical cyclone in Texas since 1919. The fatalities included a veteran Houston police officer, who drowned in his car in a flooded underpass while dutifully attempting to reach his place of work.

The scale and intensity of the deluge was staggering, even for seasoned meteorologists. Houston's branch of the National Weather Service reported an almost unimaginable 250 mm (9.92 inches) of rain in a single 90-minute period at a station in the southern suburbs of the city. Harvey deposited around 22 cubic kilometres of rainwater in total across the south-eastern coastal United States, an amount equivalent to the flow of Niagara Falls for 110 days. The weight of all the water was sufficient, scientists calculated, to depress the Earth's crust by two centimetres over the affected region. It took five weeks for all this extra water to flow back into the sea and for the land surface to gradually rebound.

Harvey was the wettest hurricane in United States history, with several places reporting 1,300–1,500 mm (50–60 inches) of rainfall. The totals were so high that the US National Weather Service had to add two new shades of purple to its flood maps to represent such extreme amounts of precipitation. 'After more than 50 inches of rain over four days,' reported the *Washington Post*, 'Houston was less of a city and more of an archipelago: a chain of urbanized islands in a muddy brown sea. All around it, flat-bottomed boats and helicopters were still plucking victims from rooftops, and water was still pouring in from overfilled reservoirs and swollen rivers.' About 300,000 buildings in the region were flooded, along with half a million cars. According to the Federal Emergency Management Agency, 30,000 water rescues took place during Hurricane Harvey's catastrophic deluge.

Even before the storm came ashore, speculation was rising about a possible role of climate change in the anticipated disaster. 'What you can and can't say about climate change and Hurricane Harvey,' read the headline of a *Washington Post* piece by the newspaper's climate specialist Chris Mooney on 25 August (the storm hit later that evening). 'Did climate change impact Hurricane Harvey?' asked CNN, as the flood waters reached their peak on 28 August. 'The Specter of Climate Change Hangs Over Hurricane Harvey', suggested the *New York Magazine*. The *Sydney Morning Herald*, publishing on the same day, took a more moralistic tone: 'Houston, you have a problem, and some of it your own making' read the headline. The author asserted – after wishing the state's residents well during the ongoing catastrophe – that 'as the self-styled "world capital of the oil and gas industry", there's a connection between rising global green-house gas levels and the extreme weather now being inflicted that some of your residents have understood for decades and had a hand in.'

Watching the disaster unfold, albeit from hundreds of miles away on the other side of the Atlantic, was a strange experience for me because the spectacle was frighteningly reminiscent of the scenario I painted of a monster hurricane hitting Houston in the first *Six Degrees*. As I wrote in an imaginary scene: 'The first of [the hurricane's] rain bands advances under the cover of darkness, dumping torrential downpours across coastal Texas, from Corpus Christi in the south right up to the border with Louisiana. The storm is enormous, and Houston is right in the middle of its projected track … The surge is now moving up the river, the first water pouring around the buildings on the eastern edge of Houston itself. With blinding rain now pounding all of Harris County for several hours, Houston's long-tamed river, Buffalo Bayou, begins to return to the wild. First to flood are underground car parks and malls. Storm drains suddenly start spouting floodwater. Manhole covers blow off with no warning, releasing fountains of foam five metres into the air. Abandoned vehicles float down the rapidly rising river, together with wind-blown debris washed out of flooded streets.'

All this bore an uncanny resemblance to the scene as it unfolded in Houston, not in my imagined future of August 2045 but right there in August 2017. Moreover, I had set this scene in my Three Degrees chapter because at the time I felt the science was not clear about whether or not hurricanes were already getting observably stronger, but that in a three-degree-warmer world 'any lingering doubts about the connection between global warming and stronger hurricanes will have been dispelled by the brutal realities of a more energetic atmosphere'. In that sense, Hurricane Harvey came 30 years too early. Like many computer climate models, I had been proved unduly conservative by real-world events.

The deluge of rain was shortly followed by a virtual avalanche of scientific papers analysing the possible contribution made to the disaster by climate warming. A November 2017 paper in *PNAS* by hurricane expert Kerry Emanuel concluded that Harvey was a one-in-2,000-year event for Houston because of the sheer magnitude of its rainfall. Emanuel wrote: 'By the standards of the average climate during 1981–2000, Harvey's rainfall in Houston was "biblical" in the sense that it likely occurred around once since the Old Testament was written.' Emanuel calculated, using both observations and climate models, that the annual probability of Harvey had already seen a 'sixfold increase since the late 20th century'. A subsequent paper, published a month later in *Environmental Research Letters*, determined that the three-day rainfall total of just over one metre recorded at Baytown was a staggering one-in-9,000-year event, and that global warming made the rainfall about 15% more intense and the storm overall three times more likely.

Hurricanes are fuelled by warmth in the oceans, and the ocean heat content in the Gulf of Mexico was the highest on record in 2017, helping drive Harvey's strong winds and intense rain. Harvey was also particularly destructive because the storm stalled over Houston, dropping enormous quantities of rain in one place over an extended period. There may be a climate change factor here too: a 2018 paper in *Nature* reported that tropical cyclone forward movement speed has slowed by 10% over the last half-century, increasing local rainfall totals that would previously have been spread over a wider area.

A similar stalling of an intense hurricane also led to the devastating flood-related disaster visited on the Bahamas by Hurricane Dorian in September 2019. This time the monster storm parked itself over the vulnerable islands for more than a day, resulting in nearly 1,000 mm of rainfall deluging the islands, accompanied by a multi-metre storm surge. As reported in *Scientific American*: 'This slow motion and extreme intensity allowed Dorian to subject the Bahamas to the most fierce and prolonged battering by an Atlantic hurricane of any populated place in recorded history.' By the time the cyclone finally drifted away to the north-east, Abaco and Grand Bahama islands were virtually flattened. With sustained wind speeds of 185 mph and gusts up to 220 mph, Dorian was 'truly exceptional … Winds of this strength would make Dorian worthy of a category 6 rating, if it existed.'

Despite Dorian's fury, 2019 was not as intense an Atlantic hurricane season overall as 2017. That year saw 17 named storms (the average is 12), 10 hurricanes and 6 major hurricanes. These included Irma and Maria, which devastated islands across the Caribbean. A 2019 study that investigated Maria found that the 2017 storm produced higher average rainfall totals than any of the 129 storms that have hit Puerto Rico since reliable records began in 1956, and that this extreme precipitation has become much more likely in recent years due to climate change. The combined storms generated 'accumulated cyclone energy' that was 245% above normal, thanks to hotter sea temperatures in the tropical North Atlantic. Hurricane Maria was the most deadly Atlantic hurricane for over a decade, causing – directly and indirectly – nearly 3,000 fatalities and leaving Puerto Rico's infrastructure devastated, with nearly all power lines, many buildings and 80% of crops destroyed.

Scientists are now beginning to wonder if something has permanently changed in hurricane climatology. Coastal North Carolina has experienced three extreme tropical cyclone-driven flood events since 1999, with experts left fearing that they are seeing the impacts of a 'regime shift' towards a permanently higher risk from hurricane-related floods. Climate models do seem to suggest that the disasters caused by hurricanes like Katrina (which submerged New Orleans in 2005), Irma and Maria would simply not have been so destructive in a pre-industrial climate that had not been altered by accumulating greenhouse gas emissions. In other words, these destructive storms were the different creatures we can now expect in our one-degree world.

Some studies have also detected a human climate-change finger-print in the rapid intensification and peak windspeeds reached by some tropical cyclones: both Maria and Irma underwent rapid intensification in the tropical Atlantic prior to landfall. The latter achieved Category 5 status and maintained that highest category longer than any storm anywhere in the world since reliable records began. Scientists have now found, for the Atlantic at least, a 'detectable increase' in tropical cyclone intensification rates as a result of global warming. Over in the eastern Pacific, in 2015 Hurricane Patricia broke records as the most intense tropical cyclone ever to form in the Western Hemisphere, with estimated sustained peak wind speeds of 185 knots, which equates to an extraordinary 212 mph. Patricia intensified explosively from a weak tropical storm to a strong Category 5 monster in just 48 hours, a rate of intensification so rapid and profound that it has probably also never been observed before in the modern era.

Underlying all these changes is the huge increase in ocean heat driven by global warming. In the western North Pacific, meteorologists have seen a doubling or even tripling of the numbers of Category 4 or 5-equivalent typhoons affecting eastern China, Taiwan, Korea and Japan over the last few decades. While the overall numbers of tropical cyclones have not changed much, those that do form are increasingly intense.

There is also evidence that the extent of the Earth's surface affected by tropical cyclones is increasing. Research shows that the main cyclone-generating regions have migrated poleward in both hemispheres during the last 30 years, consistent with broader changes in atmospheric circulation driven by global warming. This process is likely to continue. In 2017, for example, Hurricane Ophelia – the largest-ever recorded hurricane in the East Atlantic – made it all the way to the coast of Ireland, bringing strong winds and heavy rain, and causing coastal erosion.

This means that in decades to come it will not just be the coastal residents of places like Taiwan and North Carolina who will have to batten down the hatches for hurricane season. As the Irish found out in 2017 as Ophelia loomed up from the south-west, bringing strong winds, tropical warmth and peculiar yellow skies, areas that have previously been considered too cold to be at risk of landfalling tropical cyclones will increasingly find themselves in the line of fire. As if to presage this change, in late September and early October 2019 Hurricane Lorenzo blew up in the Atlantic, setting new records as it became the most northerly and easterly Category 5 storm ever recorded. 'This is something totally unusual for this kind of environment,' said Miguel Miranda, president of the Portuguese Institute of the Sea and Atmosphere. Hurricane Lorenzo 'is not normal', he added. Fortunately the storm largely dissipated before hitting the British Isles – but there will be many more 'abnormal' storms to come.

High tides

Rising seas, of course, make the threat from hurricanes even worse. Sea levels have risen by nearly 6 cm since I wrote my first book in 2004. I took its title, *High Tide*, from my experience on the threatened island nation of Tuvalu in the Pacific. I was entranced by island life and the rhythms of the day- and night-time activities, from catching tuna fish to drinking beer and dodging fights in the capital Funafuti's sleazy afterhours bar. Life was rapidly modernising – the majority of people wore jeans and T-shirts most of the time, but island traditions continued nevertheless. Most older men still wore coloured wraparound skirts, and we all gathered one evening for traditional dancing in the open-walled *maneapa* communal house, sharing plates of fish and taro. Sea level rise was impacting the community in Funafuti already, however: waves were washing into people's properties, and 'king tides' led to water bubbling up in the centre of the island and running through the streets. Things have only got worse since then, with Tuvalu experiencing a rate of sea level rise three times the global average.

The leaders of Tuvalu and other small island states are not suffering in silence as their survival is threatened. At UN meetings and climate change conferences representatives of the 'Association of Small Island States' (AOSIS) do their best to communicate their nations' plight to the rest of the world, demanding action on greenhouse gas emissions that is rapid and sustained enough to save them from drowning. I worked with AOSIS for several years in my capacity as climate advisor to President Nasheed of the Maldives, which as a coral atoll nation composed of hundreds of tiny islands is one of the countries most vulnerable to the rising seas. Nasheed was the first democratically elected president in the Maldives, and he made headlines early on in his administration when he and his ministers donned scuba gear and held an underwater cabinet meeting to illustrate the threat posed by the rising oceans. I worked with Nasheed on plans for the Maldives to lead the way towards a cleaner economy by becoming the world's first carbon-neutral country, a policy commitment announced in 2009. It has not all been plain sailing since then; a coup interrupted plans in 2012, with Nasheed forced from power and even suffering several months in prison at the hands of an autocratic new president. Fortunately, democracy has since returned, with Nasheed's Maldivian Democratic Party winning elections comprehensively in 2018.

During my time working with the Maldives and other small island states, it often seemed like the United States was the enemy, holding back progress at the UN and vetoing attempts to forge a global treaty on climate change. Now perhaps the US will need to think about joining AOSIS. Its east coast suffers some of the fastest relative rates of sea level rise in the world – about three to four times the global average – with a combination of tidal shifts and land subsidence making the 1,000-km-long, highly populated coast north of Cape Hatteras in North Carolina a 'hotspot' of accelerated sea level rise. Up and down the coast thousands of hectares of 'ghost forests' can be found in tidal estuaries and wildlife areas, where trees that have stood for decades or longer have been killed by gradually intruding salt-water. Scientists comparing the modern seashore with old maps from the 1850s suggest that 40,000 hectares of coastal forest may have died around the edges of Chesapeake Bay alone. 'Much of the dead forest has now been replaced by marshland, while former marsh areas are now open water,' reports Climate Central.

Coastal communities are now experiencing a new threat, of so-called 'sunny day flooding', where seawater inundates streets and parkland even on fairweather days without high onshore winds. According to the US agency NOAA, Boston, Massachusetts, and Atlantic City, New Jersey, both experienced 22 days of flooding in 2017, while Galveston, Texas, saw seawater invade its streets on 18 separate days. On 27 September 2015 'sunny day' high tides in the Miami region flooded several coastal communities with 0.57 metres of ocean water. Although this was only the sixth-highest water level measured in the area, the previous five flood events had all been associated with landfalling hurricanes. The NOAA report revealed that the frequency of high tide flooding on US coastlines has doubled in the last 30 years.

This is still only the beginning. Sea level rise has been accelerating in recent decades, from 1.4 mm/year before 1990 to 3.6 mm/year in the latest IPCC assessment. There are now numerous reports coming in from low-lying areas all around the world of the resulting impacts. A study of one part of the Solomon Islands in the western Pacific found five out of twenty vegetated reef islands 'have been totally eroded away in recent decades'. A further six islands are experiencing severe shoreline erosion, which at two sites has destroyed villages that have existed since at least 1935, forcing people to relocate. A study in New Caledonia in the south-western Pacific found numerous islets in a 'critical situation' and likely to disappear within just a few years. The picture is complicated, however. Global assessments show that larger islands have been remarkably resilient in the face of rising seas, with most inhabited islands not yet losing land area. Smaller atoll nations are uniquely vulnerable, however, including where I have worked in the Maldives.

Globally, 700 million people live in low-lying areas and 200 million are already within the range of extreme sea level rises. In southern Florida, weather forecasts now come with tide warnings, and stranded fish are a regular sight on flooded roads. Every year the waters rise, and residents know that while they can temporarily fight back with engineering projects and other adaptation measures, ultimately the oceans will win.

Paradise lost

It was 'like the gates of hell opened up', reported the newspaper *USA Today*. Except that this wasn't supposed to be hell – it was supposed to be Paradise. That was before the Camp Fire, however. The paper reported how the wildfire disaster that struck the small California town with the heavenly name on 8 November 2018 unfolded: 'As true darkness fell – smoke had clogged the air all afternoon – residents jammed onto winding, hilly two-lane roads. Witnesses reported blackout conditions, the smoke too thick to see through. Drivers collided, went off embankments, slammed into signs and trees as embers rained down upon them, setting trees and houses and cars alight.' The heat was so intense that windows were blown out, and streams of melted aluminium ran down the roads from burning vehicles. People stuck in traffic jams were burned alive in their cars as fiery tornados raged around them. 'It just looked like Dante's Inferno,' evacuee John Yates remembered. 'Black and red was all you could see.'

By the time the wildfire was finally brought under control ten days later, little remained of Paradise but a few charred foundations, with the survivors of its original 27,000 residents scattered into shelters and evacuation centres. The official death toll of what had become the nation's deadliest wildfire for a century climbed to 85 people. 'A whole town was wiped off the face of the Earth in a matter of eight hours,' one traumatised resident told CNN. As survivors began to return to the smouldering wreckage, they were warned to keep an eye out for bone fragments, all that might remain of residents who had not managed to escape in time. Other evacuees and relatives provided DNA samples to assist in the identification of any additional human remains.

After the fire burned out, attention moved to the role potentially played by climate change. Climate scientist Daniel Swain from the University of California, Los Angeles, explained on Twitter: 'If Northern California had received anywhere near the typical amount of autumn precipitation this year (around 4–5 in. of rain near the Camp Fire point of origin), explosive fire behaviour & stunning tragedy in Paradise would almost certainly not have occurred.' Reuters reported: 'Paradise had not seen significant rain for 211 days, and the town, on a ridge in the foothills of the Sierra Nevada mountains, was surrounded by a potential bonfire of dry or dead trees following a five-year drought that ended in 2017.' Swain's own work has shown that more of California's annual precipitation is coming in the winter months, leading to a drying trend in the summer and autumn, when fires tend to break out.

Later scientific work confirmed these preliminary conclusions. Studies show that between 1972 and 2018 California experienced a stunning fivefold increase in burned area. Each subsequent year seems to be setting new records: in 2017 modern state records were set for the largest individual wildfire (Thomas Fire, at 114,078 hectares) and for the most buildings destroyed by an individual wildfire (Tubbs Fire, 5,636 structures, leading to 22 fatalities). Both these records were to fall in 2018. In that year the Mendocino Complex Fire set a new record for the largest individual wildfire, turning 185,800 hectares to ashes. The deadly Camp Fire set a new record of 18,804 structures destroyed as it levelled the town of Paradise, and a state record was also set for the total area burned: 676,312 hectares. The costs were immense. In those two years California spent over $1.5 billion on fire suppression, itself also a new record. An analysis published in July 2019 showed that the major cause of the increase in summertime wildfires is the drying effect of rising temperatures, which have shot up by 1.4°C since the 1970s in California. Direct human influences – such as urbanisation, suppression of natural fires (which can lead to a build-up of unburned fuel wood) and so on – are potential contributory factors, but climate change is the big one.

This summer-drying trend has been measured over a large proportion of the forested areas of the western United States since 1979, and is strongly correlated with fire occurrence elsewhere as well. The number of large fires has been increasing: over the last quarter-century each year saw an average of seven additional large fires and an increase in burned area of 355 km² in the western US, according to one recent study. 'The geographically broad and coherent nature of fire and climate trends across much of the study area implicates climate as a dominant driver of changing fire activity in the western U.S.,' the authors reported. Another study, published in *PNAS* in 2016, also concluded that human-caused climate change has been drying out forests across the western part of the US, lengthening the period of 'high fire potential' by nine days on average. Between 1984 and 2015 climate change doubled the area affected by forest fires, with an additional 4.2 million hectares burned.

Canada has also seen an increase in devastating fires. The Alberta Fire that levelled a fifth of the city of Fort McMurray in spring 2016 burned for two whole months before being finally extinguished on 5 July. By that time, 2,400 buildings had been destroyed and 590,000 hectares of land burned. With 90,000 residents affected, the Alberta Fire resulted in the largest-ever wildfire evacuation in the province. Fortunately no one was killed, although the fire was the costliest economic disaster in the country's history, with an eventual price tag of 4.7 billion Canadian dollars. Ironically, perhaps, one of the fire's impacts was to shut down oil sands production in the north of Alberta province, taking one of the most carbon-intensive and environmentally destructive source of liquid fossil fuels offline, at least for a few days. A year later it was the turn of neighbouring British Columbia, which saw a record 1.5 million hectares (an area three-quarters the size of Wales) burned and 65,000 people displaced during the most extreme fire season on record. A study by Canadian scientists concluded that the 2017 disaster was made two to four times more likely by climate change, which also increased the area burned by a factor of seven to eleven.

Wildfires everywhere seem to be increasing both in frequency and destructive power. The year 2017 saw extensive and severe fires in Chile, the Mediterranean, Russia, the US, Canada and even Greenland, where fires were spotted burning in the tundra along the western coast. Across the world as a whole, researchers have found that the average fire season has lengthened by nearly a fifth, with half of the Earth's entire vegetated surface area seeing an increase in fire weather conditions during the last fifteen years. As the unfortunate residents of the Californian town of Paradise found out in the 2018 disaster, wildfire can strike with unprecedented ferocity and deadly speed – at one point the Camp Fire was spreading at the rate of a football field every single second.

In the first *Six Degrees* I used the image of Dante's Inferno, describing each degree rise in temperature as a descent into one of the successive circles of hell. This was meant to be just a metaphor. But from California to Canada, as smoke rises, it seems that we are entering the Inferno for real.

Heat refugees

Everywhere temperatures are rising, as ever-higher concentrations of greenhouse gases in the atmosphere trap heat at the Earth's surface. When I was beginning to write about climate change in the early 2000s, extremely hot summers might have been expected to occur twice a century. Now they are expected twice a decade. The shift is clear, even in temperate England where I live, with a two- to threefold increase in heatwaves since the pre-industrial period and week-long extreme heat events seemingly getting more intense each year. On 25 July 2019 a new UK all-time high-temperature record of 38.7°C was set at Cambridge University Botanic Garden, beating the previous record – set in 2003 – of 38.5°C. This seemed pleasantly cool by French standards, however. A month earlier, in June 2019, while much of western Europe baked in an unprecedented heatwave, thermometers in the southern French town of Gallargues-le-Montueux read a stunning 45.9°C, setting a new all-time record. A later study of the 2019 French heatwave found that it had been made five times more likely because of climate change.

This is what one degree of global warming looks like. Just the previous year, in the summer of 2018, almost the entirety of the Northern Hemisphere experienced drastically elevated temperatures, with extreme heat in Europe, North America, Asia and North Africa. In Oman, the coastal city of Quriyat experienced a 24-hour temperature that never dropped below 42.6°C, most likely setting a record for the highest minimum night-time temperature ever observed on Earth. In the Algerian Sahara, a high of 51.3°C was measured on 5 July, probably a new all-time record for the continent of Africa. At one point temperatures were as hot in Arctic Scandinavia as they were in southern Spain. Japan, too, set a new temperature record, with the city of Kumagaya, 65 kilometres from Tokyo, seeing 41.1°C. All around the world, records tumbled like dominoes.

A June 2019 study concluded that it was 'virtually certain' that the 2018 Northern Hemisphere heatwave – which affected a fifth of the populated and agricultural areas of the northern mid-latitudes concurrently – could not have happened in the absence of human-caused climate change. 'Virtually certain' means 99–100% probability in IPCC parlance; it is extraordinarily rare to have this level of confidence declared in any scientific finding. The authors also stated that heatwaves like that of 2018 were 'unprecedented prior to 2010'. The human fingerprint has become very clear in modern-day temperature rises – one modelling study suggests that there was only a one-in-a-million chance that the high global temperatures recorded in 2014, 2015 and 2016 could have come about through natural variability.

High temperatures may not seem as immediately dramatic as floods or storms, but they are just as deadly; more than 70,000 additional deaths were recorded in Europe during the extreme heat of August 2003, with those losing their lives primarily being the elderly and most vulnerable. According to a 2018 health review published in the leading medical journal *The Lancet*, vulnerability to extremes of heat has risen steadily since 1990 in every region, with 157 million more people exposed to heatwave events in 2017 compared with 2000. The death tolls for the 2018 and 2019 heatwaves have not yet been calculated, but they will likely be in the many thousands. Preliminary estimates are worrying: in northerly Sweden, for example, the heatwave of 2018 was associated with 635 excess deaths. In Japan, medical authorities reported more than 34,000 cases of heat-related emergency transportation during the 2018 heatwave, with nearly 100 people found clinically dead upon the arrival of the emergency medical services.

But there is another, more subtle, way in which heat kills people. Rising temperatures increase the risk of drought, and in less fortunate parts of the world drought can lead to food shortages and a loss of livelihoods, which exacerbates conflict. Drought risk is particularly increasing in the sub-tropics due to the widening of the tropical belt, a long-predicted and now observed feature of a warming planet. The Sahara is expanding both northwards and southwards, threatening the livelihoods of tens of millions more people living in the increasingly arid zones of West and North Africa. Across the Mediterranean in southern Europe, scientists have calculated that it is more than 95% likely that climate change has increased the probability of drought years. The Levant region – Palestine, Israel, Lebanon and

Syria – suffered 15 years of drought between 1998 and 2012, again due to the expanding zones of sub-tropical dry air consistent with global warming. Scientists have studied tree ring data from the region to try to estimate how often these kinds of droughts occurred in the past; they found that the recent decade was probably drier than any comparable period over the last 900 years.

The impacts on the inhabitants of the region have been utterly devastating. During the worst part of the drought after 2009, 1.5 million people were displaced from agricultural areas in Syria and forced to migrate to cities as harvests failed and livestock herds died from thirst and starvation. This led to a doubling of food prices and a dramatic increase in childhood undernutrition. 'The rapidly grow-ing urban peripheries of Syria, marked by illegal settlements, over-crowding, poor infrastructure, unemployment, and crime, were neglected by the Assad government and became the heart of the developing unrest', reported an assessment for *PNAS*, with this unrest later becoming a full-scale civil war. The failure of the Assad dictator-ship to initially address the agricultural crisis, and the dire conditions suffered by millions of displaced people and refugees who were living in terrible conditions on the edges of cities, were therefore important factors in the Syrian uprising that began in 2011. This obviously does not mean that Assad's decision to drop barrel bombs and poison gas on civilian populations can be blamed on climate change. The Syrian regime's war crimes remain its own responsibility, albeit shared with the Russian and Iranian governments that propped up the blood-soaked Syrian dictator.

However, there is evidence that climatic calamities do correlate with armed conflict, at least in the most ethnically divided countries. The authors of a recent study note that 'about 23% of conflict outbreaks in ethnically highly fractionalized countries robustly coin-cide with climatic calamities'. This is not a simple cause-and-effect relationship, but it does seem like the disruptions brought on by climate heating play out in ethnically divided countries 'in a particularly tragic way'. The ensuing conflicts can have impacts far afield, as – in the case of Syria – millions of refugees flee to neighbouring countries.

The moral challenge of climate change is writ large in the fate of refugees. Given that the richer countries have done most to cause global warming, I would argue that they have an especially strong responsibility to assist people who are suffering the impacts of drought-related conflicts like that in Syria. One of the proudest moments of my life was speaking to a crowd of 2,000 people at a 'refugees welcome' rally a small group of us organised in 2015 at a few days' notice in Oxford. The spark that made us act, and prompted so many people to come along to show their support, was the photograph of the Syrian toddler Alan Kurdi washed up drowned on a beach in Turkey. Kurdi was a victim of climate, conflict – and callousness: that of European leaders who closed their nations' borders and refused aid to millions of people in distress, forcing the young boy's family to attempt a dangerous night-time crossing to Greece in an open boat. We are all human, and as climate impacts accelerate in decades to come, maybe one day Western readers of this book will be the refugees. I hope – and it might be a forlorn hope – that we can summon up the will to address future climate impacts in a spirit of mutual solidarity rather than division. Otherwise I fear there will be many more Alan Kurdis washed up on the world's beaches in the years ahead.

Against nature

It is not only humans who are suffering from the impacts of ongoing climate breakdown. Global heating is now an increasing factor in wildlife declines and even the outright extinction of species as plants and animals lose their habitat due to shifting climate zones. According to the IPCC, 'the geographical ranges of many terrestrial and freshwater plant and animal species have moved over the last several decades in response to warming: approximately 17 km poleward and 11 m up in altitude per decade.' In terms of annual distance, that corresponds to 1.7 kilometres per year – or nearly five metres per day – that species are having to shift their ranges to keep up with rising temperatures in our one-degree world. And this is only an average: in many places climate zones are moving much faster.

It may be obvious that plants, which are generally rooted to the ground, will have difficulty keeping up with this increasing 'climate velocity'. But even those species with wings are lagging behind. One recent study found that birds and butterflies were running up 'climatic debts' by lagging 212 and 135 kilometres respectively behind the ongoing speed of climate change. When they do move long distances, butterflies may find themselves stranded in a suitable climate but without food to raise their caterpillars, if their larval host plants are slower to disperse into new areas. Birds which then depend on absent insect larvae to feed their chicks may find their own offspring facing starvation. One example is Baird's sandpiper, a species whose migration into the high Arctic used to be timed exactly to coincide with the peak of insect abundance during the short tundra summer. Insects are now emerging earlier as springtimes advance, meaning less food later in the season for hungry sandpiper chicks. Another migratory bird is the pied flycatcher, whose populations have crashed in Holland as the bird arrives from Africa too late to exploit the peak supply of caterpillars. Research has also found an increasing mismatch between the supply of caterpillars in UK oak forests and the demands from nestlings of birds such as blue tits, great tits and pied flycatchers. Such is the reality of unravelling food webs across the world as temperatures rise.

Animals and plants in mountain areas are particularly vulnerable because they are finding themselves squeezed uphill in contracting areas towards mountain summits as temperatures rise. Dubbed the 'escalator to extinction', this topographical effect is particularly worrying among mountains in the tropics, because species would have to travel thousands of miles to higher latitudes to find the same kinds of cooler regions that currently exist in tropical highlands. There is evidence that this is already happening; in 2017 a team of biologists visited a remote and densely forested Peruvian mountain ridge called Cerro de Pantiacolla, returning to an area that had been originally surveyed for birds back in 1985. With temperatures having risen nearly half a degree in the intervening period, the scientists expected to find that bird species had shifted their ranges uphill in order to stay in the same temperature zones. What they found was even worse. 'Several high-elevation species seem to have disappeared, and those that persist have generally shifted upslope and now inhabit smaller distributions with lower abundances,' the scientists reported, concluding that 'high-elevation birds on the Cerro de Pantiacolla are indeed riding an escalator to extinction.'

It is not only changing temperatures that are a concern. In California's Mojave Desert researchers found that numbers of bird species have 'collapsed' since the early 20th century, with reduced rainfall amounts being the most likely cause of an observed 40% decline. A 2016 study surveying 976 species around the world found that climate-related local-area extinctions had already occurred in nearly half of them. The casualty list included fish, insects, birds and mammals, with tropical species suffering the most. A total of 460 species had been driven out of previous habitat by rising temperatures.

When species are already under threat and restricted to very small areas, a single disaster can wipe out the entire global population. This is what is thought to have happened with the world's first documented climate-driven mammal extinction – that of the Bramble Cay melomys, a small rodent restricted to a single island in Australia's Torres Strait. With extreme high tides driven by sea level rise inundating the island and destroying vegetation, the animal lost 97% of its habitat. The last individual was seen by a fisherman in 2009, and in 2019 the government of Australia recognised it as officially extinct.

'The Bramble Cay melomys was a little brown rat,' the Wilderness Society told the *Sydney Morning Herald*. 'But it was our little brown rat and it was our responsibility to make sure it persisted. And we failed.'

Climate change is only one factor among many driving the ongoing epidemic of global biodiversity loss. The Bramble Cay melomys was one of three Australian vertebrates known to have gone extinct between 2009 and 2014. One of the others was also a mammal, the Christmas Island pipistrelle bat, which disappeared alongside another Christmas Island species, the forest skink. The last individual of the latter species, a female lizard nicknamed Gump, died in captivity on 31 May 2014. The immediate cause of the species' deaths is not known for certain, but is likely to involve predation from introduced species such as cats or snakes.

Whether caused by invasive species on islands, hunting for bushmeat in Africa, the destruction of tropical forests or rampant industrial overfishing, the ongoing wave of destruction is affecting pretty much the entirety of life on Earth. Take wild herbivorous mammals, 60% of the species of which are threatened with extinction. These include the Bactrian camel, of which only 950 survive in the wild, Przewalski's horse (population 310), the pygmy hippopotamus (2,500), our close relatives the Eastern gorilla (5,900 are left), and the mountain tapir (2,500). The total population of Javan rhinoceros is just 50, while the Sumatran rhinoceros numbers only 280 individuals.

As these dismal numbers indicate, even where species do not disappear entirely, so few individuals are left in the wild that a species may be ecologically dead anyway. Marine biologists are now observing the proliferation of 'empty reefs', 'empty estuaries' and 'empty bays'. This drastic reduction in wildlife numbers – termed 'defaunation' – means that 40% of mammal species and 32% of all vertebrates have experienced severe population declines in recent decades. Scientists writing in *PNAS* in July 2017 described this as 'biological annihilation', part of what has now become the 'sixth major extinction event' in the Earth's history.

The statistics are so overwhelming as to be almost numbing. In September 2019, for example, a team of biologists reported in *Science* that since 1970 bird populations in the US and Canada have declined by nearly a third. These declines are seen not just in rare and threatened species but in familiar backyard birds seen across the North American continent. The total number of birds lost was a staggering three billion individuals, including sparrows, warblers, finches and swallows – which, as BirdLife explains, are 'common, widespread species that play essential roles in food webs and ecosystem functioning, from seed dispersal to pest control'.

One of the biggest factors driving the decline of once-common bird species is an underlying fall in the numbers of insects. The term 'Insectageddon' is now used in the media to describe the rapid declines in insect numbers measured around the world. This seems to be happening even in areas that are not obviously directly impacted by humans; a study in German nature reserves found a 75% decline in 'total flying insect biomass' over 27 years, while in relatively undisturbed Puerto Rican rainforests another team found that insect biomass had declined by between 10 and 60 times between the 1970s and today. Not surprisingly, parallel declines were observed in the populations of insectivorous lizards, frogs and birds. A 2019 paper found that global rates of decline are now so dramatic that 40% of the world's insect species may be driven to extinction within the next four decades. Another recent study in the US Midwest found that a third of butterflies had disappeared in just 20 years.

Habitat loss due to agriculture is the number one concern identified by the researchers, followed by pollution from fertilisers and pesticides, and invasive species. However, climate change is probably now a significant factor behind insect loss too, as ecological zones shift and food webs fray. Direct impacts of heat may also be affecting insect reproduction. A 2018 study found that simulated laboratory heatwaves could damage sperm production in beetles, suggesting that this 'male reproductive damage under heatwave conditions provides one potential driver behind biodiversity declines and contractions through global warming'. The researchers found that a single heatwave (defined as a 5–7°C rise in temperature for five days) halved male fertility in the beetles, while a second heatwave almost sterilised them.

Climate change can also interact with disease. Amphibians – frogs and salamanders in particular – have suffered catastrophic population collapses worldwide in recent decades as a result of the rapid international spread of an infectious skin disease caused by the chytrid fungus. At least 501 amphibian species have been pushed into decline by the resulting chytridiomycosis disease, with 90 species confirmed or presumed extinct in the wild and a further 124 experiencing declines of more than 90% in abundance. While the global amphibian trade may have helped to spread the disease rapidly, even into protected nature reserves far from direct human disturbance, rising temperatures may also be a factor. One study looking at the critically endangered Panamanian golden frog – a native of cloud forests in central Panama – found that individuals showed especially high mortality rates when the chytrid fungus was combined with higher temperatures.

If you go trekking in the Panamanian jungle today you won't find any golden frogs. The only specimens left alive are within captive breeding programmes in zoos and conservation centres, protected behind glass and plastic walls, and isolated from the external environment by strict biosafety protocols. Annual Golden Frog Festivals – for the beleaguered amphibian is Panama's national animal, no less – feature parades, sponsored runs, and trips to see the few remaining captive animals. Much of the frog's former territory is protected in the hope that it might one day return, perhaps after the climate has been stabilised and the current wave of extinctions has passed. But for the moment the Panamanian forests that once echoed to the sound of the frog's distinctive whistling mating calls lie silent.

Global browning

For Chapman's Baobab the end came suddenly. On 7 January 2016 a loud cracking sound, followed by a mighty groan, echoed across the Kalahari. All seven trunks of the mighty tree – one of the largest and oldest in the world – suddenly split apart at the base and crashed to the ground, leaving them splayed apart in opposite directions like corpses on a battlefield. Tellingly, while the disaster arrived with no warning, it came after Botswana recorded its hottest-ever day, and following two years of punishing drought. This gigantic tree, which had stood for at least a thousand years and was one of Botswana's best-known landmarks, had died of thirst.

Ancient and stately, baobab trees have stood sentinel-like on the plains of southern Africa for millennia. Known as the 'tree of life', the baobab – with its bulbous trunk and frequently hollow base – is instantly recognisable, even from a far distance. Several individuals have been measured at over 2,000 years old. And yet these antique specimens, the oldest angiosperms (flowering plants) on the planet, have begun one by one to topple over and die. In 2018 a research team led by the Romanian ecologist Adrian Patrut, an expert on baobabs, reported that nine of the thirteen oldest, and five of the six largest individuals have died or begun to collapse in the past twelve years. They include Namibia's Homasi tree, which had stood since the end of the Roman empire and fell on 1 January 2005. Many of the trees are immensely historic; Chapman's Baobab, for instance, had initials on its bark carved by the 19th-century explorer David Livingstone. The oldest of all was Panke, a sacred baobab located in a remote part of Matabeleland, Zimbabwe. Patrut and his team carbon-dated samples from its trunks after the tree fell in 2010, finding it to be an incredible 2,400 years old. No wonder it was sacred.

'The deaths of the majority of the oldest and largest African baobabs over the past 12 years is an event of an unprecedented magnitude,' wrote Patrut and his team in *Nature Plants* journal. There was no evidence of an epidemic of disease, they made clear, and yet numerous mature baobabs had all died suddenly in a short space of time, making climate change a leading suspect. Other experts are more blunt. 'One would imagine such behemoths had survived many climatic vicissitudes over their vast lifetimes,' forest ecologist Bill Laurance told environment writer John Vidal. 'But in a climatically changing world, their great stature is a curse. They struggle to get water up to their foliage without suffering dangerous embolisms in their vascular systems. Droughts can be fatal. In a world with more drought and with higher temperatures, it does not take much to push them over the edge.'

Africa's baobabs are not the only arboreal casualties. From Spain to New Mexico, and from Argentina to Australia, there are now multiple examples of large-scale forest die-offs associated with drought and high temperatures. In Algeria, the majestic blue-green Atlas cedars have begun to dry out and die, while in Australia acacias have been dying back over large areas. In New Zealand and Patagonia one casualty is *Nothofagus* (southern beech), while across western India numerous tree species in dry tropical forests have suffered sharply increased mortality. In Europe, spruce, beech, fir, oak and pine have all experienced die-offs in the wake of heatwave and drought events. Across huge areas of the American West conditions are now too dry for ponderosa pine and Douglas fir seedlings to re-establish after wildfires, leading to fears that these iconic forests may be passing a threshold where they will eventually disappear completely. Forest experts are concerned that widespread tree death due to drought and heat may now be a worldwide phenomenon directly resulting from our one-degree world.

During California's epic 2012 to 2015 drought, tree mortality increased tenfold, from tens to hundreds of dead trees per square kilometre, a death toll that rose dramatically in the fourth year of the drought. According to a study published in July 2019, conifer trees throughout the southern Sierra Nevada had found themselves with soil moisture exhausted as deep as 15 metres into the ground, far below accessible root level. As well as direct death from thirst, the drought made trees vulnerable to bark beetle outbreaks and wildfires. While California has seen droughts before, the higher temperatures accompanying the recent record-breaking rainfall deficits seem to have been the final straw for millions of trees.

With the world's forests under threat, the next generation of climate models may have to be retuned. It has long been supposed that rising CO_2 levels in the atmosphere will have a fertilising effect on the world's plants, and that the land biosphere will therefore continue sucking up increasing amounts of carbon right through until the end of the century. Certainly CO_2 fertilisation is real, and is why some growers pump waste CO_2 into greenhouses to ramp up tomato production. And for a long time it was also the case that large areas of the Earth's surface were greening, partly in response to elevated levels of CO_2. The phenomenon used to be talked up by climate change deniers, who a decade ago ran a now-defunct coal industry front group called the 'Greening Earth Society' to tout 'the benefits to plant life from carbon dioxide fertilization' to the unwary. No more. The most recent satellite data, published in August 2016, show that a threshold was passed in 1999, after which the greening trend in many areas reversed. The culprit seems to have been a parallel post-2000 decline in relative atmospheric humidity, which has been drying out forests faster than water can evaporate from the world's oceans. Thanks to this increasing water vapour shortage, greening Earth became browning Earth instead.

If the CO_2 fertilisation effect has indeed been overplayed in climate models, it means that more carbon will remain in the atmosphere to generate further warming rather than being taken up by plants. Moreover, if sudden forest die-offs continue to be seen over large parts of the world, not only will the biodiversity crisis accelerate but new carbon may appear as ecosystems collapse. In the worst-case scenario, the land biosphere will become a net source of carbon. If that happens, the falling Chapman's Baobab – which echoed like gunfire across the arid plains of the Kalahari on the morning of 7 January 2016 – may have been the opening shot in a much wider war.

Ocean heatwaves

Rising CO_2 has major effects in the ocean too. Most directly it causes ocean acidification as carbon dioxide dissolved in seawater generates carbonic acid. Since pre-industrial times, surface ocean pH has decreased by around 0.1, a change already harming shell-building organisms – from corals to plankton – that use calcium carbonate. This pH drop may not sound like much, but it is estimated to be taking place an order of magnitude faster than any natural event for hundreds of millions of years. So much human-made CO_2 has now entered the oceans that the seafloor is even starting to dissolve in several locations around the world. As the authors of a recent *PNAS* paper point out, this 'chemical burndown' is beginning to alter the geological record of the deep sea, and 'will intensify and spread over vast areas of the seafloor during the next decades and centuries' as ocean acidification accelerates.

CO_2 of course also causes warming, and the laws of physics dictate that hotter water holds less oxygen. The slowdown of ocean circulation – also driven by warming – means that less surface oxygen is transported into the depths. Thus global warming is beginning to deoxygenate the oceans, depleting the dissolved oxygen in seawater that is essential for the survival of virtually all forms of life. Over the last half-century the ocean has lost 2% of its oxygen content, which equates to a loss of 77 billion metric tonnes of oxygen. In the open ocean so-called 'oxygen-minimum zones' have expanded by 4.5 million square kilometres, equivalent to the size of the European

Union, while the volume of fully anoxic water (seawater that is completely devoid of oxygen) has quadrupled. In addition, more than 500 dead zones now persist in coastal waters around the world. Although these smaller coastal dead zones are caused largely by nutrient pollution from agricultural runoff and sewage, the world-wide loss of oceanic oxygen bears the unmistakable fingerprint of global heating.

Ocean warming is having a direct and sometimes devastating effect on species and ecosystems. One tragic example was the 'marine heatwave' that struck the Pacific coast of North America between 2014 and 2015 and led to a mass die-off of seabirds. Populations of the robin-sized Cassin's auklets were particularly badly hit. The US Fish and Wildlife Service collected 250 carcasses on a single stretch of Oregon beach and left as many behind. 'You'd find them piled up in clusters on the wrack line, where the tide leaves sea grasses and debris,' the biologist recalled. 'Most were in these states of decay, but every now and then we'd see tracks coming out of the water and find a bird that was just barely clinging to life. They were just skin and bones.' By April 2015 more than 9,000 carcasses had been recorded on beaches from California to Washington State. 'It was so distressing,' recalled one bird-spotting volunteer, who had patrolled the beaches of Washington State looking for dead or stranded seabirds. 'They were just everywhere. Every ten yards we'd find another ten bodies of these sweet little things.' Scientists found that the carcasses were emaciated – ruling out toxic pollution or oil spills, they concluded that the little birds had starved to death in huge numbers.

The mass-mortality event closely tracked the appearance of hotter-than-usual waters over a huge area of the coastal north-east Pacific, famously dubbed 'The Blob' by Washington's state climatologist Nicholas Bond. Warmer temperatures had drastically reduced the numbers of tiny invertebrates, called copepods, that are the primary food source for Cassin's auklets, and the tiny birds had starved in their thousands as a result. The species was already listed as of conservation concern following long-term population declines, and scientists warn that marine heatwaves on the scale of the 2014–15 north-east Pacific event 'may well represent a global population preci-pice' for the vulnerable seabird. 'I've never seen anything like this, ever, and I've been here since 1985,' David Nuzum, of the Oregon Department of Fish and Wildlife, told *National Geographic*.

It wasn't just birds that were affected. The Blob was also implicated in a cetacean 'Unusual Mortality Event' (UME) that saw 46 whale carcasses – mostly fin and humpback whales – stranded on the coast-lines of British Columbia and Alaska. Another UME was declared at the same time for fur seals and California sea lions, with malnour-ished, starving and dead animals washing up along the entire California coast from January 2015 onwards. Those that could be saved were taken to rehabilitation centres where malnourished pups were provided with nutrition and hydration so that they could be re-released when conditions improved. Fisheries were also affected, and a harmful algal bloom led to toxins contaminating shellfish along the coasts of Washington, Oregon and California. All told, scientists writing in the journal *Nature Climate Change* concluded, 'it is possi-ble that the northeast Pacific warm anomaly of 2014–15 is the most ecologically and economically significant marine heatwave on record.'

Other marine areas have been hit by their own versions of 'The Blob'. On the Atlantic coast of South America a 2017 marine heatwave brought the hottest-ever recorded sea temperatures over a wide area, causing mass mortalities of fish and a toxic algal bloom just a few miles offshore from Uruguay's capital city. In 2010 to 2011 a marine heatwave off the coast of Western Australia damaged huge areas of ecologically important seagrass meadow and led to a long-term decline in the population of bottlenose dolphins. Marine heatwaves 'have already become longer-lasting and more frequent, extensive and intense in the past few decades', a 2018 *Nature Climate Change* paper concluded, reporting data showing that marine heatwave days doubled between 1982 and 2016. Another 2018 paper, published in

Nature Communications, found that 'from 1925 to 2016, global average marine heatwave frequency and duration increased by 34% and 17%, respectively, resulting in a 54% increase in annual marine heatwave days globally.' The explanation was straightforward: a rise in average ocean temperatures. In other words, the culprit was global warming.

A more recent paper, published in March 2019, concluded that marine heatwave days have increased by 50% in recent decades as compared with the first half of the 20th century. Lead author Dan Smale compared the impact of hotter oceans on marine ecosystems to wildfires on land. 'You have heatwave-induced wildfires that take out huge areas of forest, but this is happening underwater as well,' he told the *Guardian*. 'You see the kelp and seagrasses dying in front of you. Within weeks or months they are just gone, along hundreds of kilometres of coastline.'

Bleaching corals

The oceanic ecosystems most endangered by marine heatwaves are tropical coral reefs, which are experiencing devastating bleaching episodes as they are swept by ever-hotter waters. In 2016 and 2017 Australia's Great Barrier Reef suffered back-to-back mass bleaching events that virtually wiped out large areas of this 2,300-km-long ecosystem. Terry Hughes, a world expert on corals, surveyed 900 sections of the reef during and immediately after the 2016 bleaching event from the air. 'I showed the results of aerial surveys on bleaching on the Great Barrier Reef to my students,' he tweeted on 19 April 2016. 'And then we wept.'

Hughes and colleagues subsequently published a paper in *Nature* that detailed an 'unprecedented ecological collapse, extending southwards from Papua New Guinea for up to 1,000 km'. In the worst-hit northern 700-km section of the reef, where heat exposure was most extreme, 50% of coral cover on reef crests was lost within eight months. With the staghorn and tabular corals suffering a 'catastrophic die-off', the three-dimensionality and ecological functioning of nearly a third of the 3,863 reefs that together comprise the world's largest coral reef system was transformed. Mass bleaching was easy to spot from the air, with large sections of reef converted into areas of deathly white visible through the clear water. The southern section of the reef was only saved from the same fate by pure luck, when cooling wind, cloud-cover and rain from a passing tropical storm rescued it from the rising temperatures that were devastating corals elsewhere.

Any lingering optimism about the longer-term fate of the reefs must surely be misplaced. Coral bleaching was virtually unknown in the world's oceans before the mid-1980s. This means that corals have evolved little protection to rising heat that might help them adapt or speed ecological recovery. For example, a bleaching event in 1998 killed large areas of staghorn coral surrounding Orpheus Island off the Queensland coast. Now, 18 years later, photographs of the same site show it still covered with muddy debris and exhibiting no sign of recovery. Even when some ecological rebound does take place, bleaching events are now arriving too frequently for the reefs to recover anything like their previous diversity before the next event strikes. The latest studies now show that marine heatwaves are becoming sufficiently intense to skip the bleaching process altogether and kill coral organisms directly. The exposed reefs, left vacant by the dead coral polyps, are draped with a layer of algae within a few days, and later begin to dissolve.

The 2016 worldwide bleaching event, as well as devastating the Great Barrier Reef, also had 'catastrophic impacts' – according to scientists later reporting in *Nature* – in the Red Sea, central Indian Ocean and across the Pacific Ocean and the Caribbean. In some areas corals were bleached right down to what should be much cooler areas 90 metres below the sea surface. In the Arabian Gulf, where corals were assumed to be reasonably accustomed to higher sea temperatures, reefs spread over 350 kilometres of the southern basin of the

Gulf were bathed in lethally high temperatures for over a fortnight. Mass bleaching ensued, and two-thirds of corals were killed outright. By the next year, just 7.5% of the original coral cover was left. Reef scientists were particularly shocked at the scale of this loss because the Gulf corals were supposed to be more resistant to bleaching as they were used to higher temperatures. Yet they still died.

The coral die-off has transformed once thriving reefs into 'more degraded systems, with just a few tough species remaining,' scientists report. No wonder so many coral experts are in despair. A recent feature in *Nature* reported that many marine biologists who work on the Great Barrier Reef are experiencing 'ecological grief' at witnessing the real-time breakdown of one of the world's most beautiful and valuable ecosystems, something that they have loved and studied throughout their careers. Researchers also feel the weight of knowing what has been lost, and the reality that their children will never enjoy the pristine and thriving reefs that they themselves remember.

Meanwhile, the extinction clock is ticking. The final demise of the reefs may come sooner than even many scientists expect, not just because of increased bleaching or thermal stress, but because corals are increasingly failing to reproduce at all. Researchers have found that juvenile corals, which need a solid anchor point on the seafloor to start growing, cannot establish new colonies on a bed of algae and mud-covered rubble. Although new coral colonies are moving pole-ward in a desperate effort to stay within thermally tolerable waters, studies have found a more than 80% reduction in their worldwide reproductive success since the 1970s. Recent work on the Great Barrier Reef found a 90% collapse in the reproductive capacity of the corals, though perhaps this is hardly surprising since most of the sexually mature adults over large areas are already dead.

Coral reproduction used to be one of the great wonders of the world. Despite being unable to communicate directly, corals are somehow able to spawn over hundreds of kilometres simultaneously on a single night, this miraculous synchrony coordinated through a complex combination of environmental cues and the phases of the moon. Eggs and sperm can only survive in the water for a matter of hours, so successful fertilisation depends critically on coral colonies all releasing their sexual material at the same time. However research conducted in the Red Sea, published in *Science* in September 2019, suggests that this system, which evolved over millions of years, is beginning to break down in the face of record-breaking sea temperatures. Corals are losing their spawning 'synchrony' – in other words they are going out of tune, with colonies spawning in an irregular way over different nights or even failing to spawn at all. This synchrony breakdown drastically reduces the probability of successful fertilisation, which in turn reduces the numbers of young corals and may eventually 'drive aging populations to extinction'.

I don't know whether the researchers wept when they saw what was happening to coral spawning in the Red Sea. But it would be strange not to suffer 'ecological grief' at the sight of billions of coral eggs dispersing uselessly into the warming ocean, and at the thought that the prospects of the next generation of these spectacular corals has been stolen. This is a future stolen ultimately not just from tropical corals, Cassin's auklets or golden toads. It is also stolen from our own children, who will never know the amazing and spectacular world that we enjoyed when we were young. Already, at one degree, our globe is becoming impoverished and reduced. We might all weep for what we have done.

2°

Day Zero in the Arctic

No one knows exactly when it will happen, but at some point in the two-degree world we will see the complete disappearance of Arctic sea ice, resulting in an ice-free North Pole for the first time for about three million years. It is already fairly likely that most people alive today who are middle-aged or younger will witness this event, a historical milestone by any description. No other humans in the whole history of our species would have been able to sail right across the North Pole without hitting a substantial ice cap. Even during previous interglacials – warm periods between successive ice ages when the Greenland ice sheet was reduced to a much smaller size, forests advanced northwards and the Sahara flourished with lakes and wetlands – there was still permanent ice in the Arctic. The date that we lose it – Day Zero in the Arctic – will surely be a global warming marker like no other.

Scientists are now confident that the threshold for an ice-free summertime Arctic lies somewhere in the two-degree world. To be classified as 'ice-free', the entire Arctic does not have to have melted; some ice will probably remain attached to the coasts of Ellesmere Island and northern Greenland for many years after the rest of the wider Arctic Ocean becomes open water. Instead, the generally recognised definition for 'ice-free' is therefore the first year when

September (late summer) sea ice extent falls below one million square kilometres. A 2017 study in the journal *Nature Climate Change* found that a 'summer ice-free Arctic is virtually certain to be avoided if the 1.5°C target of the Paris Agreement is met', but the chance of avoiding an ice-free Arctic falls to 1 in 3 if global warming is only limited to two degrees.

Different models yield different estimates, however. A 2018 study, also published in *Nature Climate Change*, found that by the year 2053 in a two-degree world it is certain – a 100% probability, in other words – that ice-free conditions in the Arctic will have been reached at least once. When exactly the first ice-free year happens is something of a lottery, because it depends on the chaotic year-to-year variation of weather patterns. Clearly, however, the probability keeps on rising the longer that warming is sustained. Another 2018 study confirmed that with two degrees of warming it is more than 99% likely that summer Arctic sea ice will have disappeared at some stage, with the final threshold probably lying somewhere between 1.5 to 1.9°C of average global warming. A fourth study, using a different 'earth system' model, found that in a 1.5°C scenario an ice-free Arctic September remained a relatively rare 1-in-40-year event, while at two degrees one in every three years was simulated as being ice-free.

Unfortunately these model projections may be unduly optimistic. The majority of the more than two dozen models on which these forecasts are based fail to accurately simulate the dramatic rate of sea ice loss that is already being observed by scientists monitoring the Arctic. Why exactly the models are so conservative is still being debated, but clearly if the Arctic sea ice is melting faster than the models represent, their projections for the future may also underestimate how quickly the ice will disappear. Indeed, once models are retuned to take observed summer sea ice declines as a starting point, they instead predict 'a nearly sea ice free Arctic in September by the year 2037', with the possibility that the first ice-free year may occur as early as the late 2020s. The most recent generation of updated climate models also suggest a nearly sea ice free Arctic in the 2030s, once they are tweaked to take the current rapid ice disappearance as a starting point.

Projections for an ice-free Arctic are not only based on computer simulations. Ocean drilling expeditions have recovered sediment cores from an Arctic seafloor ridge, with the aim of analysing the region's long-term climate history via the balance of carbon molecules utilised by different marine plankton species present at the time. These seem to show that back in the Late Miocene, five to ten million years ago, summer sea ice was absent when atmospheric CO_2 levels were about 450 parts per million (ppm). We are currently, in 2019, at about 408 ppm and rising at between 2–3 ppm per year. At current emissions rates, we could therefore see 450 ppm, and an ice-free Arctic, by about 2034 – assuming that other factors remain the same and that CO_2 therefore acts as the main driver of polar temperatures. The comparisons are not exact, because during the Miocene the Earth's climate was in long-term equilibrium, whereas currently we are changing it rapidly as we make the transition to a new, hotter climate state.

The disappearance of the Arctic sea ice matters for more reasons than just its epochal historical significance. For a start, it could play havoc with the world's weather. As we saw in the previous chapter, there is evidence that the ongoing drastic reductions in Arctic sea ice are already affecting atmospheric circulation, thereby contributing to extreme weather events across the Northern Hemisphere. With the transition to a seasonally ice-free Arctic, this process can only intensify. If there is no cap of sea ice on the ocean, the whole region becomes much warmer, changing the pressure dynamics of the upper atmosphere over the polar region. The northern continents warm faster than they would otherwise, and the tropical rain band in the Pacific is displaced southward and intensifies. Because of the reduced temperature gradient between the much warmer polar region and the mid-latitudes, the Northern Hemisphere jet stream weakens, altering storm tracks and perhaps leading to more 'blocked' weather, with associated intense heatwaves in summer and cold outbreaks in winter. Climate models are virtually unanimous in associating lost Arctic sea ice with a strengthening of the hydrological cycle worldwide (floods, droughts and extreme rainfall) and a shifting of the equatorial rain bands. These altered weather impacts ricochet around the planet, even reaching Antarctica. The Arctic region itself sees a big increase in precipitation in a warmer world, and shifts towards a rain- rather than snow-dominated system, transforming the landscape and ecosystems.

Arctic warming can directly damage ecosystems and will affect wild species in numerous ways. 'Rain on snow' events are a particular threat to grazing animals like reindeer and musk oxen because coatings of ice can stop the animals digging through the snow layer to feed on plants underneath. These events have been implicated in mass die-offs, such as the deaths by starvation in 2017 of nearly 50 caribou, whose emaciated carcasses were discovered in a remote part of Nunavut after the spring melt. As many as 20,000 musk oxen starved to death on nearby Banks Island, also in northern Canada, after what scientists called a 'humungous' rain-on-snow event in the fall of 2003. A study in Svalbard found simultaneous population declines after extreme weather events – including rain and icy winters – in reindeer, ptarmigan and voles. More dramatic was the unfortunate fate that befell a herd of 50 musk oxen sheltering from a blizzard on the western coast of Alaska on 14 February 2011. A wind-driven tidal surge led to an 'ice tsunami' that literally entombed the entire herd. When researchers visited the area by helicopter, they could see only a horn and hair from some of the animals protruding above the ice.

Summers can be almost as bad. During a three-day hot spell in June 2019 local Alaskans watched a herd of panting musk oxen retreat towards the last snow patches in the hills to seek relief from the heat. Offshore from Nome in Alaska, migrating baleen whales 'often show up emaciated because the timing and extent of the [sea] ice melt has changed', altering the springtime plankton blooms and arrival of fish, reported the *New York Times*. Those algae that do bloom are increasingly of the toxic kind, contaminating shellfish on which local people depend and poisoning thousands of seabirds.

The Arctic is of course famously the habitat for the polar bear, *Ursus maritimus*, whose dependence on the sea ice as its primary habitat has made it the iconic global warming victim. So what will happen to the polar bears as the sea ice declines and eventually disappears? Currently, there are estimated to be about 26,000 polar bears scattered in various sub-populations across the Arctic region. Sea ice is essential as a platform for them to hunt their main prey, ringed and bearded seals, which come up to breathe through holes in the ice. Some polar bears remain on the ice all year round, but others in more southerly regions are forced to spend summers on land, largely fasting until the autumn freeze-up allows them to return to the ice. Photos of single emaciated polar bears have led to worldwide concern – although the specific reasons for the poor condition of individual bears cannot conclusively be determined, scientists have estimated that more than half of young polar bears would die of starvation after being marooned on land for 180 days. Already reduced sea ice off northern Alaska has been linked with poorer polar bear body condition and lower survival rates for cubs. When or whether the species will be driven extinct in the wild is uncertain; even two degrees will leave sea ice in the Arctic during winter, albeit for shorter periods. However, studies do project severe population declines as the bears' frozen marine habitat is available for a shorter season each year.

The Arctic meltdown will also directly affect human populations. When I visited Alaska in 2000 to research *High Tide*, I was struck by how permafrost melt was already affecting infrastructure in the state as the melt zone moved gradually north with the warming climate. There were 'drunken forests', with trees collapsing into holes in the ground as ice masses thawed below them. In Fairbanks whole streets had buildings pitched higgledy-piggledy in different directions, while roads and paths undulated as the ground beneath them sank away. One of my expert guides in investigating this phenomenon was scientist Vladimir Romanovksy from the University of Alaska, Fairbanks, whom I joined on an expedition to study ice lenses wedged in exposed sections of thawing permafrost.

Romanovsky has kept up his interest in the field. He was co-author of a 2018 paper in the journal *Nature Communications* that calculated nearly four million people and 70% of current built infrastructure is located on permafrost zones that will thaw in the two-degree world. The 2050 'highest hazard' zone included more than 36,000 buildings, 13,000 km of roads and 100 airports across high-latitude and high-altitude regions. Three entire cities of more than 100,000 residents – all in Russia – are built on areas that are currently continuous permafrost. This means that railways, roads and pipelines will buckle, airport runways will crack, and houses and other buildings will split apart as the ground underneath them gives way, leading to tens of billions of dollars' worth of economic damage.

Perhaps the greatest threat posed by permafrost thaw is that it will further accelerate the breakdown of the world's climate. In the two-degree world, one study projects that enough of the Arctic permafrost will melt to release 60–70 billion tonnes of additional carbon into the atmosphere. There are considerable uncertainties here; a second study projects a smaller loss of 22–41 billion tonnes in a two-degree world by 2100, but with hundreds of billions more tonnes released over subsequent centuries. Not all of this is CO_2; as much of half of it could come as methane, a much more powerful greenhouse gas. There is a substantial difference between the area of permafrost that melts in a 1.5°C-warmer world as opposed to two degrees. While about 4.8 million km² of permafrost is lost in the former scenario, two degrees of global warming sees the loss of 6.6 million km², with 40% of the entire permafrost area of the Arctic region disappearing.

Whatever the exact numbers, with both CO_2 and methane pouring out of these newly melting areas, humanity's chances of keeping to the Paris Agreement targets diminish further. Another study suggests that the additional carbon from thawing permafrost reduces the two-degree-allowable 'budget' of future emissions by 30–50 billion tonnes. Yet another finds that as much as 345 billion tonnes of carbon will eventually be released from thawed permafrost, even if we successfully stabilise temperatures at two degrees. Unless humanity can somehow wave the magic wand of negative emissions, we do not therefore have a high chance of staying permanently in the two-degree world once the Arctic begins to melt. This additional greenhouse gas release from thawing permafrost will not happen instantly – it will take many decades to play out. But the ultimate destination is clear: unless curbed by carbon cuts, the Arctic permafrost carbon feedback is a shortcut to the three-degree world.

Tipping point in the Antarctic

It is not just the Arctic. Recent surveys have shown the Antarctic sea ice is in what scientists call 'precipitous' decline, with 'decreases at rates far exceeding the rates seen in the Arctic', according to a *PNAS* paper published in July 2019. The sudden drop was particularly notable because it reversed a gradual increase in Antarctic sea ice that had been tracked by satellites over the last 40 years.

Even the usually cautious IPCC warns that a potentially disastrous Antarctic tipping point may lie somewhere in the two-degree world. In its 2018 report on 1.5°C, it states: 'The threshold of global temperature increase that may initiate irreversible loss of the West Antarctic ice sheet and marine ice sheet instability (MISI) is estimated to lie between 1.5°C and 2°C.' The West Antarctic Ice Sheet (WAIS) is cited as of particular concern because it is mostly grounded far below sea level, so a collapse could become self-sustaining once the grounding line is crossed. Warmer oceans would then penetrate hundreds of

kilometres into the Antarctic interior, fragmenting the entire continental ice sheet and ultimately delivering – alongside East Antarctica
and Greenland – more than five metres of sea-level rise. None of
today's coastal megacities could survive such a huge boost to global
sea levels – not London, not Jakarta, not New York, not Shanghai.
Coastal defences can only do so much. They could protect against a
metre or two at most, but five metres would require a large-scale relocation of humanity inland, involving upwards of a billion people.

The vastly larger East Antarctic Ice Sheet (EAIS) has similar points
of vulnerability. As with the West Antarctic, sections of the eastern
ice sheet are in direct contact with the warming Southern Ocean, and
have grounding lines which similarly lead inland via reverse-sloping
beds down to troughs that are as deep as 1,500 metres below sea level
in the continent's interior. If the floating ice shelves that protect these
glacial outlets collapse, and ocean waters begin to penetrate underneath the vast ice sheet into the Antarctic's very heart, the result could
be catastrophic, delivering as much as 20 metres of additional global
sea level rise.

Greenland also has glaciers that are retreating rapidly because of
their contact with a much warmer ocean. Numerous massive glaciers
draining the Greenland ice sheet have sped up, retreated and thinned
in recent years as the climate warmed. As I showed in the previous
chapter, surface melt has also increased dramatically, far in advance
of that predicted by models. The most recent science suggests that
Greenland too has a threshold after which, in the words of a 2018
study in *Nature Climate Change*, 'the ice sheet enters a state of irreversible mass loss and complete melting is initiated.' There are not one
but two positive feedbacks that lead to this unstoppable melt. The first
is the fact that as the ice sheet diminishes, it will lose altitude and
therefore be exposed to increasingly high temperatures due to the
lower elevation. The second is the 'melt-albedo feedback', where, as
the snow surface thaws, it darkens and thereby absorbs more solar
radiation. The ice sheet surface is also darker than any overlying

snow, so once it is fully exposed to the sun's rays on account of the receding snowline, this too acts as a positive feedback to speed up the melting process.

So where does this fateful threshold lie? The experts, based on a combination of observations and model simulations, put their best guess at a regional Greenland summer temperature increase of 1.8°C. Given that overall Arctic warming is happening much faster than global temperature rise, this 1.8°C point of no return would be right at the very start of the two-degree world. In fact, there is a good chance – as I suggested in the previous chapter – that we have crossed this line already. While it will take millennia for the entire ice sheet to melt and deliver its full complement of seven metres' worth of sea level rise, the gradual elimination of the Greenland ice sheet means that our descendants will be faced with irreversibly rising oceans for centuries to come.

There is evidence that both Greenland and the West Antarctic ice sheets did indeed collapse during the Eemian, 116,000 to 129,000 years ago. As I discussed in the previous chapter, this interglacial had a global temperature roughly similar to today, and much lower CO_2 levels, and is therefore a conservative analogue for the two-degree world. However, this very moderate warmth was enough to result in sea levels six to nine metres higher than now. These dramatically raised sea levels can only have come via less land ice at the poles, suggesting that moderate levels of global warming will eventually be enough to significantly reduce both the Greenland and Antarctic ice sheets over the longer term. The question now is by how much forecasts of sea level rise need to be raised for the two-degree world, given the latest science on the vulnerability of both polar ice sheets.

The IPCC, in its September 2019 report on oceans and the cryosphere, points out that the loss of ice on Greenland – which totals 250 billion tonnes per year – is unprecedented over at least the last 350 years and that this high rate of melt represents a two to five times increase over pre-industrial levels. The IPCC also warns that 'rapid mass loss due to glacier flow acceleration' both in West and East Antarctica may indicate the beginning of 'instability' in these ice sheets which leads to 'irreversible retreat'. It adds that the combined sea level rise contribution from both ice sheets has risen by a staggering 700% since the decade 1992 to 2001.

Even using very moderate estimates of sea level rise, the IPCC projects that 79 million people will be displaced as their homes and communities are inundated in a two degrees world (ten million fewer will lose their homes if temperatures are kept below 1.5°C). Bangladesh would face having more than a million of its citizens permanently displaced by the invading oceans. Even as soon as 2050, large parts of the world's coastlines will be experiencing what was previously a once-in-a-century flood event every single year. In the longer term, even in a 1.5°C stabilisation scenario, the IPCC points out that countries with 50 million people or more on large areas of land exposed to sea level rise include China, Bangladesh, Egypt, India, Indonesia, Japan, the Philippines, the United States and Vietnam. At least 136 megacities are at risk of being at least partially flooded in a two-degree scenario, with flood damage costs totalling $1.4 trillion per year by the end of the century.

These numbers can be reduced with aggressive coastal protection measures, but the costs will be astronomical; one recent report found that the US alone faces more than $400 billion in coastal defence costs over the next 20 years, with longer-term costs for those living in smaller communities as high as $1 million per person. I suspect no one will want to pay for sea walls at such vast expense, and the most vulnerable (and the poorest) communities will simply be abandoned. The gradually rising list of abandoned areas will not just include coastal portions of larger nations such as China and the US. Entire countries will face being submerged or eroded away by the end of the century, with small island nations like the Maldives and Tuvalu first on the list. This process could begin much sooner than we would like to think. According to a 2018 study in *Science Advances*, within as little as 30 years from now many atoll islands will find themselves washed over annually by ocean waves. Once this happens, ground-water will salinise, vegetation will be destroyed, buildings repeatedly damaged and the long-term habitability of the islands fatally under-mined. Their residents will eventually have to join the millions of climate refugees all over the world who will be looking for a new home.

Deadly dengue

Sea level rise is clearly a long-term threat to the Maldives, but many people living there have a more immediate concern. Virtually all the islands are infested by mosquitoes; these can transmit dengue fever, a disease that often strikes suddenly and with little warning. This happened to a friend of mine who has an eight-year-old son, a lively boy with blond hair and quick smile. One day the boy was running, jumping and eating sweets at their home in the local island of Eydafushi, on Baa Atoll. The next he had a fever, and three days later was in hospital hooked up to a drip and with a critically low blood platelet count. Desperate doctors gave him a blood transfusion as the disease steadily worsened; dengue can progress to a haemorrhagic stage, and the first signs of bruising were beginning to appear on the boy's feet. They knew any blood loss into the brain could be fatal. Dengue is caused by a virus, so antibiotics are useless – his mother, a medical professional herself, could do little more than pray. The boy was the fourth member of the same family to be struck down with the disease in the space of a few months.

Fortunately the child in this case made a full recovery, but some Maldivians have not been so fortunate. A nine-year-old boy died from dengue in July 2019, after an emergency evacuation from the northern island of Kulhudhuffushi to the main hospital in the Maldives' capital Malé. The disease can strike young and old alike – fatalities in 2016 included a seven-month-old baby and a 61-year-old woman. The incidence of the disease seems to be rising, with a 200% increase between 2018 and 2019, and 506 cases reported in the single month of April 2019. A similar trend is occurring globally. Dengue was present in only nine countries in 1970 but is now endemic in over a hundred nations throughout the tropics and sub-tropics. It is estimated that there could be as many as 390 million new dengue fever infections worldwide each year, leading to approximately 12,000 deaths, mainly in young children.

There is an obvious link between dengue and climate change because the two mosquito species that transmit the disease, *Aedes aegypti* and *Aedes albopictus*, are warmth-loving insects whose potential range will increase with rising temperatures. As the IPCC points out, projections of the 'prevalence of dengue fever generally conclude that there will be an increase in the number of mosquitoes and a larger geographic range at 2°C than at 1.5°C', and that 'the risks increase with greater warming'. Specific projections can be quite alarming. While dengue is widely prevalent in Mexico, and the current range of *Ae. albopictus* includes southern states of the US, one study suggests that the mosquito might shift north by up to 1,000 kilometres, even establishing itself in central and eastern Canada. In Mexico dengue incidence might increase by as much as 40%, especially as minimum temperatures rise in areas of higher rainfall. Dengue is also expected to jump into Europe from North Africa, establishing new hotspots of potential infection on the northern side of the Mediterranean, including Spain, France and Italy, and even reaching as far as the south-east of England. Parts of Africa may be spared, but only because they become too hot and dry for the mosquito to successfully breed.

Small temperature changes can make a big difference to disease transmissibility. One study published in 2018 in *PNAS* estimated that limiting global temperature increases to 1.5°C would potentially avoid half a million dengue cases in Latin America by the end of the century as compared with a rise of two degrees. And two degrees is much better than the 'no-policy' scenario of a global temperature rise of 3.7°C, reducing the additional number of dengue cases in Latin America by 2.8 million as compared with what would occur in a four-degree world. Better health systems could help offset this rise, however. This is well illustrated for dengue by the different rates of incidence of the disease across the US–Mexican border. While both *Ae. aegypti* and *Ae. albopictus* are present throughout the south of the United States, dengue outbreaks are rare and tend to involve US citizens who have recently travelled to parts of the world where the disease is endemic. Mexican towns adjacent to Texas have much higher incidence of dengue not because mosquitoes are deterred by the border fence but because Texans tend to have access to air-conditioned homes, better health services and a higher standard of living generally.

There are also strategies to control mosquitoes directly that can be implemented independently of climate change. Some are as simple as bed nets and encouraging people to cover bare skin to reduce the chances of them being bitten. Mosquitoes breed in stagnant water – sometimes in an item as small as a discarded bottle-top – so people are also encouraged to empty containers that might collect rainwater and to pick up plastic litter. Fogging with insecticides can also kill mosquitoes, although resistance is becoming an increasing problem, and pesticides also affect other species and can damage the wider environment. A more environmentally friendly option is being trialled by a British company called Oxitec, using genetic engineering to produce sterile males (male mosquitoes don't bite) that are then released to mate with wild females. These fail to produce viable offspring, reducing the mosquito population and thus the rate of disease transmission. While trials have proved successful in Brazil and elsewhere, the use of genetic engineering has raised widespread suspicion and generated hostility among activist groups that undermines the potential viability of this strategy. A better option might be a vaccine, but at the moment dengue vaccines do not offer reliable protection.

And dengue is only one of a number of insect-borne diseases that might spread as a result of rising temperatures. *Aedes* mosquitoes also transmit chikungunya, yellow fever and the Zika virus, while another mosquito genus, *Anopheles*, is the main carrier of malaria. In Africa, malaria has already begun to appear in highland locations that were once too cold for the disease. Malaria kills a child somewhere in the world every two minutes, with nearly half a million deaths overall in 2015. While a huge international effort is under way to eliminate malaria entirely – and its incidence has been diminishing in recent years – it is likely that climate warming will complicate this challenge. Other diseases of concern include West Nile fever, Rift Valley fever and the tick-borne Lyme disease, all of which have a climatic component.

The greatest human health risk of all in a two-degree world does not involve transmissible disease, however. This risk is just as urgent, although more prosaic and familiar. It is the risk that hundreds of millions – or even billions – of people will run short of food.

Food facts

Climate change is already harming food production in the one-degree world, although this was never supposed to happen. Up until fairly recently the consensus was that moderate warming up to two or even three degrees would be broadly beneficial to global agriculture. Now these rosy expectations look dangerously naïve. A study published in 2019 looked at the impact of current climate change on yields of the world's ten most important crops – barley, cassava, maize, oil palm, rapeseed, rice, sorghum, soybean, sugarcane and wheat – and found identifiably negative effects across large areas. Instead of the expected broad increase in productivity thanks to warming, on aggregate these crops have seen about a 1% decrease, reducing caloric availability in nearly half of the world's most food-insecure countries. Although some crops have benefited, this is more than offset by the

1.6 million tonnes shaved off the world's rice crop and 5 million tonnes of lost wheat production resulting from decreased yields across Europe, Australia and sub-Saharan Africa. Indeed, for Africa the impacts on harvests of all ten crops added up to a 1.4% reduction in food calories. That might not sound a lot, but we are talking about a continent where several hundred million people, mostly subsistence farmers at the margins of existence, already suffer from food shortages and resulting malnutrition. There can be little doubt from this analysis that climate-related undernutrition is already causing deaths in poorer countries due to decreased yields.

There will be many more deaths in the two-degree world. A recent paper in the medical journal *The Lancet* projected that global temperature rises of about two degrees – expected in their scenario by mid-century – would lead to a 'relative reduction of global food availability in 2050 of 99kcal per person per day' when compared with a scenario with no warming. The result is hundreds of thousands of underweight and malnourished people, especially (though not exclusively) in poorer countries. In the model, the two-degree scenario leads to 529,000 climate-related deaths worldwide by 2050, a death toll that 'far exceeds other climate-related health effects that are projected to occur in 2050'. This is a pretty sobering conclusion – at least half a million people will die from malnutrition in a two-degree world because of climate change.

This half-million projected death toll could be a significant underestimate. Scientists looking at individual crops – rather than broad model outputs – increasingly fear a downwards trend in agricultural production as large areas of current-day breadbaskets become too hot to sustain today's harvest levels. The issue here is not changing average temperature, but the increasing frequency of extreme temperatures that cross critical heat tolerance thresholds of different cultivated species. Maize, for example, is the world's most important staple crop, but is particularly sensitive to drought and heat stress. I have seen at first hand in Kenya and Tanzania how smallholder farmers struggle to produce much of a harvest in hot, dry conditions. Often all these farmers would have is an acre or two of parched, shrivelled plants. They would be desperately poor, with ragged, undernourished children and little hope of improvement. Maize yields are already critically low in sub-Saharan Africa, and rising temperatures combined with increasing drought can only worsen the outlook. Maize has a critical temperature threshold of about 32°C while setting seed, and temperatures above this level reduce photosynthesis and increase the amount of water lost from the leaves.

As mentioned, impacts are being seen in Africa even in the current one-degree climate. Historical data published in a 2011 paper show that each day spent above 30°C reduces yield by 1%, and by closer to 2% under drought conditions. A three-week heatwave, in other words, could slash yields by a quarter. Experts agree that the relationship between warming and yields is non-linear; if the temperature soars past critical levels, yields will decline much more rapidly than you might expect. Farmers in Africa have few adaptation options; water for irrigation is rarely available, and other inputs such as fertiliser can also be scarce or too expensive. While in recent years crop breeders have developed drought-tolerant maize seeds, these still need some rain, and the more advanced versions have been subject to vociferous opposition from environmental activists who oppose the use of genetic engineering.

The global picture for maize is not much better. The most recent study, published in February 2019 in the journal *Earth's Future*, predicted that once-in-a-decade extreme climate events – heat stress and drought – would become 'the new normal' in a 1.5°C-warmer world, from about the mid-2020s onwards. By the 2030s, with 2°C global warming in this scenario, 'maize areas will be affected by heat stress and drought never experienced before, affecting many major and minor production regions.' The biggest area of concern is also the world's largest producer, the United States, which suffers from increasing heat stress throughout its Corn Belt. As much as 100 million tonnes are wiped off global production in a two-degree world, which would eliminate most of the world's maize trade. This would be a disaster for importing countries such as Mexico and Japan. Because maize is important for animal feed, any reduction in global supply would have knock-on effects across world food markets. The *Earth's Future* paper authors suggest that efforts should be made to identify potential new regions that might become suitable for maize cultivation given that the US, China, Argentina and Brazil are likely to be seriously affected by heat and drought.

Other studies have also backed up this dire forecast for maize in the world's major grain farming areas. A 2017 paper in *PNAS* projected a 10% loss of the United States' maize crop, accompanied by 8% losses in China, and 5% in Brazil and India, per degree Celsius of global temperature rise. And it is not only maize that is at risk. The same paper also projects a 6% loss of global wheat yield with each degree of global warming, and a 3% reduction in rice. The US, the world's largest producer of soybeans – a critically important protein crop – also loses nearly 7% of its soybean harvest per degree Celsius. These worrying figures are consistent with other studies, which have shown, for example, a 6% fall in global wheat production for each degree rise in temperature.

And there is more to global warming than heat and drought, bad as they are. At the risk of sounding warnings reminiscent of the biblical ten plagues of Egypt, scientists also predict that insect crop pests could dramatically multiply with increasing temperatures, seriously affecting harvests of rice, maize and wheat. Yield losses may increase by as much as 25% per degree of global warming due to increased insect attacks. And while increasing CO_2 could still have a small fertilisation effect, this is offset by another previously unanticipated impact: higher levels of CO_2 make crops less nutritious. With atmospheric CO_2 at 550 ppm, researchers reported in *Nature Climate Change* in 2018, many food crops will have protein, zinc and iron contents that are reduced by 3–17% compared with current conditions. The human impacts could be dire. 'We estimate that elevated CO_2 could cause an additional 175 million people to be zinc deficient and an additional 122 million people to be protein deficient,' they warn, thereby adding hundreds of millions more people to *The Lancet*'s two-degree malnutrition casualty list.

All forecasts for global food production also need to consider the 'elephant in the room' – world population growth. Feeding a much greater world population, of 9.5 to 10 billion people by mid-century – and doing so without ploughing up the rainforests and destroying the Earth's last wild areas – is already considered by experts to be an almost insuperable challenge, even without considering the impacts of climate change. All the mainstream forecasts call for a 70% or more increase in global aggregate food production to deal with population growth and changing lifestyles by 2050. It is very difficult to see how this can be delivered in a world suffering simultaneous major yield declines due to accelerating drought and heat impacts on the world's major breadbaskets. Of course, dire forecasts of famine resulting from population growth have been wrong before. Paul Ehrlich's notorious prediction, made in his 1968 book *The Population Bomb*, that hundreds of millions would die from famine in the 1970s and 1980s as a result of overpopulation, fortunately never came to pass. But this was no accident. Those hundreds of millions of lives were saved by the dramatic yield increases delivered via the Green Revolution, for which one of the world's leading crop breeders, the American wheat scientist Norman Borlaug, rightly won the Nobel Peace Prize.

So what can we do? Borlaug's lesson from history is that predicted famines can be averted through a concerted multi-decadal effort to breed better crops and improve agricultural productivity around the world. And given that two degrees is about the best-case outcome in terms of global temperature rise, we do not have the option of just wringing our hands and waiting for hundreds of millions to die from famine in the 2030s or 2040s. Norman Borlaug was certainly no population denier. During his lifetime he warned repeatedly that future global population increase would require unceasing efforts on the part of the world's crop breeders and agronomists to enable harvests to keep pace with demand. All that was before global warming became an issue, of course. The task of feeding the future world just got much, much harder.

Heat stroke

I admit that two degrees doesn't sound like much. A two-degree change in ambient temperature is barely even perceptible. So why all the fuss? Recognising the danger that people simply won't understand the magnitude of a two-degree global temperature change, in July 2019 researchers based in Switzerland published an innovative study pairing cities based on their current and expected 2050 climates. Madrid's climate by mid-century would resemble today's in Marrakech, Morocco, they suggested, while in North America, Seattle in Washington State would move two states south to the current latitude of San Francisco, California. Reykjavik would become like Edinburgh in Scotland, while Edinburgh itself would move to Lille in the north of France. London, meanwhile, would be transplanted all the way to Barcelona, Stockholm to Budapest, Moscow to Sofia and Tokyo to Changsha in southern China.

As a general trend, the researchers pointed out, 'all the cities tend to shift towards the sub-tropics', with cities in the Northern Hemisphere moving to warmer conditions on average 1,000 kilometres further south. This translates to an average 'climate velocity' of about 20 km per year. Wherever you are, therefore, if you live in the Northern Hemisphere mid-latitudes you are effectively moving south by 20 km per year, which is about 54 metres per day, or 2.25 metres per hour. This in turn is just over half a millimetre a second, easy to see with the naked eye. It is as if every major city – London, Moscow, Stockholm – were on a slow-moving giant conveyor belt, transporting them deeper and deeper towards the sub-tropics at the same speed as the second hand on a small wristwatch. This change in temperature will mainly be felt in terms of increasing heat, but moving outside a city's 'normal' climate envelope will also alter species composition in the surrounding regions and lead to changes in water supply.

Of course, this is just an imaginary exercise. In reality it is the climate zones that are shifting, not our cities. But it does provoke all sorts of very real questions. Barcelona, for example, has small and fairly ephemeral watercourses flowing through it, a consequence of the surrounding region's Mediterranean climate. Does that mean that London's parks and streets will be lined with palm trees, as is the case in Barcelona today? Will the River Thames dry up in the 2050 world? Barcelona itself, moving to the climate of North Africa, will presumably be seeing a hotter, semi-arid climate that befits a region only a mountain range away from the world's greatest desert. (Cross the Atlas mountains from Marrakech and you will find yourself at the northern edge of the Sahara.)

The real story here is heat. Another way to look at two degrees, used by researchers who published a 2017 paper in *PNAS*, is not to move cities south into hotter environments but to look at their most deadly recent heatwaves and predict how much more frequently these conditions will hit in the future. For example, conservative estimates of the lethal heatwave that struck Karachi in Pakistan in 2015 suggest that it caused around 1,200 heat-related deaths. With two degrees of global warming, Karachi will be experiencing those extremes every single year. Globally, over 40% of the world's 44 largest megacities will see dangerously high heat conditions each year with 1.5°C of warming, exposing 350 million more urban residents to 'deadly heat' by 2050. In response to this looming threat, the International Federation of Red Cross and Red Crescent Societies put out a 98-page guidebook designed to help city officials deal with heatwaves and reduce heat-related mortality.

Deadly heatwaves also hit the higher latitudes. A glimpse into the heatwave of the future came in Russia in the summer of 2010 when a 'mega-heatwave' seared the country for nearly two months, sparking devastating fires and blanketing Moscow in smog. Bodies piled up in the city's morgues, while out on the streets tanker trucks sprayed water to try to stop the asphalt on the roads melting. Baffled Russian meteorologists declared the heatwave the worst in the country's millennium-long history: 'No similar heatwave has been observed, neither by ourselves nor by our ancestors', said a meteorological official, while more than 500 fires burned around the country. 'This is a completely unique phenomenon.' With a fifth of Russia's grain production either incinerated by wildfires or parched in the heat and drought, wheat exports were banned. Overall about a million hectares were burned, while the eventual human death toll may have reached as high as 55,000 across the country as a whole.

While the temperature reached 38.2°C in Moscow, further south Volgograd (formerly Stalingrad) reached 41.1°C, and Yashkul measured an extraordinary 44°C during July and August. These kinds of temperatures are certainly considered life-threatening; the US National Weather Service issues 'excessive heat warnings' at temperatures of above 40°C (105°F) because 'mortality begins to increase exponentially as the heat increases or stays above a heat index of 104°F.' ('Heat index' includes humidity, so the ambient temperature may be substantially lower than that.) Even below 40°C, the incidence of heat-related illness – where the human body cannot cool itself quickly enough to maintain a healthy temperature – shoots up. Confusingly, the symptoms of heat exhaustion and heatstroke are almost the opposite of each other. While a patient with the former will exhibit symptoms including dizziness, heavy sweating, cool clammy skin and a fast, weak pulse, someone suffering from heatstroke is more likely to have hot, dry skin and a rapid, strong pulse. Heatstroke is considered a severe medical emergency. The US National Weather Service advice is to call 911 or get the victim to a hospital immediately as 'delay can be fatal'.

The 2010 heatwave in Russia exceeded in magnitude even the other recent European mega-heatwave of 2003, which killed between 35,000 and 70,000 people. Both were off the scale in terms of the current climate, and were hotter than anything seen in the continent for at least 500 years (and probably much longer). But projections suggest that mega-heatwaves such as these will be returning much more frequently in future. In fact this already seems to be happening: 2017 also saw another Europe-wide mega-heatwave, while 2018 saw record-breaking temperatures throughout virtually the entire Northern Hemisphere. The latest generation of climate models show that with a global warming of only 1.5°C, the heatwaves of 2003 and 2017 would become just a normal European summer. Another half a degree – taking us into a world two degrees warmer – would make the average European summer as hot as July 2010, when Moscow baked and Russia burned. Overall, 90 million people in Europe would be exposed to historically unprecedented summer heatwaves in a 1.5°C warmer world. This number rises to 163 million – twice the population of Germany – in a two-degree scenario. A second set of climate models confirms that high-impact heat extremes such as the deadly summer of 2003 would 'occur in most years in a 2°C world'. Another study has estimated that EU member states will be experiencing 30,000 heat-related deaths per year by the 2030s, with the death toll rising much higher towards the end of the century.

Heat is rising in the Southern Hemisphere too. During Australia's 'angry summer' of 2012–13, the country as a whole saw an *average* temperature of 40.3°C on 7 January, setting a new record for the hottest-ever day, and temperatures hit 49°C at weather stations in three different states during the month. This record-breaking summer heatwave was made at least five times more likely on account of human influence on the climate, researchers later calculated. In the two-degree world, 'angry summer' events would be at least 50% more frequent as compared with the world of today, making these deadly heat events commonplace in the Australia of the future. Scientists also emphasise that it would be a mistake to imagine that worldwide temperature rise is linear; global warming of two degrees does not mean that extreme heat records will be only two degrees higher. Instead, extremes of heat are likely to increase much faster than the global average. In Australia, heat extremes are expected to be at least double the average rise in a two-degree world, setting the scene for temperature highs that humanity has never experienced before on the continent.

China also suffered a record-breaking heatwave in 2013, which led to increases in deaths – especially among the elderly – in several cities. Excessive heat then returned in 2016, 2017 and 2018. In the two-degree world, models project that the 2013 summer in China would be considered on the cool side, with almost every year seeing the mercury rise past the extreme levels experienced in 2013. Areas of China that are currently spared extreme heat will begin to see heat-waves for the first time, increasing the exposed population by 25–50% in the two-degree scenario. In a country the size of China, this means hundreds of millions of people becoming exposed to extreme heat that is outside their previous experience. Whole cities of tens of millions of people will need to be heat-proofed, and crop yields will fall as farmers struggle to cope with temperatures rising above the thermal-tolerance thresholds of different crops.

In July 2018 it was Japan's turn to suffer extreme heat. A new national record of 41.1°C was set in the city of Kumagaya, resulting in a 'natural disaster' being declared by the government as 1,000 people died and tens of thousands more were hospitalised. A later study, published in May 2019, concluded that this event would never have happened without human-caused global warming, and warned that heatwaves such as this 'could become a usual situation with warming levels of 1.5 or 2°C in the next few decades'. Globally, the numbers affected are huge; the most recent aggregate study found that more than two billion people would be exposed to extreme heat-waves at least once every 20 years in a two-degree world. Half a degree makes a huge difference. Limiting global heating to 1.5°C reduces the population exposed to severe heat waves by 1.7 billion, by around 420 million for extreme heat waves, and by approximately 65 million for 'exceptional' heat waves. Even storms will bring little relief. A 2019 study warned that millions of people on exposed coastlines will face combined tropical cyclone/extreme heat events in a two-degree world.

This threat from tropical cyclones is particularly serious because strong storms tend to knock out electricity supplies, and would therefore cut off access to air conditioning for heat-affected populations, who might also be suffering from shortages of drinking water and other critical supplies. This concern applies more widely too in terms of global inequalities in access to cooling services. It is one thing to experience 40-degree temperatures inside a modern air-conditioned suburban home in Adelaide, quite another to try to survive the same kind of heat in a tin-roofed shack on the edge of Mumbai, even without a tropical storm. India saw a new all-time temperature record of 51°C set in Rajasthan during the pre-monsoon heat of May 2016, with severe heatwaves projected to rise by 30 times as compared to the current climate for India as a whole, meaning an up to 92 times increase in the numbers of people exposed to extreme heat. Unless India becomes a rich country with wide access to air conditioning, tens of thousands will die in an average summer, those labouring outside in fields or on roads and building sites being particularly affected.

One study has found that developing countries in Africa could be spending tens of billions on air conditioning to try to survive heatwaves in the two-degree world. The International Energy Agency (IEA) estimates that air-conditioning demand will require additional electricity supply equal to the combined generating capacity of the United States, the EU and Japan by 2050. I see this as a sort of positive feedback, where extreme heat means that humans consume ever more energy for cooling, thereby generating increased CO_2 emissions that in turn go on to cause yet more heat. Once on this treadmill, there is no way off – humanity would have to go on running, faster and faster, for ever.

The dry continent

It is one of the great injustices of our times that those who have done least to cause global climate change are often the people most affected by its impacts. Perhaps nowhere is this more true than Africa. In sub-Saharan Africa, per-capita carbon emissions are typically a tenth of what they are in rich, developed economies. Average annual CO_2 emissions per person in sub-Saharan Africa are 0.8 tonnes, as compared with 16 tonnes in the United States, 15 tonnes in Australia and 6 tonnes in the European Union. Yet the fact that Africans have contributed very little to global warming does nothing to help them avoid its impacts. In fact, some of the most intense climate change hotspots lie on this continent. One of these can be easily spotted in a 2017 paper published in the journal *Geophysical Research Letters*, whose authors used a climate model to investigate the risk of drought in the two-degree world. The paper includes a figure showing a world map, the continents shaded with colours ranging from blue, yellow and orange to red, indicating expected changes in precipitation in a warmer world, with red showing a drying trend and blue a wetting trend. Africa is particularly brightly coloured, showing a swathe of intense red from Cape Town in the south to the Zimbabwe–Congo border in the north, this zone of drought spreading east from Namibia to cover virtually the entire island of Madagascar. Judging by the intensity of the colours, these areas lose substantially more rainfall than drought areas elsewhere in the world, indicating – if the model is right – severe hardships to come for the millions of people who already struggle to eke out a living from the parched soil.

Right at the centre of this drought hotspot lies the southern African nation of Botswana. I wrote about the country in the first *Six Degrees* because the earlier generation of climate models already suggested substantial drying was to come in the region. In 2007 I put this case study rather conservatively in the Three Degrees chapter, although the section also has a very short-term climate model prediction. As I wrote back in 2007: 'Even as early as 2010, southern Africa stays consistently dry in the projections, eventually losing 10 to 20% of its rainfall'. So how did this play out so far? One might ask the residents of Botswana's capital city, Gaborone, who watched alarmed as the taps ran dry for weeks at a time during a particularly intense drought in 2015. The culprit was the Gaborone Dam, optimistically dubbed 'Old Faithful' by journalists, and the subject of such intense ongoing interest that water levels in its reservoir are relayed via a neon sign in the city centre.

A local reporter from the daily newspaper *Mmegi* relayed the scene:

> For the first time in its history, Gaborone Dam is dying, its once proud 141 million cubic metres of water drying up to barely four metres above silt level. Of the seven water draw-off points in the Dam, six are exposed and the last is halfway in the water. Once the water reaches below this last water draw-off point, Gaborone Dam will have failed, depriving the 500,000 or so residents and businesses of Greater Gaborone their primary and traditional source of water … As far as the eye can see lies rock upon rock, muddy ground where waters once stood, and in the far distance, a small herd of cattle risk being stuck in the mud to tug at blades of grass.

Abandoning journalistic neutrality, the news crew from *Mmegi* offered silent prayers to the dam before returning to the parched capital. Two months later, with the dam at only 1.4% capacity, Botswana's official Water Utilities Corporation declared the dam failed.

For Botswana the future looks even grimmer than the present. The latest generation of climate models forecast severe losses in rainfall, with over 10% of the nation's water disappearing in the two-degree world and dry spells lasting 15–19 days longer on average. Not all models agree on the exact location of the worst drying, but the broad trends are clear. A second study forecasts a loss of 10–20% of average rainfall over most of the central subcontinent and parts of western South Africa and northern Mozambique. Added to an additional 80 days of heat, this reduction in water supply will be catastrophic.

Botswana is already adapting to a hotter, drier future. Measures include the construction of a 360-kilometre pipeline – the largest engineering project in the country's history – to carry water from the Letsibogo Dam in the north-east of the country all the way to the thirsty capital Gaborone. A second pipeline is already operational, carrying water from the even larger Dikgatlhong Dam, which holds more than three times the capacity of the troubled Gaborone Dam and now supplies on average nearly half the city's water. Even this may not be enough; there is talk of an even longer 500-kilometre pipeline to transfer water virtually the whole length of the country, from the Zambezi River on the northern border down to Gaborone in the arid south. Droughts do not last for ever – the model projections described above detail changes in broad average rainfall patterns, hiding the day-to-day detail of weather that Botswanans will experience.

For now, the parable of the 'failed' Gaborone Dam has a happy ending. Following three weeks of heavy rain in February 2017, the dam was declared '100% full', with excess water flowing over the spillway. Local journalists again flocked to the scene, with one describing the 'heart-stopping excitement of watching Gaborone Dam filling to the brim'. Writing in the *Botswana Daily News*, reporter Baleseng Batlotleng declared:

On Saturday afternoon, hope was finally restored to many Batswana [Botswanans] after the majestic dam finally hit the 100 per cent mark. After several years of despair following

frequent drought occurrences, communities in the greater
Gaborone region are on the edge of real hope that change from
the dark times of water rationing will now be a thing of the
past.

That may be a forlorn hope. The good times will last only a few more
years, until the next big drought grips the region.

Botswanans also have another difficult choice to make. The country's main export is diamonds, and the government wants to diversify
the economy away from reliance on this single foreign-currency
earner. Top of the list for exploitation are the country's enormous
deposits of coal, which at 200 billion tonnes are considered among
the largest untapped reserves in the world. In July 2019 Botswana's
first privately owned opencast coal mine began production, aiming
to supply the South African power market and new coal-fired power
stations elsewhere in Africa. *New Scientist* asked an expert to calculate the carbon implications of Botswana's coal ambitions. The result
was striking: the country's reserves contain enough carbon on their
own to use up a quarter of the remaining budget for the total amount
that can be burned if the world is to keep to the target of 1.5°C.

So can Botswana be blamed for its own coming climate misfortunes? It hardly seems fair that with rich countries having industrialised on the back of fossil fuels, poorer nations in Africa are now to be
denied the same opportunity. So far Africa has contributed only a
tiny proportion of the carbon now in the atmosphere. But this is the
logic of mutually assured destruction. In reality Africa has no choice
but to pursue a different path, using clean energy technologies –
which were not available in earlier decades – to achieve prosperity.

Glacial loss

One of Africa's most iconic landmarks is Mount Kilimanjaro, the huge ice-clad volcano on the border of Kenya and Tanzania that rises above the surrounding dust-dry plains like a glimmering mirage. Kilimanjaro's icefields are steadily vanishing, however, as temperatures rise and the volume of snowfall plummets. What were once colossal ice masses draped atop the mountain's summit plateau and flowing down its flanks have lost 85% of their mass over the last century, and most have begun to split apart. Some formerly mighty glaciers are now just a few forlorn triangular wedges stuck in a sea of dark volcanic dust and withering slowly under the harsh equatorial sun. Simply extrapolating present-day rates of loss forwards means, according to the latest projections, that the remaining ice fields on the plateau and southern slopes will most likely disappear by 2040. Moreover, 'it is highly unlikely that any body of ice will be present on Kilimanjaro after 2060,' even without any increase in the rate of global warming. Kilimanjaro – whose name is reputed to mean 'shining mountain' – will be brown, not white, in the two-degree world.

Far away to the north-west, the Lewis Glacier – the largest remaining ice body on Mount Kenya – has lost half its mass in just the last decade. It has also split into two rapidly diminishing parts. If the current rate of retreat continues the glacier will be extinct by 2030, ending the longest ice monitoring record anywhere in the tropics (the glacier was first measured in 1899). Elsewhere in the world's tropics it is a similar story. Eight glaciers have already disappeared from the Colombian Andes, and the six remaining glaciated areas will be unlikely to survive much past the middle of the century. Two degrees of global warming will raise the height of the freezing level in the Peruvian Andes by about 230 metres, eliminating most of the smaller icefields altogether and shrinking the extent of those that remain. Pastoruri, the popular glacier in Peru's Cordillera Blanca that is already a noted casualty of climate change, will also be entirely gone.

The global picture is just as dire. Under current rates of ice loss, most of today's glacier volume will vanish in the Caucasus, the European Alps, the tropics, North America and New Zealand by the second half of the century. Even for a warming of just 1.5°C, most likely to be reached in just a decade or two, a third of the ice in 'High Mountain Asia' (the Himalayas, Karakoram, Pamirs, Hindu Kush and Tien Shan) will melt. Mountain glaciers are already so far out of equilibrium with the current climate that even drastic cuts in emissions will have little impact on melt rates during the 21st century.

These mountain glaciers contain a huge amount of water. Their rapid melt means that they are already adding an estimated 335 billion tonnes to global sea levels each year, raising the height of the oceans by nearly a millimetre a year. In volume terms, most of this meltwater comes not from the tropics but from the enormous glaciers on the higher-latitude mountain ranges of Alaska and the southern Andes, as well as ice caps in the Russian and Canadian Arctic regions, all of which are seeing warming rates much faster than the global average. While there is no water shortage in these areas, some glacierised river basins in the tropics are projected to suffer increasing water stress during this century as the ice caps that maintain river flows in the dry season shrink and eventually disappear. Particularly hard-hit will be river basins in Central Asia, such as the Aral Sea and the Tarim Basin, which lose a substantial portion of their late-summer water once the glaciers shrink, as well as South American rivers that drain from the high Andes through arid coastal areas.

The greatest concern, however, lies in South Asia, where around 900 million people depend on waters supplied by the Indus, Ganges and Brahmaputra rivers, all three of which rise in the high mountains of the Karakoram–Himalayas. Although both the Ganges and the Brahmaputra receive substantial inflows from downstream rainfall in the monsoon season, during the pre-monsoon months meltwater is an important component of their overall flows. The situation is even clearer for the Indus River in Pakistan. Most of the areas through which the Indus flows are hyper-arid, so the majority of the river's water originates from mountain melt all year round. In July 2019 researchers quantified the numbers of people who are directly dependent on meltwater carried by these three great rivers for drinking water and food production. They calculated that 129 million people in the South Asia region are 'substantially dependent on upstream meltwater for their livelihood', and that the amount of food produced with meltwater in the plains is equivalent to the rice consumption of 52 million people and the wheat consumption of 64 million people. These numbers are 'in addition to the 48 million farmers who live in the Indus, Ganges and Brahmaputra mountains, many of whom depend directly on local glacier and snowmelt'.

The situation is even more critical further north in Central Asia. A May 2019 study in *Nature* reported that seasonal glacier meltwater is equivalent to the basic needs of 221 million people, or most of the municipal and industrial needs of Pakistan, Afghanistan, Tajikistan, Turkmenistan, Uzbekistan and Kyrgyzstan. These countries are particularly vulnerable during drought years, when the meltwater portion from mountain glaciers can be critically important to cover the deficit from failing rain or snowfall. Researchers warn that 'social instability, conflict and sudden migrations' can be triggered by water scarcity, exacerbating problems in what is already a war-torn and desperately poor region of the world. However, projections show that parts of this region expect to experience 'peak water' as early as the 2020s, with a subsequent sharp decline through the rest of the century as the glaciers wither and die. 'The days of plenty might soon be over in glacierized Central Asian catchments,' is the ominous title of one recent study.

The loss of mountain glaciers is now also recognised as a major threat to the planet's natural heritage. A 2019 paper projected that a third of the glacier volume will disappear from UNESCO World Heritage Sites – such as Huascarán National Park in Peru, Te Wahipounamu in New Zealand and Jungfrau-Aletsch in the Swiss

Alps – under a two-degree scenario by the end of the century. This loss of natural heritage will lead to more and more of these precious sites being given an 'in danger' rating.

We should all mourn for the loss of world heritage implied by the disappearance of the glaciers from Colombia, East Africa, Switzerland and Peru. It is true that in water terms some of their function can be replaced by dams and reservoirs. But as the 'world heritage' status implies, there are more than just utilitarian reasons for regretting the disappearance of snow and ice from the world's high mountains. In the Peruvian Andes, many people believe that mountain gods, known as 'apus', live in the highest reaches amid the snow and ice. Traditionally, apus are protectors of remote villages and highland regions, but perhaps now – as the mountains turn from glistening white to drab, dusty brown – the apus will punish us for destroying their homes. We would certainly deserve it.

Future floods

While vanishing glaciers are a major concern for South Asia, at certain times of the year much of the continent may find itself with too much water rather than too little. A glimpse into this far wetter future came in 2010, when Pakistan suffered its worst-ever floods. During the two months of July and August unimaginable quantities of water swept down the usually arid Indus river valley, submerging a fifth of the entire country and leading to the deaths of nearly 2,000 people. The then UN Secretary General Ban Ki-moon pleaded for international aid, stating: 'Almost 20 million people need shelter, food and emergency care. That is more than the entire population hit by the Indian Ocean tsunami, the Kashmir earthquake, Cyclone Nargis and the earthquake in Haiti – combined.' As well as the human death toll, 20,000 cattle were drowned, irrigation systems left destroyed and crops valued at $500 million washed away, along with numerous barrages, bridges and roads. The BBC journalist Jill McGivering wrote movingly about the moral dilemma she faced when she found a mother with a sick baby who had just been born at the roadside: 'When covering disasters, reporters can face the ethical question of whether they should help, or remain detached. When is it right for a journalist to help a weak and possibly dying baby?' (McGivering did help, by finding a doctor at a nearby clinic, and the baby survived.)

The flooding in Pakistan was particularly severe because it hit in what is usually a very dry area that is unused to extreme downpours. The South Asian monsoon normally drops its heaviest rains far to the east, reaching its greatest intensity over the mountains and wetlands of north-east India and Bangladesh. (The so-called 'wettest place in the world', Mawsynram in Meghalaya state in north-east India, receives an incredible 12 metres of rainfall annually.) However, in a two-degree future the forecast is for a widespread intensification of the monsoon – not just in South Asia, but also for other monsoonal systems across the world. According to a 2018 study by Chinese scientists published in the journal *Nature Communications*, 'extreme precipitation in the South and East Asian monsoon regions is the most sensitive to warming,' with roughly a 10% increase in intensity for each degree of temperature rise. Across all the world's monsoon regions, the scientists predict, two degrees of warming means that 146% more land area and 149% more people will be exposed to extreme five-day precipitation events.

In 2017 the rest of the South Asian subcontinent got a glimpse of this future when severe flooding killed over 1,200 people in India, Nepal and Bangladesh, with over six million temporarily affected in Bangladesh alone. Researchers plugged river discharge data into a flood model after the 2017 flood and found that such events would also become more extreme in the two-degree world. They also noted that increased melting of glaciers and snow in the higher reaches of the Brahmaputra will augment the flooding rains. Another major study, led by the UK Met Office, found that the flow of the Ganges could increase by 30–110% in the two-degree world. These increased flows would be partly driven by a 25% increase in the incidence of the most extreme, once-in-a-century downpours, a significant increase in which would also be seen by the Brahmaputra. Scientists predict 'more frequent and stronger heavy precipitation events, exerting devastating impacts on the human and natural systems over the Asian monsoon region'. As if on cue, in 2019 the strongest monsoon for a quarter of a century killed 1,600 people across India.

With more energy in the Earth system, the intensification of the global hydrological cycle means that severe flooding becomes more likely almost everywhere in the world. A 2018 study by Chinese scientists found that two degrees of warming would increase the probability of historical once-in-a-century floods in China by a factor of 2.4, more than doubling their occurrence. In Europe, similar once-in-a-century floods are also projected to double in frequency within three decades from now, by about 2040. One of the greatest dangers comes from the potential failure of dams during more intense flooding events. For example in February 2017 the spillway at the Oroville Dam in California began to fail during the floods that swept the state, forcing the evacuation of 200,000 residents who live downstream. A subsequent study found that in the warmer future world, the risk of dam failure increases for most of the major dams in California. In August 2019 summer downpours led to the partial collapse of a dam in Derbyshire in the UK, resulting in the hurried evacuation of more than a thousand residents from the nearby town of Whaley Bridge. As the mass evacuation took place, the Royal Air Force deployed Chinook helicopters to drop hundreds of tonnes of rubble onto the dam to try to shore it up.

The rest of the world faces similar dangers. According to a major 2018 study, a fifth of the world's land area will see a significant increase in severe week-long flooding in the two-degree world, with low-income countries most seriously affected. Heavier rainfall events mean that average flow in streams and rivers increases across the Northern Hemisphere by as much as 50% at 2°C global warming. The IPCC's

2018 report suggests that 'global warming of 2°C above the pre-industrial period would lead to an expansion of the area with significant increases in runoff, as well as the area affected by flood hazard'.

As with many climate impacts, deaths and injuries can be reduced with increased preparedness. If you live near a river or other watercourse, even in a part of the world that is usually arid, check carefully what the maximum flood heights have been in the past. Remember that in the two-degree world, flash floods beyond historical experience will occur and severe floods previously thought of as once-in-a-century events will come significantly more frequently. If you have just been through a drought in your area, the danger is amplified because water runs more rapidly off hardened, bare soils and hillsides denuded of vegetation. If you think you might be in the danger zone, be prepared and heed weather warnings. Seriously consider permanent relocation – the best time to move is before, not after, the heavens open and that once-in-a-century flood strikes.

Climate breakdown

As Hurricane Harvey demonstrated when it hit the Houston area in 2017, some of the worst floods come when tropical cyclones strike land. In 2019 Mozambique suffered two cyclone strikes in close succession. Hundreds of communities were cut off as floodwaters rushed down what are usually dry river channels. According to the UN's Reliefweb service, 1.8 million people were left in need, over 600 died, and 240,000 houses were damaged or destroyed. With 70,000 people living in temporary accommodation, malaria and cholera outbreaks affected thousands more. But it is important also to appreciate that relief efforts do work. During the Mozambique emergency, 1.1 million people were given food and 900,000 provided with fresh drinking water. The cholera outbreak quickly peaked and cases fell rapidly thanks to an oral vaccination campaign targeted at young children. No doubt thousands of lives were saved thanks to the kindness of strangers, perhaps including readers of this book. If so, I salute you.

Bad news for some is also good news for others. In 2017, as I mentioned earlier, Botswanans celebrated watching their main city dam at Gaborone fill with heavy rains, brought by the remnants of a tropical cyclone that had already caused significant damage in Mozambique. Botswanans – perhaps unlike Mozambicans – may not therefore be pleased to hear that the two-degree forecast is for a *decrease* in the number of tropical cyclones making landfall over southern Africa. This, as the authors of a 2018 paper in the journal *Environmental Research Letters* acknowledge, will likely lead to decreased rainfall over the interior of eastern and southern Africa, harming agricultural production in already arid areas.

This prognosis of decreasing tropical cyclone incidence does not just apply to southern Africa, but to the tropics and sub-tropics as a whole, with the overall number of tropical cyclones projected to be significantly reduced in a two-degree world. This is perhaps a counter-intuitive prediction for many people, who might expect to see an increase in hurricanes and tropical storms in a hotter world. But there is more to cyclone occurrence than just warm ocean water. Atmospheric conditions, with cooler air aloft and gentle winds at height (high-level vertical 'wind shear' can tear a developing cyclonic vortex in half) are also key. Climate models do not do a perfect job of representing tropical cyclones in their simulated Earths, however, so the IPCC states that it has 'low confidence' in this conclusion. Nevertheless, it predicts that 'the global number of tropical cyclones will be lower under 2°C compared with 1.5°C of global warming'.

Unfortunately, there is a sting in the tail of this long-term weather forecast. While the overall number of tropical cyclones might decrease, the frequency of the most intense – and therefore most damaging – Category 4 and 5 storms is expected to go up. The IPCC warns that 'these very intense storms are projected to be associated with higher peak wind speeds and lower central pressures under 2°C versus 1.5°C of global warming,' and that these stronger hurricanes will be accompanied by 'further increases in heavy precipitation' and hence a higher likelihood of catastrophic flooding. According to the 2018 paper on which the IPCC largely based this conclusion, the actual number of additional intense tropical cyclones is likely to be 'small' – just a couple of extra-intense hurricanes per year around the world. Even so, damage costs for coastlines in the firing line will be immense. It has been suggested that economic losses from hurricane strikes in the Caribbean nearly double in a 1.5°C scenario, to $1.4 billion per year. China, with its higher rates of economic growth and long, highly populated coastline faces economic costs four times higher than today in a 1.5°C scenario, rising to a sevenfold increase in a two-degree world. This translates into 'normalised' – adjusted for economic growth and other factors – losses of up to $65 billion per year. The global annual damage cost could therefore be in the hundreds of billions of dollars.

These changes are signs of a planet where weather systems are beginning to move into a more chaotic and unpredictable state, with global circulation patterns increasingly different from today's. Hence the aptness of the recently popularised term 'climate breakdown', as familiar weather patterns fall apart and transform into significantly different types of circulation. The shifts are still subtle at 1.5°C and 2°C warming, and the specifics vary substantially between different climate models. However, some broad assessments can be made. The jet streams – bands of fast-moving air high in the atmosphere that act to steer storms and high-pressure areas across the mid-latitudes – gradually move away from their current positions, towards the equator in the North and South Pacific, and poleward in the North Atlantic. While storm tracks in the Southern Hemisphere intensify, the North Atlantic storm track shifts east, bringing increasingly heavy precipitation, and greater wind extremes and storminess to the north-western coasts of the British Isles and Scandinavia. In contrast, southern Europe is marooned in the meteorological doldrums, with fewer winter storms bringing less and less much-needed rainfall and exacerbating the drying trend already afflicting all sides of the Mediterranean in today's world, from Spain to North Africa to Greece. A 2019 paper in *Nature Climate Change* projected that long periods of both wet and hot weather would become more frequent in a two-degree world as the jet stream becomes more meandering. This means lengthy summer heatwaves, but also a higher risk of floods as rain-bearing depressions stall for long periods throughout the mid-latitudes.

Particularly worrying is the prognosis for El Niño, the periodic swing in temperature and wind direction across the equatorial tropical Pacific that often sparks domino-effect weather chaos throughout the world, with floods in dry regions and prolonged droughts in usually humid areas. According to a 2017 paper published in *Nature Climate Change*, the frequency of extreme El Niños doubles at 1.5°C warming. The potential implications can be judged from the 2014–15 El Niño, one of the three strongest such events since 1950. Impacts might include extreme drought in an arc stretching from Brazil to Central America, combined with drying in southern Africa, India, East Asia and Australia, plus heavy rainfall in the southern US, Spain, Argentina and coastal China, and additional tropical cyclones across the Pacific. El Niño's Indian Ocean equivalent – the so-called 'Indian Ocean Dipole', which often precedes extreme El Niños – may also intensify; its extreme version doubles once global warming reaches 1.5°C, from one event every fifteen years in the historical climate to one every seven years in the future. This means floods in East Africa, combined with wildfires and drought in Indonesia and Malaysia, the latter spreading smoke and haze across areas inhabited by hundreds of millions of people and leading to the accelerated destruction of the remaining Asian tropical forests.

Perhaps the greatest danger, however, is drought. One 2018 paper comparing multiple different models warns that 'increasing aridity is projected in nearly all the land areas over the world except northern

Asia'. The two-degree projection in this study condemns virtually the entire African continent, Australia, the Middle East, western India and China, south-east Asia, most of South America and the western half of North America to increased drought duration and frequency, adding up to a 20% global increase in drought overall. The typical drought length increases from 2.9 months to 3.2 months, meaning three more weeks of failed rains during the average dry spell. Globally, 410 million more people will be exposed to severe drought conditions in the two-degree world. For them, this future means long queues for water tankers, the drying out of rivers, streams, lakes and wells, and the failure of harvests. As droughts become hotter, what water is left evaporates more quickly, leaving land even drier than before and killing vegetation. This is a future not so much of climate breakdown, perhaps, as scorched earth.

The fate of the Amazon

Perhaps the most worrying drought hotspot is not actually in Africa. Nor is it in Europe, nor even the Middle East, although the impacts of lost rainfall there will certainly be disastrous for millions of people. Instead, the worst and most prolonged area of drought in the world could lie in a sparsely inhabited region that is nevertheless of critical global importance because it encompasses the world's greatest river and most important land-based ecosystem – the Amazon rainforest.

This colossal and magnificent rainforest covers 5.3 million square kilometres across Brazil, Peru, Bolivia, Colombia, Venezuela and Guyana. The river from which it takes its name pours some 200,000 cubic metres of water per second into the Atlantic, representing about 15% of the entire global freshwater input into the world's oceans. All this will be under threat. Scientists used 11 different climate models to study precipitation changes in the two-degree world. The model outputs, pictured on a map of the world, show red swathes across the

Mediterranean, Australia and southern Africa. But the darkest red of all – indicating drastically reduced precipitation – sits in the top half of South America, encompassing much of Brazil and the surrounding countries, and covering virtually the entire Amazon rainforest. A 2017 paper by American researchers on two degrees of warming reached the same conclusion, with the Amazon area right up to the eastern Andes blotted out by the most intense drought response seen anywhere in the world.

Climate models have long raised a red flag about the potential fate of the Amazon in a warmer world. Not only does the Amazon rainforest store some 150–200 billion tonnes of carbon in biomass and soils, but it also contains anywhere between 6,000 and 16,000 species of tree alone, making it a critically important store of global biodiversity. If anything is worth fighting to save on Earth, it is the Amazon rainforest, and any projections of climate-driven destabilisation of the rainforest are therefore worth studying closely.

Back in 2000, a landmark paper by experts at the UK's Hadley Centre proposed that a future tipping point might exist whereby the Amazon rainforest ecosystem would collapse and shift to a drier savannah or even desert-like state, releasing vast quantities of additional carbon into the atmosphere. I put this scenario in the Three Degrees chapter of the 2007 version of this book, in accordance with predictions at the time. Later models seemed to reduce this projected risk somewhat, moving the likely threshold up to four degrees of global warming. In its Fifth Assessment Report, published in 2014, the IPCC devoted a whole section to 'A Possible Amazon Basin Tipping Point'. Its conclusion – representing the broad scientific consensus of the time – was that 'modeling studies indicate that the likelihood of a climate-driven forest dieback by 2100 is lower than previously thought.' It added: 'There is now medium confidence that climate change alone will not drive large-scale forest loss by 2100 …', although it warned that fires and drought – particularly in the eastern Amazon – might well drive a gradual shift to drier forest types.

But the illusion that the Amazon will be safe for the foreseeable future has been shattered, as is so often the case, by fast-moving events in the real world. The region's climate seems to be becoming steadily more extreme, with severe droughts and drastic flooding alternating in quick succession, alongside a temperature rise in the last few decades that is nearly twice the global average. In 2010 the rainforest was struck by such an intense drought that the Rio Negro, a tributary of the Amazon, fell to its lowest level in half a century, and other tributaries dried up altogether. This was followed, in 2012, by a once-in-a-century flood that in turn caused the Rio Negro to over-flow and put most of the Amazonas region in Brazil into a state of emergency. (Note that the previous 'flood of the century' was only three years earlier, in 2009.) Then in 2015 another drought struck, this time related to a monster El Niño in the Pacific that was setting high-temperature records worldwide.

Scientists examining the event reported that 'the drought during August 2015–July 2016 was one of the two most severe meteorologi-cal droughts since 1901.' The water shortage badly affected the forest, meaning that it absorbed a billion tonnes less carbon than it would have done in a normal, well-watered year. Long-term studies show that the region as a whole is beginning a transition towards a drier climate regime, with over two-thirds of the tropical evergreen forest now having seen a decline in precipitation since the year 2000. One 2014 study – unfortunately appearing too late to be incorporated into the IPCC report – found 'widespread tree mortality and forest degra-dation across southeastern Amazon forests', with one forest plot subject to experimental burning during a drought in 2011 making a rapid shift to savannah. This drying trend, towards a less resilient forest absorbing less carbon each year, now seems to be taking place across a vast area. Studies of more than 300 plots scattered through-out the Amazon rainforest show – perhaps as a result of this extreme cycle of drought and flood – an increase in the number of dying and dead trees, a trend that is already weakening the forest's ability to absorb carbon from the atmosphere. The authors note that their 'observed decline of the Amazon [carbon] sink' is once again 'contrary to expectations based on models'.

Then came the disastrous 2019 'fire season'. As the *Guardian* reported from Rondônia state: 'From afar, it resembles a tornado: an immense grey column shooting thousands of feet upwards from the forest canopy into the Amazonian skies. Up close it is an inferno: a raging conflagration obliterating yet another stretch of the world's greatest rainforest.' Up by 84% in a single year, the 2019 Amazon fires were apocalyptic, producing so much smoke that NASA satellites tracked the resulting carbon monoxide as it spread across the Pacific, and faraway São Paulo was plunged into midday gloom. 'In the height of daytime, the sky suddenly blackened, and day became night in São Paulo,' reported the *Washington Post*. World leaders became involved, with France's Emmanuel Macron pressuring Brazil's president Jair Bolsonaro to accept international aid to tackle thousands of simultaneous blazes. Bolsonaro was impervious; hardly surprising for a man who rose to power on a promise to allow cattle ranchers, soy farmers and gold diggers free rein over the Amazon region. Indeed, when the head of Brazil's National Institute for Space Research released figures showing a dramatic increase in deforestation, he was unceremoniously sacked.

Perhaps in retrospect it was a mistake for experts to focus for so many years on the precise numbers spat out by climate models, when human agency is so directly involved with the immediate future of the forest. According to Carlos Nobre, Brazil's leading expert on climate and the Amazon, deforestation must not be allowed to exceed 20–25% of the original forest area or a threshold may be crossed that then inevitably converts the majority of the remaining rainforest to hot savannah. Given that we are currently at something like 15–17% deforestation in the whole Amazon basin, this threshold is already perilously close. Large dams are also a major threat to the forest; 154 hydroelectric dams are already operational in the region, with 21 under construction and another 277 planned. If all are built, only three free-flowing tributaries to the Amazon will be left intact.

As Nobre well knows, with Brazil's political system now focused on intensifying the destruction to reap maximum reward for loggers, ranchers and dam-builders, and a president nicknamed 'Captain Chainsaw' in charge, the future is grim. Just like the climate-change deniers who become louder and more influential as heatwaves and droughts devastate their countries, the people who profit from destroying the Amazon seem determined to intensify their onslaught, even as the remaining rainforest becomes more vulnerable to collapse. Never mind atmospheric physics – perhaps the climate models need an equation for human idiocy.

Nature's peril

The decades-long conflagration of the Amazon rainforest will probably release somewhere between 25 and 55 billion tonnes of carbon into the atmosphere. This is not just lost biomass from trees and other vegetation; like other tropical forests around the world, Amazonia also stores immense quantities of peat in its saturated soils, much of which could be emitted as CO_2 as the ground dries out and burns. This peat – up to seven metres thick in places – has lain undisturbed, gradually accumulating under the root systems of the giant rainforest trees, for thousands of years. Once the trees fall, it will be exposed to decomposition or to incineration from wildfires. Either way the carbon enters the atmosphere, adding a further boost to global warming. If we can protect the Amazon rainforest, we can help to stabilise the world's climate and safeguard tens of thousands of endemic species. If we allow it to burn, the additional carbon will help push the planet beyond the guardrails of two degrees, and into an even hotter future.

Any substantial loss of the Amazon will be a human tragedy for the indigenous people of the rainforest, many of whom already live in island-like reserves amid a sea of deforestation. Members of some tribes who have lost their land to the invading ranchers and loggers are now forced to live under tarpaulins by the side of highways. There are some 305 tribes living in Brazil today, totalling around 900,000 people, and probably about 100 uncontacted groups still living in the more remote regions of the rainforest. As Brazil's far-right president declares open season on indigenous reserves, researchers predict an increase in violent attacks and murders by well-armed invaders, abetted by corrupt local officials and carried out in the safe knowledge that violent crimes against indigenous people almost always go unpunished. When Europeans first arrived in the year 1500 there were an estimated 11 million Indians living in Brazil. At least 90% were wiped out within a century by diseases, slavery and massacres. It is important to bear witness to this history and to defend the interests of the surviving indigenous peoples as we discuss the fate of the forest today. The Amazon rainforest is more than just leaves and carbon – for hundreds of thousands of people, with many centuries of history and culture, it is home.

The rainforest is also home to numerous species of wildlife that today inhabit this vast and precious ecosystem. These include an estimated 1,000 different bird species, including macaws, owls, vultures and kingfishers. Mammals include jaguars, capybara, freshwater dolphins, sloths, armadillos and tapirs. It is critical to note that, unlike many other more arid biomes, the rainforest ecosystem is not accustomed to being burned. 'In the Amazon, nothing is adapted to fire,' explains a researcher at the National Institute of Amazonian Research in Manaus, Brazil. 'Basically, the Amazon hadn't burnt in hundreds of thousands or millions of years'. While fast-moving or large animals, like some birds or pumas and jaguars, may be able to escape an expanding wildfire, sloths and anteaters, as well as frogs, lizards and other reptiles, may be unable to move to safety quickly enough. Some newly discovered species are already threatened. Milton's titi, a small, long-tailed monkey with a grey forehead stripe and ochre sideburns, was only discovered in 2011, yet its habitat was at the centre of 2019's blazes. Another recently identified monkey, the Mura's saddleback tamarin, is 'also threatened by encroaching wildfire', *National Geographic* reported in August 2019. Even those animals that escape the initial flames will not survive for long. Once the rainforest is gone, so are 99% of all species.

The species lost from burning rainforests will be added to the sad toll of depleted biodiversity throughout the two-degree world. With climate zones shifting towards the poles at several kilometres per year, species from every biome on Earth are already having to shift their geographical ranges to keep pace with the changing climate. Scientists have tried to model the specific range changes that are required, and calculate how much habitat different species are likely to lose. The most recent and comprehensive study found that 18% of insects would lose over 50% of their climatic range by 2100 in a two-degree warming scenario, while plants would lose 16%, and mammals and birds 8% and 6% respectively.

This is actually an optimistic scenario, because it assumes that these species can shift their ranges unimpeded. In reality, they are likely to be blocked by both human-made and natural barriers: roads, cities, agricultural deserts and rivers, mountain ranges and real deserts all stand in the way of successful dispersal. Species that are based on islands are blocked by water, and so are particularly vulnerable to extinction. In a no-dispersal scenario, 26% of insects, 19% of amphibians, 14% of reptiles, 12% of mammals and 11% of birds will lose more than half their range by the end of the century. In terms of their total geographic habitat, this means that in the two-degree world plants, insects and amphibians lose roughly a third of their range, while mammals, birds and reptiles lose about a quarter. These climate change pressures will come on top of the existing biodiversity loss that is driven by farming, hunting, invasive species and numerous other more direct human pressures.

So should we just watch all these species sleepwalk to extinction? We could try to restrict global warming to 1.5°C; doing so cuts the numbers significantly. But staying at 1.5°C warming requires extraordinarily rapid rates of emissions cuts in a world where policy is moving in the opposite direction. As well as unrealistic emissions cuts, keeping to a 1.5°C carbon budget also requires the direct removal of billions of tonnes of CO_2 that has already accumulated in the atmosphere. Doing that could mean planting colossal areas of land with fast-growing forestry monocultures for burning in power stations so the resulting CO_2 can be sequestered underground. This is called Bio-Energy with Carbon Capture and Storage (BECCS). One study has found that allowing business-as-usual emissions with the resulting carbon sequestered using BECCS would require the elimination of 'virtually all natural ecosystems', rendering the whole exercise somewhat pointless if the objective is to conserve some semblance of the Earth's original biodiversity. Even in a lower-emissions scenario, using BECCS to constrain global temperatures to 2.5°C would require converting 1.1 billion hectares of the planet's most productive cropland (three times the total area of India) to plantation forestry or the removal of over half the current area of natural forests. This is a Catch-22 if ever there was one; in order to limit global warming sufficiently to protect biodiversity using CO_2 removal, biodiversity must be largely eliminated.

Fortunately there is another option. This requires cutting emissions as rapidly as possible while allowing restored natural ecosystems to soak up the extra carbon by themselves. This approach is termed 'natural climate solutions', and can provide a substantial part of the carbon reduction needed to keep the planet's temperature from rising above two degrees. This represents a huge opportunity. The humdrum restoration of the planet's ecology may not be as sexy for some as techno-fantasies about colossal banks of carbon-scrubbing machines or giant sunshades in the sky, but it is the only option that can both protect biodiversity and mitigate climate change at the same time. Natural Climate Solutions is now the subject of a campaign backed by writers, environmental campaigners and political leaders around the world. 'By defending, restoring and re-establishing forests, peatlands, mangroves, salt marshes, natural seabeds and other crucial ecosystems, very large amounts of carbon can be removed from the air and stored,' declared George Monbiot and co-authors in a letter to the *Guardian*. 'At the same time, the protection and restoration of these ecosystems can help to minimise a sixth great extinction, while enhancing local people's resilience against climate disaster. Defending the living world and defending the climate are, in many cases, one and the same.'

The most promising approach of all, of which Natural Climate Solutions can be a part, is large-scale rewilding. This means allowing the natural regeneration of forest and scrubland over large areas, and the recolonisation of vanished species in restored habitat with a minimum of ongoing intervention. With the warming climate, restored ecosystems will be constantly changing, but they offer at least a chance of saving threatened species by regenerating large areas of connected semi-wild habitat. Multiple species have to move all at once in order to keep the integrity of food webs; butterflies need to shift along with their food plants, for instance, while birds that prey on caterpillars will need to move at the same time. In most cases this will not be possible, but either way it is better for nature to be left to manage the process than for humans to attempt to engineer it. Successful rewilding also means sparing large areas of land from agriculture, something that can only happen if we can sustainably improve agricultural productivity, reduce food waste, and persuade people to adopt healthier and less meat- and dairy-intensive diets.

For me, rewilding presents a positive vision, at a time when there are precious few reasons for optimism. Instead of shifting climate zones meaning the inexorable elimination of habitat and eventual extinction for each species, it is possible to imagine a different scene, with a more natural, less fragmented landscape, and a diverse range of plants, birds, butterflies, predators and other animals ranging across it. These will be novel ecosystems, of course, and will not bear much resemblance to the vanished Edens of the past. But our task is to protect as much of the living world as we can from rising temperatures, not to try to bring back what is already gone for ever. For all its flaws, a rewilded world can still be a world of colour, of birdsong, of insect noise – a world of life.

Empty oceans

Unfortunately, one of the planet's most biodiverse and important ecosystems will not survive two degrees intact. The science on corals and global warming has got steadily more alarming over recent years, in tandem with the accelerated destruction of reefs by rapidly rising temperatures around the world's tropical coastlines, as has already been described. In 2018 the IPCC had to admit that 'tropical corals may be even more vulnerable to climate change than indicated in assessments made in 2014.' Marine biologists watched in horror as the Great Barrier Reef suffered back-to-back bleaching events in 2016 and 2017, losing fully half its coral cover in the process. The IPCC's latest predictions for the two-degree world are dire: even if global temperatures stay under 1.5 degrees, 70–90% of reef-building corals will be lost. With two degrees of warming, this increases to 99%.

A death sentence does not get much clearer than that. Mass mortality could come as soon as 1.2°C, according to the IPCC, with corals down to zero in many locations and dying reefs flattened across the seabed. Given that we could see global temperatures hit the 1.2°C mark as soon as 2025, it is clear that coral reefs around the world are critically endangered in the very imminent future. Recent projections in fact suggest that two-thirds of the world's reefs could be gone within just a decade from now. Coral reefs throughout the tropics will be reduced to flattened, algae-covered rubble, with the chances of survival for substantial reefs anywhere being little better than zero. As if this were not enough, what is left of coral reef structures will be steadily dissolving across the whole world by mid-century due to ocean acidification.

The IPCC reminds us that 'as corals disappear, so do fish and many other reef-dependent species.' A whole ecosystem, which for millions of years has provided habitat for an immense number of marine species – a quarter of the ocean's total biodiversity – will be wiped out in just a couple more decades from now. Corals as organisms may not be extinguished entirely – it is possible that some will be able to migrate to cooler waters and re-establish smaller, impoverished reefs that allow species to hang on in temporary refuges. Others may survive in deeper waters less susceptible to surface heatwaves. Some corals seem more tolerant of heat than others, so it is also possible that some more adaptable species will be able to take over from the rest, even as the majority of reef-building corals die off. Evidence from fossil corals – and from an endangered Mediterranean species – suggest that polyps can abandon dying large reef structures and lurk as emaciated refugees for long periods while waiting for more favourable conditions to return.

Coral scientists across the world, from Hawaii to Hong Kong, and from Florida to the Maldives, are frantically racing to figure out what adaptation mechanisms might exist, and whether evolution can be speeded up to try to encourage corals to survive higher temperatures. Some are even looking at genetic engineering to try to develop coral genomes that are more durably resistant to heat. Meanwhile the most threatened corals are being preserved in onshore tanks, partly to be studied for potential resilience, but also to safeguard them from total extinction in their natural environment. Some have tried 3D printing to provide better structures for corals to attach to, as well as 'coral gardening' to try to keep some semblance of reef diversity alive. These are all desperate measures, however, and none offer the prospect of keeping coral reefs in anything like the state we have always known them. The glory days of coral will be over, never to return in our lifetimes at least.

And coral reefs are not the only threatened oceanic ecosystem. The IPCC now warns that 'risks from climate change may have been underestimated for mangroves as well.' In recent years mangrove forests have seen mass die-offs, driven by drought and high temperatures brought by more intense El Niño events. In 2015–16 a huge area of coastal Australia suffered mangrove dieback, from Roper River in Northern Territory to Karumba in Queensland, stretching along 1,000 kilometres of largely uninhabited, supposedly pristine coastline. Aerial images show a brown swathe of dead trees stretching like a scar through the otherwise vibrant green of the mangroves. This dense network of salt-tolerant trees is a vital nursery for fish, as well as providing habitat for birds and numerous other species. With their above-ground vegetation and rich, organic sediments, mangrove ecosystems are also significant carbon stores.

In shallow coastal environments, seagrass meadows are another critically important marine habitat. They too store tens of billions of tonnes of carbon in sediments. As thermal zones move through the warming oceans, seagrass meadows will be forced to migrate polewards over hundreds of kilometres, meaning large areas of existing meadow will die off while new areas take decades to establish. Out in the wider oceans, vitally important food-chain species such as krill, which are prey for whales, seals, fish, penguins and other seabirds, are potentially threatened too. The IPCC notes that 'record levels of sea ice loss in the Antarctic translate into a loss of habitat and hence reduced abundance of krill, with negative ramifications for the seabirds and whales which feed on krill.' As the oceans acidify, krill, plankton, and pteropods – tiny floating sea-snails – will see their shells begin to soften and eventually dissolve altogether.

None of these dire predictions mean that we should abandon existing conservation measures or other additional efforts to protect the oceans. It stands to reason that marine ecosystems that are covered in plastic litter, polluted by nutrient runoff and damaged by trawling and overfishing are going to be less resilient to the additional stresses brought about by climate change. As with land-based ecosystems, probably the best we can do is to rewild the oceans as much as possible, urgently establishing large marine conservation areas where all fishing and other extractive activities are permanently prohibited. (In the longer term we must shift entirely away from capture fisheries and towards a fully sustainable aquaculture system to support human demands for fish.) There are fewer barriers to species dispersal in the oceans than on land, and so long as marine ecosystems are not excessively degraded or destroyed outright by humans, there is at least a chance for some adaptation.

The most important conservation measure we can take, however, is to reduce emissions of greenhouse gases and prevent the planet's temperature from rising any further. While two degrees will stretch many ecosystems to breaking point, three degrees will usher in a wholescale mass extinction. As this chapter has shown, human societies can aim to survive the two-degree world in some semblance of their current condition. Another degree, however, will stress our civilisation towards the point of collapse. If we choose to enter the three-degree world – and to do so still remains a choice – we must do so with our eyes open. We must not shrink from looking directly at what awaits over the precipice.

3°

Hotter than history

Entering the three-degree world means we are now living in a hotter climate than any experienced on Earth throughout the entire history of our species. You have to wind the geological clock back about three million years, to an epoch called the Pliocene, to encounter a world where global temperatures averaged 2–3°C higher than at the start of the 20th century. In other words, you have to travel to an earlier time than all the ice ages, beyond even the definitive emergence of *Homo* as a genus, to a world where our great ape ancestors roamed the savannahs but were yet to set foot outside Africa.

The ancestral lines of gorillas and chimpanzees had already diverged from the evolutionary tree of Pliocene great apes, but if you could travel back four million years and meet one – say in the Turkana Basin of modern Kenya, where fossils of *Australopithecus anamensis* were discovered in 1994 – you would be hard-pressed to recognise them as even proto-humans. *A. anamensis* was just about bipedal, but the researchers concluded from the shapes of the fossil bones that the species still spent an awful lot of time in the trees. Not surprisingly, perhaps, they mostly ate leaves and would have looked more like chimps than humans. *Homo* might just plausibly appear in the Pliocene; a single broken lower jawbone, discovered in 2013 in Afar, Ethiopia, dates from the Late Pliocene around 2.8 million years ago, and may be a missing link between the *Australopithecus* and *Homo* genera.

The Pliocene world was unfamiliar in many other ways too. Although the continents were close to their modern positions, the Isthmus of Panama only closed at the very end of the epoch, about 2.7 million years ago, uniting North and South America and leading to a mass invasion of northern species and the extinction of South America's distinctive large marsupials. At the very beginning of the Pliocene – about 5.3 million years ago – the Strait of Gibraltar was closed, with the dried-out bed of the Mediterranean left as little more than a gigantic salt-pan. Eventually the Atlantic broke through the barrier and refilled the entire Mediterranean basin in a truly awesome event known as the 'Zanclean flood' – most of the water surged through the strait within as little as a few months at a rate a thousand times the flow of the Amazon River. If our *Australopithecus* ancestors had made it from Kenya to the shores of North Africa, they would have been confronted with sea levels rising at the astonishing rate of ten metres per day – roughly the speed of an incoming tide.

The three-degree-warmer Pliocene climate led to a very different distribution of vegetation zones on the planet. In the early 2000s palaeontologists visiting Ellesmere Island made a tantalising discovery illustrating just how different the Pliocene climate was. They came across the traces of a four-million-year-old beaver pond, complete with the preserved remains of gnawed wood and sticks that the beavers had used to build their dam. Pollen studies showed that the pond was surrounded by a diverse and thriving forest, with trees including larch, spruce, pine, alder and birch, while animal bones showed the presence of primitive rabbits, shrews, wolverines, bears, horses and deer. This might all seem normal enough, except that Ellesmere Island lies between Greenland and Arctic Canada, with the Pliocene beaver pond today stranded more than 2,000 kilometres north of the treeline. Modern wintertime temperatures average around -40°C, which is why much of Ellesmere Island is covered in ice caps, glaciers and bare rock. Needless to say, no beavers frolic there now. Subsequent researchers analysing bacteria, tree rings and fossil vegetation later concluded that average temperatures in this part of the Arctic were as much as 19°C higher than today, with average growing-season temperatures in the Pliocene Arctic a pleasantly temperate 14°C, similar to the northern half of the British Isles today. The Arctic Ocean was at least seasonally ice-free.

On the other side of the planet, Antarctica also has fossil forests dating from the Pliocene, which indicate a climate very different to that of today. Outcrops of the Oliver Bluffs, part of a bleak, rocky mountainside above the Beardmore Glacier, contain remnants of dwarf beech trees and other shrub tundra vegetation that then grew a mere 480 kilometres from the South Pole. To say that the region is cold is an understatement; temperatures today average -26°C in summer, while back in the Pliocene summer temperatures probably reached a balmy 5°C. Although these southern beech fossil leaves were first described to science in the mid-1990s, the story has a fascinating historical origin; it now seems very likely that Captain Scott's ill-fated polar expedition of 1912 was actually the first to discover these important Pliocene remains.

Scott's team were traversing the Beardmore Glacier on their return from the South Pole, and although desperately cold and short of supplies, the expedition scientist Edward Wilson stopped to gather geological samples on the surface of the glacier. The fossil leaves he found embedded in these rocks were largely of much older geological age – dating from the Permian, roughly 300 million years ago – but Wilson also found some imprints that were very different. As he wrote in his diary: 'Most of the bigger leaves were like beech leaves in shape and venation. In size, a little smaller than British beech and the venation much more abundant and finer in character, but still distinctly beech like.' Six weeks later Wilson, Scott and their companions froze to death only 18 kilometres short of their relief supplies depot on the Ross Ice Shelf. Extraordinarily – and testament to the determined characters these men were – they had dragged a sledge containing numerous heavy geological finds all the way to their final resting place. These specimens, together with notes, diaries and final letters, were all recovered by a search party a few months later. Although there were no Pliocene-age beech tree fossils, Scott and Wilson's Permian fossil leaves helped scientists later understand that Antarctica had once been covered with forests when connected with South America, Africa and Australia in the supercontinent Gondwana.

These Antarctic beech shrubs could only grow in the Pliocene because the gigantic East Antarctic Ice Sheet periodically retreated back into the interior of the continent due to intervals of sustained warmer temperatures. Just how much ice melted – and how far that contributed to dramatically higher sea levels at various points during the Pliocene – has been tantalisingly revealed by offshore seabed drilling projects further west around the Antarctic coast, near Adélie Land. Here part of the East Antarctic Ice Sheet drains from the Wilkes Subglacial Basin into the ocean via several ice shelves, but evidence preserved in seafloor sediments reveals that during warmer intervals in the Pliocene the ice sheet possibly retreated several hundred kilometres inland, uncovering areas that are today buried under ice thousands of metres thick. This monumental change might by itself have contributed to a rise of between three and ten metres in global sea levels. Clearly this part of the Antarctic may be more sensitive to the three-degree world than previously thought.

There is increasing evidence, in addition, that the smaller West Antarctic Ice Sheet (WAIS) was largely absent during the Pliocene. As a landmark 2009 *Nature* paper put it, during the Pliocene epoch the WAIS 'periodically collapsed, resulting in a switch from grounded ice, or ice shelves, to open waters in the Ross embayment when planetary temperatures were roughly 3°C warmer than today'. The Greenland Ice Sheet, if not completely melted, waxed and waned between something close to today's extent and a small remnant stranded on the eastern side of the landmass. Researchers have drilled right through the modern ice sheet from its highest point and found to their surprise that 'an ancient landscape underlies 3000 m of ice', a landscape composed of frozen tundra soil laid down before the ice sheet formed 2.7 million years ago. This is further strong evidence that Greenland was largely ice-free during at least the early part of the Pliocene.

All that water – from the absent West Antarctic Ice Sheet, the tiny rump of Greenland, and the much-reduced East Antarctic Ice Sheet – had to go somewhere, and as a result of this colossal outpouring of meltwater, sea levels during the Pliocene were as high as 22 metres above where they are today. There is abundant evidence for this, from model reconstructions to beach-like terraces left tens of kilometres inland from the modern coastline along continental edges from South Africa to Australia to the south-eastern United States, showing how the oceans flooded much further inland thanks to higher Pliocene sea levels. The estimates are complicated by the fact that the redistribution of water and ice mass on the Earth's surface itself affects relative sea level, as does the uplift (or sinking) of land on continental coastlines. The latest calculations – published in March 2019 – have revised estimated Pliocene sea levels downwards somewhat, to between 8 and 14 metres above the modern tide-line, but even so, this means that the world of three million years ago saw drastically reduced ice sheets in the polar regions.

So what made the Pliocene warmer? Climatologists now agree that CO_2, the main greenhouse gas, is the primary driver of Earth's surface temperature. The precise average level of atmospheric carbon during the Pliocene is the subject of some uncertainty, but reconstructions and models have now converged around a value of about 400 ppm, slightly lower than today. No wonder glaciologists have suggested that the melt of Greenland is now irreversible, and that the ice sheet would be unable to form at all with CO_2 concentrations anywhere close to today's level. Researchers now suggest that we'll be back in the Pliocene as soon as 2030 with current emissions trends. What this means for the planet – in terms of higher sea levels, vanished ice sheets and drastically altered ecosystems – is written in the rocks all around the world, if only we choose to look.

Collapsing ice, rising seas

Our return to the Pliocene, with its drastically reduced ice sheets, is already well under way.

As I mentioned in the previous chapter, much of the West Antarctic Ice Sheet (WAIS) – which holds enough water to raise the oceans by several metres – sits on bedrock that lies hundreds or even thousands of metres below current sea levels. The WAIS is stabilised by vast floating ice shelves: the Ross Ice Shelf in the Ross Sea and the Ronne Shelf in the Weddell Sea. If these shelves meet the same fate as Larsen B, the WAIS will be vulnerable to collapse as the ocean penetrates underneath it into the low-lying West Antarctic basin. Experts have already noted that warming oceans are nibbling away at the under-sides of some of the ice shelves holding back the largest ice streams in West Antarctica such as the Pine Island and Thwaites glaciers.

In the first *Six Degrees* I put West Antarctic collapse in the Four Degrees chapter because it seemed unlikely to take place without rapid and sustained global warming. Now, as I suggested in the previous chapter, it is a concern even at two degrees. For the three-degree world, the total collapse of the West Antarctic Ice Sheet seems a virtual certainty. Larsen B's fate gives us a glimpse as to why – the final breakup was presaged by a huge melt event, during which thousands of small lakes dotted the surface of the ice shelf. When some of these began to drain through crevasses into the sea below, the stresses of changing weight began a fracturing process that radiated out from the centre of the ice shelf and set in motion an irreversible chain reaction of collapse. As the meltwater opened up fractures to the base of the ice shelf (in a process termed 'hydrofracturing'), individual icebergs began to break free, toppling over and capsizing into the sea with enormous force, triggering minor tsunamis and further chaotic disintegration at the ice front.

This is the process that scientists fear could at some point in the future begin to take place on the giant Ross and Ronne ice shelves, which are several hundred metres to a kilometre thick. Although they are much further south than Larsen B, and therefore colder and closer to the South Pole, they are already subject to occasional surface melt during the summer months. As glaciologists warned in 2016: 'Summer temperatures approach or just exceed 0°C on many shelves, and their flat surfaces near sea level mean that little atmospheric warming would be needed to dramatically increase the areal extent of surface melting and summer rainfall.' This widespread summer melt could eventually trigger a rapid collapse and breakup of both gigantic ice shelves, pretty much as already happened further north at Larsen B.

So how much warming is enough to trigger this collapse process? According to researchers, a sustained global warming of three degrees is enough to eliminate virtually the entire WAIS, delivering five metres of sea level rise as a result. They report their model results showing that a mid-range-emissions scenario 'causes almost complete WAIS collapse within the next five hundred years, primarily owing to the retreat of the Thwaites Glacier into the deep WAIS interior'. (The collapse happens within about 250 years in higher-emissions scenarios.) The much larger East Antarctic Ice Sheet will also begin to decline, committing our descendants to continually rising oceans until at least the year 5000. The East Antarctic Ice Sheet will not disappear completely in a three-degree scenario; a paper published in 2018 in *Nature* suggests that the Antarctic continent has been partly under ice for at least eight million years, indicating that there was substantial ice on Antarctica throughout the moderately warmer world of the Pliocene.

The concern is not just Antarctica, however. Greenland will see intense and sustained melt in a three-degree world. The latest calculations suggest that between a quarter and a half of the Greenland ice sheet will melt in this scenario, delivering between two and four metres of global sea level rise within the course of the next millennium. The ice sheet contracts towards the interior of the island, pulling away from the warmest south-west quadrant, and even retreating a long way from the colder north coast. As with the West Antarctic, there are areas in central Greenland that are below current-day sea levels, suggesting that warming ocean waters may penetrate inland there too.

The resulting inevitable multi-metre sea level rises – in effect returning global sea levels to where they were in the Pliocene – take centuries to play out. It is difficult to comprehend the policy implications of timescales such as these, still less the moral ones. We're talking about our great, great, great, great, great, great, great, great (etc) grandchildren being affected by decisions we take this century in terms of how much coal, oil and gas we burn. Maybe these future generations will curse us for the fact that there is no longer such a thing as a stable coastline, and that today's cities have to be continually rebuilt further inland. (New New New York, perhaps?) Maybe they will tell Atlantis-style stories about the fabulous mythical capitals that were once London, Washington DC and Bangkok, which now lie under the ocean waves. Or maybe today's great coastal megacities will still be inhabited, but trapped behind enormous barricades holding back the angry ocean – while residents cower in terror on the roofs of buildings as each new storm arrives and threatens an eventual cataclysmic Zanclean flood.

Looking just at this century, the most recent science has led to significant upward revisions in the projections for sea level rise. In particular, adding in the higher rates of mass loss from the Antarctic – which the IPCC in its 2013 report felt were too uncertain to quantify – has upped the sea level rise estimates for 2100 significantly in a three-degree scenario. The result is a couple of new estimates – of a 50% chance of sea level rise of just over a metre by the end of the century, and a 5% chance that the rise in the oceans could be as high as 177 cm. Even if the extent of sea level rise is limited to half a metre by 2100, this will inundate land currently inhabited by 50 million people. If the more pessimistic projections are correct, and both Greenland and the West Antarctic deliver large amounts of melt during this century, hundreds of millions of people will be forced to relocate.

It is important to be clear that sea level rise is not necessarily a gentle, slow, incremental process. Higher sea levels mean that extreme high tides and storm surges can combine to suddenly flood new areas that had previously been considered well above the danger zone. And extreme events will be arriving much more frequently too. A 2018 study suggests that New York could suffer three annual once-in-a-century flood events in a 2.5°C-warmer world. This means three Superstorm Sandys *every year* – an extremely worrying projection given that this was a disaster that cost close to $20 billion and killed 43 New Yorkers as large areas of coastline were flooded. In California over $150 billion of property, equating to more than 6% of the state's GDP, along with 600,000 people, could be impacted by extreme sea level events by the end of the century. Even using relatively moderate assumptions, about 2,500 km² of Bangladesh will be flooded in a three-degree scenario, affecting densely populated and highly vulnerable coastal zones that are currently inhabited by tens of millions of people. When stronger cyclones and monsoon floods are factored into the equation, the high-risk zone encompasses a significant fraction of the entire country.

While direct measures to stabilise the Greenland and Antarctic ice sheets are not practical, there is much that can be done to save lives. In Bangladesh, the vast expansion of the zone at risk of flooding during tropical cyclones means that at minimum 320 new cyclone shelters must be built. Climate-proofing measures such as this will save tens or even hundreds of thousands of lives during this century by giving families somewhere to take refuge when storms threaten the low-lying coast. Billions of dollars more will need to be spent raising the heights of roads and railways, improving dykes and erosion control measures, and upgrading drainage systems in Bangladesh. Climate justice suggests that richer, developed countries should foot the bill for these vital damage-reduction measures. After all, Bangladesh has made only a small contribution to the stock of atmospheric CO_2 that is beginning to impact its coastal regions. If justice is to be served along the lines of the 'polluter pays' principle, the government in Dhaka should send the bill to Europe and the United States.

The US will also need to spend significant amounts of money at home, however. Noting that Hurricane Sandy had put 51 square miles (132 km²) of the city underwater, in March 2019 New York's mayor Bill de Blasio proposed a major programme of coastal fortifications to protect against future superstorms. 'We don't debate global warming in New York City. Not anymore,' de Blasio wrote by way of introducing the plan. 'The only question is where to build the barriers to protect us from rising seas and the inevitable next storm, and how fast we can build them.' The plan would secure subway lines, sewerage systems and other vital city infrastructure, as well as the Financial District in Lower Manhattan, by pushing an artificially raised edge of Manhattan Island several hundred metres out into the East River. 'When we complete the coastal extension, which could cost $10 billion, Lower Manhattan will be secure from the rising seas through 2100,' the mayor claimed.

This may be overly optimistic. The $14 billion programme of dykes and sea wall improvements around New Orleans that was undertaken following the disaster of Hurricane Katrina – one of the largest public works programmes in world history – could become outdated within as little as four years, according to *Scientific American*. In total, according to one estimate, at least $400 billion will need to be spent just in the US over the next 20 years – and trillions more during the rest of this century – to combat sea level rise along US coasts. This is a colossal amount of money, but almost certainly much less than paying for the damage that will arise if no attempt is made to adapt to the rising oceans. Escalating damage costs, repeatedly affecting cities all around the coastline, cannot be borne indefinitely. Either cities adapt, or they will eventually have to be abandoned.

Once again the question arises of who should foot the bill. The introduction to a report about the costs of protection against sea level rise written by the Center for Climate Integrity suggests it should be the companies that produced the polluting products:

> As things stand, oil and gas companies and other climate polluters who knew their products caused climate change at least 50 years ago, and then masterminded an exquisitely effective denial campaign for 30 years, are paying none of these costs … Regardless of your political persuasion or your views on energy policy or climate change, there is no avoiding the conclusion that the companies that made and promoted the products that they knew would irrevocably and radically alter the global climate, and then denied it, must pay their fair share to help the world deal with it. Failing to hold polluters to this basic responsibility would be to knowingly bankrupt hundreds of communities, standing idly by as they are slowly and inexorably swallowed up by the sea.

The cost to society of 21st-century sea level rise will be more than just economic. Humanity also stands to lose part of our irreplaceable cultural and natural heritage: a 2014 study found that three degrees of global warming would put at risk 136 sites on the UNESCO World Heritage List. These include the ancient ruins of Carthage, Venice and its lagoon, the statues on Easter Island, the Roman remains of Herculaneum, the old city of Tyre, the Tower of London and the castles built by Edward I in Wales. The list also includes more recent World Heritage Sites, such as the Statue of Liberty and the Sydney

Opera House. These sites are not necessarily expected to be eroded away or inundated by 2100; the timescale for the study was 2,000 years, during which time sea levels could rise by nearly seven metres. But this does not mean we should dismiss these impacts as impossibly far off, for many of the cultural sites on the list are already much older than two millennia. Consider the value of the ancient horse paintings in the Cosquer Cave, near Marseille in France; these are 18,500 years old, and have already been partially submerged by natural sea level rise after the last ice age. Future sea level rise may destroy them completely.

In any case, the long time horizon may be instructive. By 2100, as one recent study puts it, 'sea level will be rising faster than at any time during human civilization'. A new world will be emerging, one humans have never experienced before, with ever-higher tides, steadily eroding shorelines and catastrophic storm surges combining to inundate vast areas increasingly far from the current coastline. This is not the stable, relatively benign Holocene world that our ancestors enjoyed and within which human civilisation developed and flourished. That world is gone, never to return – not in our lifetimes, nor even those of our very distant descendants, assuming they survive at all.

Hotter than hell

'Delhi is burning. You can't imagine the heat. As you step out, it's a furnace on your body.'

So described an India-based correspondent on 11 June 2019. That same day, the *Times of India* reported that Delhi had just recorded an all-time high temperature of 48°C, beating the previous record of 47.8°C set in June 2014. A day earlier, the India Meteorological Department issued a rare red warning of extreme heat, with heatwave conditions expected not just in the capital but across large parts of neighbouring states: Haryana, Uttar Pradesh, Madhya Pradesh,

Chandigarh city and Saurashtra. Amid a 50% increase in heatstroke cases compared with a 'normal' summer day, doctors warned Delhi residents to wear light-coloured clothes, carry umbrellas and drink three to four litres of water per day. Even so, four passengers in a non-air-conditioned train carriage on the Kerala Express died from the heat during the journey from Agra to Coimbatore.

Further west, temperatures rose to a blistering high of 51.1°C in Jacobabad, Pakistan, as dangerous heat conditions spread across much of South Asia, from the Iranian border in the west to Bangladesh in the east. The heatwave paralleled the one that affected large areas of India and Pakistan in 2015, killing 3,500 people. In 2010 1,344 people died from a heatwave in Ahmedabad, Gujarat.

The extreme heat of 2019 will be considered an unusually cool summer in the three-degree world. Vast regions of South Asia are projected to experience heatwave episodes 'considered extremely dangerous for most humans' in a world that is just 2.25°C warmer than pre-industrial times. A heatwave so extreme that it might currently be expected only four times a century will become not just a regular occurrence, but take place every other year. The projections show that over half of South Asia's population – hundreds of millions of people living in dozens of major cities – will be experiencing 'dangerous heatwave' conditions never before seen in today's climate. While higher-altitude areas like the Deccan Plateau and the Himalayas will escape the worst, the model projections show an arc of bright red – indicating dangerous heat – encompassing both the Indus and Ganges river valleys, including Bangladesh and the eastern coastal half of India.

While some adaptation is possible – power demand spiked during Delhi's 2019 high-temperature record as people turned on air conditioners – there is a limit to how much normal life can go on in heat conditions that make it dangerous for humans to venture outside unprotected, still less work or move about in the searing heat. All agricultural labour ceases, except for work that uses air-conditioned machinery such as farm tractors. Road mending and building projects also grind to a halt, and all outside sporting activities stop, with people essentially being trapped indoors. Those who do not have access to an artificially cooled environment risk hyperthermia and death. And while humans may be able to take shelter, livestock are decimated as extreme heat leaves even shade temperatures too hot for survival.

And of course it is not just South Asia. A study projecting the heat-wave impacts of three degrees on Africa showed a tenfold increase in extreme heat across the tropical belt and the Horn of Africa. Looking at model projections for 'hot nights' (many people who die do so at night because they are unable to cool down), data visualisations show a huge swathe of the continent – across a vast area from Guinea in West Africa, to Angola in the south, to Tanzania and Somalia in the east – experiencing between 100 and 300 hot nights each year. A second study found that cities in West Africa would be experiencing dangerous heat conditions (defined as maximum air temperature above 40.6°C) for 145 days per year in a simulated three-degree world in the 2090s. Across the whole of the continent, and depending on population and emissions scenarios, African cities would be facing a 20- to 50-fold increase in exposure to dangerous heat.

Heat extremes will not just be affecting the tropics. One 2018 study looking at a three-degree scenario showed that up to a quarter of the global land surface will experience every year the kind of heatwave events that might now be expected only once every 20 years, with the largest changes hitting the US and Canada, Europe and northern Eurasia, as well as central South America. Excess mortality will also affect US cities; in New York, for example, a 1-in-30-year heatwave in the three-degree world will kill at least 2,700 more people than if global warming is kept to a moderate 1.5C. The number 2,700 is a significant one to New Yorkers, as it is roughly the same number of people who died at the World Trade Center on 9/11. For Los Angeles, 1,000 extra heat deaths can be avoided. At the risk of stating the obvious, the US spends hundreds of billions on military operations to combat terrorism, yet the prospect of the same death tolls caused by heatwaves merits scarcely a mention, or is even faced with outright denial.

Vast areas will be affected – a 2017 study found that a third of the global land area will be exposed to temperature and humidity conditions exceeding the 'deadly threshold' for more than 20 days each year in a three-degree world. This being a scientific paper, the word 'deadly' is not used for dramatic effect but has a precise meaning: it refers to climatic conditions that have caused documented increased mortality in the past and are projected to be repeated ever more frequently in future as the world heats up. While 30% of the world's population is already exposed to 20 or more days of 'deadly heat' in today's one-degree world, by the time the global average temperature reaches three degrees that number will have risen to 53%, meaning that half the world's population will be annually exposed to heatwave conditions that can kill. The heatwaves of the future will be 'devastating mega-heatwaves' according to a 2018 study, which the authors point out will 'adversely affect human mortality and morbidity'. In other words, they will injure and kill people, probably in large numbers.

Scientists writing for august publications are now beginning to use terms like 'habitability' and 'survival' in discussing the future state of the planet. A December 2018 paper in *The Lancet Planetary Health* reported that multiple climate models now predict that at least 50 million people worldwide will be exposed to temperatures 'above the survivability threshold' in a three-degree world. One model – the Hadley Centre's HadGEM2 Earth System model – projects a sudden jump in the number of people exposed once global temperatures cross the Paris Agreement level of 1.5°C, with 140 million people being catapulted above the heat survivability threshold in a 2.5°C-warmer world. Over a billion people worldwide would be exposed to temperatures that exceed the 'workability threshold', where it becomes impossible to safely work outside artificially cooled environments, even in the shade.

The zone of 'extreme risk' in the three-degree world – indicating that working outside is physically impossible without risk of fatal heatstroke – includes parts of 40 countries each with current populations above 10 million. This includes large areas of North Africa, the Middle East and South Asia, encompassing virtually all of India, two-thirds of Pakistan, half of Thailand and Cambodia, with 'extreme risk' heat even intruding into northern regions of Australia. Developing countries are worst hit: in Africa, most of Algeria and parts of Nigeria, Ghana and Cameroon are badly affected, with North and South Sudan, Chad, Niger, Burkina Faso and Mauritania almost completely within the extreme risk zone. In South America much of northern Brazil is in the zone, as are eastern Peru, southern Colombia and lowland parts of Bolivia, while in North America it covers much of coastal Mexico and border areas of the southern United States. The authors warn that 'habitability' will be affected throughout large areas of the tropics, leaving millions of people with no option but to migrate once the 'survivability threshold' is exceeded in their regions.

With entire nations experiencing heat above this survivability threshold, the world potentially faces drastic population movements, with hundreds of millions of people leaving tropical and subtropical countries no longer considered tolerably habitable. These will be refugee flows of greater magnitudes than those provoked by a world war, causing incalculable social and political consequences across the globe.

Invading deserts

And it's not just heat. The lack of moisture in parched soils means that temperatures will soar far higher than is ever the case today. With plants wilting or dead, and no water at all in the ground, there will be nothing to hold back the rising heat. Wildfires will burn vast areas during the long, hot summers; one model projects an increase of 187% in burned area in the three-degree world, with the Iberian Peninsula, southern France and eastern parts of Italy particularly affected. Virtually all climate models agree that the Mediterranean region will be the centre of drastic precipitation declines in the three-degree world. Some rain will still fall, but it will be the exception rather than the rule; according to projections published in 2018, the average Mediterranean drought will last a decade or more when three degrees is reached.

In North Africa, Morocco, Algeria, Tunisia, Libya and Egypt stand to lose virtually all their rainfall. Desert-like conditions will also creep into all of Spain and Portugal except perhaps for their western and northern Atlantic coastal fringes, extending over southern France, encompassing the Balearic Islands and Sardinia, all of Sicily, Malta and Cyprus, most of Italy up to the Alps, all of Greece, most of Turkey, then completing the arc of aridification along the eastern Mediterranean shoreline, including Lebanon, Syria, Jordan, Palestine and Israel. None of these countries will have sufficient water to maintain their current populations without relying on desalinated seawater. While irrigated food production will be possible so long as freshwater can be found, rainfed farming as we know it today will largely cease to exist. Olive groves, vineyards, citrus orchards – all will vanish from the desiccated landscape. Only the most resilient trees and shrubs will still be visible through the shimmering heat haze, surrounded by spreading sand and cacti. Meanwhile, today's Mediterranean climate will spread up into central and northern Europe.

Climate models currently undersimulate the observed drying trend in today's world, meaning their forecasts for the future are likely to be unduly conservative. Take this into account, as one study published in *Nature Climate Change* did, and the result is predicted to be arid areas 'covering half the global land surface' in a three-degree scenario. This is a world where drylands extend over almost all the continental areas of the world, including most of Africa, Eurasia and western North America, in the process threatening the water resources of an additional billion people. Developing countries are most affected because of their geographical latitude in the tropics and sub-tropics. The authors point out that these projections imply that human survival in developing countries will be increasingly imperilled.

To build up a global picture, instead of describing the drier areas it perhaps makes more sense to point out those regions that the climate models simulate as still receiving sufficient rainfall – though with the caveat that longer and more intense droughts might also occur in between the rainy periods here too. A three-degree map published by climatologists in 2018 shows areas of blue – approximating to sufficient rainfall – across a narrow equatorial zone of Africa, some of South America and the island of New Guinea. Bangladesh and central India also see increased rainfall, thanks to a more vigorous monsoon, as do Cambodia and some of western and central China. The higher mid-latitudes, including Alaska, western Canada, eastern Canada (but not the prairie provinces, which dry out), the northern half of the British Isles, Scandinavia, Siberia, Korea and Japan are also shaded blue.

The rest of the globe is bright red, indicating up to 500% increases in the magnitude of drought, and includes all the remaining areas of the Americas, Africa, Asia and Australia, with the globe-girdling region of drought engulfing a substantial majority of the world's current population and land area. Combined with the heat impacts discussed earlier, this new era of mega-droughts will further reduce the habitability of large areas of the tropics and sub-tropics, with aridity increases affecting the globe right up to the high mid-latitudes. In the United States, for example, the red area extends as far as the border with Canada. Perhaps Canadians will be the ones building a border wall in the three-degree world.

Food shocks

Even assuming sufficient water remains in sub-tropical regions to grow crops, the *Lancet Planetary Health* paper mentioned earlier projects that farmers and agricultural labourers will find it virtually impossible to work outside during daylight hours for most of the hot season. The paper's authors caution that its conclusions are 'conservative' in that they only assess shade temperatures; in full-sun conditions the threshold of workability is much lower. The three-degree world will therefore most likely see the elimination of subsistence and smallholder farming from almost all of Africa and South Asia, destroying the livelihoods of more than a billion people. Livestock will not be able to survive in such temperatures either, removing a vital source of protein for many of the world's poorest people.

Even ignoring the physical challenges faced by farmers working in extreme heat, climate projections show that in a three-degree scenario, large parts of the continent of Africa – the Sahel in the north, and across Zimbabwe, Zambia and South Africa in the south – will see failed harvests and drastically reduced yields due to soaring temperatures and reduced rainfall. One paper even uses climate models to forecast 'when and where cultivation of key crops in sub-Saharan Africa becomes unviable'. It warns that African governments will need to prepare for large-scale harvest losses, and that even shifting back into drought- and heat-tolerant traditional crops like sorghum and millet will not save farming in the Sahel and drier parts of southern and eastern Africa from virtual extinction. This time it is not just maize; vital food crops from bananas to beans get wiped off large areas of the map as the temperature rises. With no food, no water and no cattle, people throughout sub-Saharan Africa will face famine on a scale not seen in the modern era.

Like humans and animals, plant crops also have heat tolerance thresholds. Studies in India show that wheat suffers drastic yield declines once temperatures pass 34°C, while experiments elsewhere indicate that a 2°C warmer-than-average growing season leads to a wheat yield reduction of 50%. In the US, which produces 41% of the world's corn and 38% of the world's soybeans, scientists have found critical temperature thresholds of 29°C for corn and 32°C for soy, beyond which productivity declines drastically. As the experts point out, these crops comprise two of the four largest components of the human food supply and are therefore critical to avert global hunger. Once the critical temperature thresholds are factored in to the projections, US production for these two vital crops declines by between a half and two-thirds in a three-degree scenario this century.

Global projections for food production in a three-degree world are hardly any more reassuring. The areas most affected by summer heat-stress events – the interiors of large continents, where summer temperatures are projected to rise much faster than the global average in a three-degree world – overlap with all the world's most crucial grain-producing areas: the central and northern US and southern Canada, the plains of eastern Europe and southern Russia, southern Brazil and eastern China. According to one recent study, the 'global hot-spots of heat stress on agricultural crops' include the northern part of the Indian subcontinent, perhaps humanity's single most important food-producing area given the direct dependence of hundreds of millions of South Asians on food produced there. Cooler higher latitudes are not much better off, as heatwave-induced damage to harvests occurs throughout the Northern Hemisphere – even as far north as Scandinavia, Canada, Russia and Alaska.

Ironically, these are exactly the areas that earlier climate models projected would most likely gain from global warming. In its 2007 report, for instance, the IPCC predicted that world agriculture outside the tropics and sub-tropics would mostly benefit from up to two degrees of warming. For mid- to high-latitude regions, the IPCC wrote, 'moderate to medium local increases in temperature (1–3°C) … can have small beneficial impacts on crop yields.' These forecasts, which were based on models looking at long-term gradual changes in average temperatures, now look worryingly complacent. The latest projections, published in *Environmental Research Letters* in 2019, now show that even Canada – once the great hope of future food production – will see production declines of wheat, canola and maize once global temperatures pass 2.5°C.

A glimpse of this future came with the European heatwave of 2003, which would be considered a normal to cool summer in the three-degree world. According to a subsequent analysis, during that scorching summer 'Italy experienced a record drop in maize yields of 36% from a year earlier, whereas in France maize and fodder production fell by 30%, fruit harvests declined by 25%, and wheat harvests (which had nearly reached maturity by the time the heat set in) declined by 21%.' While it is conceivable that European farmers might adapt by growing substitute crops – perhaps swapping maize for pineapples or palm oil in the second half of this century – it is difficult to imagine how the world as a whole can make up for the loss of vast areas of arable land currently devoted to growing humanity's most vital food crops.

In the three-degree world, therefore, we face drastic harvest losses at the same time as the global human population is projected to rise to 10 billion. To feed these extra mouths, and to do so at the same time as reducing poverty, requires doubling food production globally by mid-century. Instead, in a three-degree scenario we could see food production cut by half. We do not have to – indeed we should not – passively accept this fate, which is nothing less than a recipe for global mass starvation. First and foremost, we must take any and all measures to keep global temperatures from ever reaching the three-degree level. At the same time, crop breeding can increase drought tolerance and perhaps improve the ability of major food plants to withstand heat, using new genetic techniques where necessary. We will also have to shift major areas of crop production north, and substitute different kinds of food crops as climate zones move. There are some important fixes necessary to secure the world's food supply, which include protecting soils, eliminating biofuels, reducing food waste and encouraging more plant-based diets. Much more food, especially proteins, will also need to be produced in thermally controlled artificial environments. And we must beef up the World Food Programme to ensure that the world shares fairly the food it can produce, helping buffer harvest failures in one place with aid from another.

If these efforts fail, the scene is set for a new era of escalating food commodity price shocks as we tip from relative global sufficiency into increasingly desperate scarcity with rising world temperatures. Again, we can look to recent history for a glimpse of what this might mean. Between 2006 and 2008 food and energy prices soared, increasing poverty rates by 3–5% globally – in effect plunging 100 million people back into poverty. Rice prices shot up by 255%, while wheat and maize costs rose by 80–90%. Increased scarcity fuelled violent street protests as prices soared in local markets, hitting the urban poor hardest of all. Food riots swept Africa, affecting fifteen countries from Morocco and Egypt in the north, to Senegal and Burkina Faso in the west, Mozambique and Zimbabwe in the south, and Ethiopia and Somalia in the east. Droughts and food-price rises were also associated with the 2010–11 Arab Spring revolts, and subsequent wars and crackdowns in the Middle East and North Africa.

In my view, worldwide food shortages are the most likely trigger of large-scale civilisational collapse in a three-degree world. A burgeoning global population facing a simultaneous crash in global food supplies, regional conflicts and the resulting failed states means millions of people fleeing from famine and war. They will join those pushed out of their homes by the direct impacts of drought and extreme heat, which will be threatening the overall habitability of many of these same countries. The subsequent outflows of refugees will have predictable consequences, seen to an extent during the Syrian civil war, where millions of people seeking safety and shelter triggered anti-immigrant sentiment in destination countries in Europe, leading to the greatest resurgence of ugly far-right politics since the Second World War.

The Syrian conflict gives a glimpse of what lies ahead, but instead of being limited to a single region, entire continents will be falling into chaos: Africa first, but South and West Asia too, with even the Americas succumbing sooner or later. Forget survivalist fantasies. Nowhere will be 'safe' – countries that still grow enough food might find themselves ruled by latter-day eco-fascists, as unscrupulous politicians stir up hate and division in order to cement their power behind rigidly policed national boundaries. Recent events have demonstrated the fragility of modern liberal notions of freedom, democracy and international solidarity. A few years ago I'd have confidently predicted that people would not stand idly by as millions elsewhere died from famine. Now I am not so sure.

Dark mountains

It was not until 2011, when the US Cold War-era spy satellite programme was declassified, that engineer Phil Pressel could finally tell his family what really went on 'at the office' during his spell at the Perkin-Elmer Corporation in the 1970s. While Pressel knew that the high-resolution satellite photos he helped secure for the Pentagon might give the Americans an edge in any combat against the Soviet Union, he could not have known that the pictures would prove just as helpful decades later to scientists investigating the impacts of climate change. The Hexagon KH-9 Reconnaissance Satellite, on which Pressel worked for 30 years, is still considered one of the most complicated systems ever put into space, and served as a model for the Hubble Space Telescope, launched many years later. Its two cameras, shooting onto several miles of tightly wound, ultra-thin Eastman Kodak film, could obtain a resolution of six to nine metres from satellites orbiting at 17,000 miles per hour, 100 miles up above the Earth's surface, all before the invention of digital technology or even computers – the designers used slide rules to make most of their calculations. The canisters of exposed film were then dropped automatically by parachute over the Pacific Ocean, where they were retrieved in mid-air by Hercules military aircraft. The film resolution was so high that 'you could see a picnic blanket and count the number of people on it,' Pressel recalls. 'Under certain conditions you might even see a ball tossed.'

The incredible precision of these Cold War photographs has recently proved useful to scientists tracking changes in Himalayan glaciers. Using three years of images taken between 1973 and 1976 as a baseline, a US team of scientists compared this data with modern satellite imagery to calculate how much ice had melted in the Earth's highest mountain range between the 1970s and today. They found that the rate of glacial melt had doubled in the 2000–16 period as compared with 1975 to 2000, from 20 cm to nearly 45 cm per year of vertical ice averaged across all the 650 largest glaciers. Himalayan glaciers are now melting so fast that scientists have calculated that another third of the ice in the high-altitude regions of Central Asia is already committed to disappear because of past greenhouse gas emissions. As with the Arctic and Antarctic melt, a precise number can be put on our individual responsibilities: each tonne of CO_2 emitted by fossil fuel users is responsible for eliminating 15 tonnes of glacier mass from the highest slopes of the Himalayas. It is a sobering thought, perhaps, for the climbers and trekkers visiting India and Nepal that their international flights are contributing measurably to the deglaciation of the mountains they love so much.

And that is only the start, with impacts in our one-degree world. As worldwide temperatures climb towards three degrees, at least 50% of the remaining ice in the Himalayas will melt away. Although projections of future glacier loss are usually based on complex computer climate models, simply extrapolating existing rapid rates of melt into the future yields a pretty dire prediction, not least because the current rates of global glacial melt are now estimated to be a fifth larger – representing 47 billion tonnes of lost ice per year – than was stated in the last major IPCC report in 2014. As one international group of glaciologists wrote in *Nature* in 2019: 'Under present ice-loss rates, most of today's glacier volume would thus vanish in the Caucasus, Central Europe, the Low Latitudes, Western Canada and the USA, and New Zealand in the second half of this century.' Exactly what 'most of today's glacier volume' means has been quantified precisely for a three-degree warming scenario: it means a loss of 86% of Western Canada's ice, 88% of Scandinavia's, 89% of the ice in the European Alps, 42% of Alaska's (which has some of the largest mountain glaciers on Earth), 72% of Central Asia's, and 92% of the glacial mass in the tropical Andes and other low-latitude regions.

This colossal melt will threaten many of our most precious natural heritage areas. One recent paper looked at the probable future for thousands of glaciers in 46 UNESCO World Heritage Sites, ranging from Patagonia to the Italian Dolomites. The researchers calculated that a three-degree scenario would lead to a loss of 43% of the volume of ice from these spectacular locations, currently highly valued for their rich biodiversity and stunning natural beauty. My personal favourite, Huascarán National Park in Peru, will lose 82% of its glacial mass, while Sagarmatha National Park (the location of Mount Everest) loses two-thirds and the Canadian Rockies shed nearly 90%. In the Swiss Alps the spectacular Jungfrau-Aletsch glaciated area will have only a fifth of its mass remaining, while only 10% of ice remains in the West Norwegian Fjords, and just 3% in the Western Tien-Shan in Central Asia. Meanwhile several of the sites – including Siberia's Putorana Plateau, Monte Perdido in the Pyrenees, the Rwenzori and Virunga national parks in central Africa, Mount Kenya and Lorentz National Park in West Papua – face what the researchers unambiguously term 'complete glacier extinction'.

It is not difficult to imagine how the mountains of the future – denuded of their snow and ice – will look. As I suggested in the first *Six Degrees*, the best analogue for the future European Alps might be the Atlas Mountains of North Africa. Here, while some snow still falls in the winter months, it melts rapidly away in the heat of the early summer, leaving the baking mountainsides exposed as bleak expanses of dark rock and scree. Snowmelt streams quickly dry up, leaving the downstream areas in the hottest months parched and dry. The loss of snow and ice will be so rapid that vegetation will have little time to grow on the newly exposed slopes, leaving them vulnerable to erosion and landslides. Thawing permafrost will also threaten high-mountain infrastructure, while the ski industry of the future will have to focus on hiking instead.

Without glaciers to keep streams flowing and rivers full, seasonal water shortages will affect cities, hydropower and agriculture across large areas of the world. This includes much of the western United States, the tropical Andes, Pakistan and the dry nations of Central Asia, as well as the regions of Europe whose rivers rise in the Alps. All told, hundreds of millions of people around the world face the loss of vital meltwater supplies from disappearing glaciers in the three-degree world. Once these 'water towers in the sky' run dry, irrigation systems will fail and croplands vanish, putting further pressure on the global food supply. Without water, as the saying goes, there is no life.

Fatal floods

Climate warming speeds up the global hydrological cycle by putting more heat energy into the system. One side of this equation means hotter, longer droughts and diminishing water supplies. The other means too much water – in other words, floods. While hydrological and climate models reach differing conclusions about which places are affected most, there is virtual unanimity among them that flooding will become increasingly catastrophic as the world's temperature climbs towards three degrees.

One major study published in 2018 which pooled the results of numerous different models found that as many as 200 million people worldwide could be affected by river flooding every single year in a three-degree global heating scenario. Global flood mortality could almost quadruple from today's levels, to more than 20,000 deaths per year. The number of people exposed to river floods could more than triple in India, Bangladesh, Niger, Egypt, Ireland, the United Kingdom and Ecuador, while those countries expected to be stricken by drought – the Middle East, eastern Europe and North Africa – might see a reduction in floods as they receive less rainfall overall. The damage to property and economies would be colossal, rising by over 1,000% to €1.2 trillion per year.

Flooding will particularly affect those areas spared the worst of heatwaves and droughts because of their location in the higher mid-latitudes. Along with the western coasts of Scandinavia, the British Isles – the UK and Ireland – face some of the most worrying projections for future high river levels, with floods expected to be more severe and more frequent as the atmosphere heats up. Northern Europe can expect damages of €17 billion every year, with 780,000 flood-affected people annually in a three-degree world. Europe's north–south divide means that areas in the northern half of the continent will be drowning even as Mediterranean countries gradually desiccate.

Anyone with a house in a floodplain would be well advised to relocate; while flood-control measures can help alleviate the worst in some parts, it is not realistic to expect existing flood defences to protect life and property against the quantities of rainfall that are expected in the future. This would mean reversing the trend of late 20th-century construction, which has seen millions of new homes built close to rivers by profit-seeking developers with no incentive to think about the future. While collectively worth trillions of dollars today, these will be stranded assets – literally – in future. Historic high-water marks will be little guide to what is coming; humans have never lived in a world three degrees hotter and never experienced the dramatic intensification of the hydrological cycle that will result.

Much of the continental United States also lies at the mid-latitudes and can expect similar increases in flood magnitude. Averaged across the US, flood damage more than doubles in a three-degree scenario, according to one 2019 study. The worst-hit parts of the country are expected to be the Midwest and northern Great Plains, with a more than tripling of damage expected here. People may have got a foretaste of the future in the great 2019 Midwestern floods, which saw the Missouri River and its tributaries inundate large areas of Nebraska, Missouri, South Dakota, Iowa and Kansas after record-breaking rainfall, subsequently acknowledged by Nebraska's governor Pete Ricketts as 'the most extensive damage our state has ever experienced'. A separate study found that the expected once-in-a-century flood magnitude in the Mississippi would increase by a sixth, while floods would come 13 days earlier in the season on account of more rapid snowmelt and a larger area of the catchment receiving its winter precipitation as rain.

Perhaps rather counter-intuitively, increased flooding does not necessarily result in more rainfall overall. In India, for example, the summer monsoon – which supports the livelihoods of 1.6 billion people – has been weakening in recent decades, raising concerns about long-term water shortages. While global warming – because it heats land areas faster than the much more massive oceans – is expected in general to intensify monsoons, pollution has dimmed solar radiation over South Asia and may be to blame. Even so, the warmer atmosphere potentially holds more water vapour, so rainfall during the monsoon months has been in shorter, more intense bursts. This is bad news in several ways if the trend continues in future. Not only does it mean that more people will lose their lives or livelihoods in extreme floods, it also means that less of the water remains on the land to help crops grow or replenish diminishing groundwater supplies. With much of central India, West Bengal and Bangladesh a gigantic flood-plain for the Ganges and Brahmaputra rivers, hundreds of millions of people will be in harm's way.

Within just 30 years from now, the damage totals from flooding around the world could already be enormous. One study found that 'in 2050 the current 100-year flood [i.e. to be expected once a century] would occur twice as frequently across 40% of the globe,' affecting 450 million people and 430,000 square kilometres of cropland with a doubling of flood frequency. In terms of the regional specifics, increases in flooding are projected across tropical Africa, south and east Asia, much of South America, and high latitude Asia and North America, with decreases in areas subject to extensive drying such as the Mediterranean, south-west Africa and Central America. This is a world of extremes, of biblical inundations followed by extreme heat and months of drought. As the shocks to our civilisation – in terms of lives lost, declines in food production, increasing incidence of disease and economic damage valued in the trillions of dollars every year – stack up, life will become increasingly precarious for an ever-greater proportion of the world's population.

Wildlife refugees

The three-degree world will also see escalating threats to the non-human inhabitants of our planet. A 2018 *Science* paper assessing more than 115,000 terrestrial species concluded that half of insects, a quarter of mammals, 44% of plants and a fifth of birds will lose more than half their climatic range by the end of the century with a global temperature rise of three degrees. All these species see their climate-suitable habitat diminish drastically because they simply cannot keep up with the speed of the changing climate. In effect, the trailing edge of their climate envelope contracts much more rapidly than the leading edge expands, leaving them with diminishing habitat. Plants, which at an individual level mostly cannot move at all, face a particular challenge; while some plants produce wind-blown seeds that can travel great distances, most are highly constrained by how far their seeds can disperse, with distances of 10–1,500 metres from the parent plant being typical. Given that many plants take years – or even, with some trees, decades – to reach maturity and reproduce, most long-lived plants will be left stranded in a temperature zone for which they are not adapted and that will eventually kill them.

Moreover, the 2018 assessment is conservative because it treats species as individual entities and does not consider the interconnections that make up ecosystems as a whole. This is because the disruption of predator–prey relationships, plant–pollinator relationships or mutually beneficial interactions between plants and fungi – the tearing apart of ecosystems involving species that have co-evolved over millions of years – is too complex to be realistically represented by models. The assessment also assumes that species can disperse at relatively rapid rates. The numbers for a no-dispersal scenario look even more pessimistic, with roughly a half of plants, insects and amphibians, and over a third of birds, reptiles and mammals losing more than 50% of their climatic range by 2100 for a three-degree scenario. While some refuges may exist in isolated areas, most of those left behind will be doomed to extinction. This process is already well under way. Hundreds of local extinctions have already been recorded around the world due to current climate warming, and this rate is expected to increase fivefold during the century.

Species lagging too far behind in future decades will accumulate so much 'climatic debt' that they will become bankrupt – in other words, they will go extinct. And it is not just birds and butterflies; one study of nearly 500 Western Hemisphere mammals found that 40% may be unable to track shifts in suitable climates, and that nearly 90% will experience a range reduction as a result of climate change. This study projects that primates will be one of the worst-hit mammal groups, with small animals like shrews and moles also left behind by the rapidity of climate change.

While you might imagine that birds – which can mostly fly rapidly, and often great distances – might be able to track the changing climate better than most, in reality things are more complex. Research carried out by the National Audubon Society and published in 2019 projected that two-thirds of North American bird species are at risk of extinction in a three-degree world. There are numerous different threats: while the orange-headed Blackburnian warbler stands to lose its forest breeding grounds, the sanderling could find its sandy beach feeding grounds engulfed by rising seas. Razorbills – the closest living relatives to the vanished great auk – face the loss of food sources as marine ecosystems shift, while the insectivorous wood thrush is at risk of fragmented forests. It has been called a 'bird emergency'. In Africa, Ethiopian bushcrows – noisy, charismatic birds that live in the hot acacia bush savannah – have a physiological limit that means they need to move into the shade when temperatures exceed 30°C. 'Even under cover, bushcrows start panting and are unable to feed,' reports *Science* magazine. 'Sadly, as the climate warms, it seems inevitable that the Ethiopian bushcrows will disappear.'

There is a worrying overlap between species that are already threatened and those most vulnerable to climate change; one recent study found that as many as 851 bird, 933 amphibian and 73 coral species 'are both highly climate change vulnerable and already threatened with extinction on the IUCN Red List'. In Antarctica, scientists are recommending the Red List status for emperor penguins be upgraded from 'near threatened' to 'vulnerable', because the iconic species stands to lose half its population as sea ice melts and marine ecosystems collapse. Globally, the most vulnerable birds include hummingbirds, antbirds, hornbills and manakins, all especially threatened because they are habitat specialists, mainly living in forests, and with a narrow temperature niche and slow reproductive rates. None of these can be expected to make it through the three-degree world alive.

It is not just the latitudinal shift of climate zones that is a concern: species will also be pushed uphill and die out when their climate envelope is pushed off the tops of mountains. For example, the critically endangered Hawai'ian silversword, a spiky plant found only on a single volcanic summit on the island of Maui, will be left with no climate space in future decades. This iconic conservation species, currently viewed by 1–2 million visitors annually, will be an early casualty in a much larger war. Mountainous areas around the world, while providing a refuge for species pushed up from rapidly heating lowland areas, will also be centres of biodiversity extinction as species that are currently adapted for cooler upland climates are reduced to ever-shrinking islands of habitat and eventually pushed off the map altogether.

Even where species do successfully shift their ranges, the results may not be pretty. Off Australia's south-western coasts, seaweed kelp forests stretch for over 800 kilometres, nurturing a highly productive and biodiverse ecosystem that includes valuable fisheries. Or at least they used to. In 2010 a marine heatwave destroyed 100 kilometres of this kelp forest and severely degraded much of the rest. It was not just the direct effect of the high temperatures that killed the kelp, however. In this region, rates of ocean warming equate to a southward 'climate velocity' of two to five kilometres per year, leading to an ongoing 'tropicalisation' of the northern parts of the reef as warm-water species move in.

One particularly destructive new arrival is the tropical rabbitfish, which is a voracious herbivore. Not only did it eat the kelp directly, but in areas where the seaweed had already been killed by heat, continual grazing by rabbitfish stopped it re-establishing on the rocky seabed once temperatures cooled. One study called this sudden transformation a 'climate-driven regime shift' that 'saw temperate species replaced by seaweeds, invertebrates, corals, and fishes characteristic of subtropical and tropical waters'. There will be many more such 'regime shifts' as ecosystems established over thousands of years fragment and disperse, sometimes within days or weeks, under the constant pressure of the warming climate. Models suggest that the biomass of plants and animals in the oceans will decrease by 5% with each degree of global warming, but given the chaos of multiple ecosystem collapses this is likely to be yet another underestimate.

As the marine heatwave in the Australian kelp forests illustrates, this heating process will not simply be one of gradual change; extreme events such as droughts, heatwaves, floods and cyclones may knock out entire species over large areas in one fell swoop. (This issue is also not captured in the broad-brush model approaches to quantifying the climate threat to biodiversity.) Ecologists studying lakes across the US Midwest have seen extreme summer heat driving an increase in fish mass die-offs, which they forecast will double or quadruple this century. If future mass mortality events affect vulnerable species with small, geographically restricted populations, extinctions could come suddenly and with little warning. A study in the journal *Nature Climate Change* found that a sixth of primate groups were vulnerable to cyclones – particularly in places like Madagascar – while a fifth were vulnerable to droughts, particularly those living in Malaysia, Borneo, Sumatra and the tropical forests of West Africa.

Meanwhile, novel ecosystems will increasingly cover both the Earth's terrestrial surface and its oceans, comprising assemblages of plants and animals that have never existed together before throughout evolutionary history. The existing paradigm of conservation – which often aims at protecting a single threatened species or valued ecosystem – will have to give way too alongside its target species, as shifting climate envelopes make protecting anything in perpetuity in a single location virtually impossible. Probably the best conservation strategy will simply to be to let go; to watch on the sidelines as new communities come into being while trying to enhance ecological connectivity so that species can migrate through or around human and natural barriers as easily as possible. Conservationists will need to remember that as with human refugees, 'invaders' into one place are often 'refugees' from somewhere no longer suitable. We will also need to let go of some of our concerns about 'invasive species' threatening 'our' native wildlife. Everything will change, for ever, and the best ecological adaptation strategy will almost certainly be to tear down the fences and let it happen.

I am not suggesting that ecologists sit idly back and watch species go globally extinct. Anything and everything should be tried to prevent that happening, including assisted migration and colonisation, habitat protection and restoration, the removal of hunting and agricultural pressures, the establishment and maintenance of targeted refuges, and – in the most desperate circumstances – keeping seeds, eggs and DNA of critically endangered species in cold storage for some point in the future when climate collapse can be contained and reversed. But just as we cannot air condition coral reefs, or put out every forest fire, we do not realistically have the option of micromanaging the maintenance of increasingly artificial ecosystems adapted to a former climate that no longer exists. Trying to do so will just prolong the agony and probably make things worse.

Watching ecosystems collapse is an extremely painful experience, but there will be little anyone can do. We will have crossed that particular Rubicon many decades earlier by deciding not to make the effort of reducing fossil fuel emissions sufficiently to avoid three degrees of global warming. Now we will have to live with the consequences of this failure as life on Earth is displaced, fragmented and destroyed. To get a sense of what this will feel like, consider how Tasmanian wildlife managers felt as they desperately tried to fight multiple wildfires during a combined heatwave and drought in January 2016. Sparked by lightning during an intense electrical storm, these were not just any bush fires – they were reducing to ashes ancient coniferous forests that have survived on Tasmania since it was part of the Gondwana supercontinent more than 180 million years ago. No wonder they called it 'Gondwana on fire'.

Many more such scenes of devastation are in store in the three-degree world. It is perhaps grimly appropriate that the Gondwanan forests, having survived multiple previous mass extinctions over nearly two hundred million years, should finally succumb to the climate-driven human extinction that is bearing down on us this century. When future humans can finally emerge from their air-conditioned houses and workplaces after the heatwaves subside, it will be an empty and silent world that greets them.

Amazon dieback

The burning Tasmanian forests are tiny compared with the Amazon rainforest. As I have mentioned, current omens are not good for the latter. The dry season is getting longer, leaving the trees in the less rainy southern part of Amazonia gasping for water later and later into the year. So-called 'once-in-a-century' droughts scorched large areas of the forest in 2005, 2010 and then again in 2016. Even in regions of virgin forest, more and more trees are dying, leaving an increasing fraction of the Amazon's carbon as dead 'necromass' rather than living biomass, and the Amazon carbon sink is in 'long-term decline'. Meanwhile soy farmers and cattle ranchers continue to encroach year on year, cutting their 'arc of deforestation' ever further into the heart of the rainforest. All this is presided over by a head of state in Brazil whose response to increased rates of deforestation has been to cook up a conspiracy theory blaming environmentalists and scientists while giving the nod to loggers, ranchers and gold miners.

Even if a majority of the rainforest survives this onslaught, it will probably not survive three degrees of global warming. 'We find that the risk of significant loss of forest cover in Amazonia rises rapidly for a global mean temperature rise above 2°C,' wrote Chris Jones and colleagues at the UK's Hadley Centre in 2009 in a paper for *Nature Geoscience*. Later work has confirmed this gloomy prediction. While some models have suggested that the forest could survive a temperature increase even up to 4°C, these projections depend heavily on the CO_2 fertilisation effect. In the real world rainforests are losing rather than gaining biomass, probably because of increased pressure from drought. (For water-stressed trees additional CO_2 is like being force-fed dry food when you are dying of thirst.) Some scientists now argue that the 'critical threshold' for forest collapse in Amazonia is more likely to be 2–3°C than a higher number.

If this is true, the forest will be critically endangered very early on in a three-degree world. Once the ecological breakdown process begins, it may well be irreversible; rainforest trees generate much of their own rainfall through evapotranspiration, recycling water numerous times over the whole region. As the trees are lost, the forest dries out, raising local temperatures and drastically reducing rainfall elsewhere. Scientists have found that this positive feedback could lead to an unstoppable collapse in the forest. In addition, the models tend to simulate more rainfall than Amazonia has actually received in recent years. Once the observed droughts are factored in, even the most conservative models shift towards a projection of more arid, savannah-style ecosystems with less and less tropical forest.

It is conceivable, perhaps, that the forest might move away from the deep tropics to keep up with the pace of planetary heating. However, the 'climate velocity' implied in such a shift is almost impossibly rapid. One recent study, based on a projected 2.5°C regional warming by 2050, found that distances to future comparable temperatures would be as far as 500 kilometres away from current forest areas. If deforestation continues at current rates, moreover, much of the remaining forest will have no temperature analogue at all. Species will also find it difficult to move across an increasingly fragmented landscape; many tropical forest birds are reluctant or unable to cross open spaces, while tree species will find it impossible to keep up with climate velocities tracking ten or more kilometres per year. It is depressing but hardly surprising, given this grim forecast, that half the Amazon rainforest's tree species are expected to be added to the IUCN Red List by the middle of the century.

These threats do not just apply to Amazonia. Although other tropical forests around the world have been given much less scientific attention, they may be even more vulnerable because of their locations and smaller extents. Studies in Bangladeshi forests already show a negative correlation between rising temperatures and tree growth. Tropical forests in Costa Rica are showing a productivity decline due to drought and warming, with no sign of any positive impact from the much-vaunted CO_2 fertilisation effect. Given their location in a region of intense future drought impacts, Central American rain-forests are unlikely to survive even two degrees of global heating, and will face rapid conversion to more arid ecosystems as the climate warms. Tropical forests in Malaysia and Indonesia are if anything even more threatened by direct human impacts – from palm oil plan-tations and intentional fires – than Amazonia, and are also likely to suffer severe increases in drought due to stronger El Niños. Little work has been done on the future prospects for Central African rain-forests, but there is no reason to expect them to be spared the impacts of rapidly shifting climate zones and increasingly erratic rainfall.

This combination of soaring temperatures and extreme drought greatly increases the risk of fire. The Amazon is not an ecosystem that is adapted to regular burning; once the forest canopy is incinerated, rough grasses invade opened-up areas. These flammable invasive plants stop the forest recovering by increasing fire risk in future and accelerating the long-feared transition from moist tropical rainforest to arid savannah. Models project hundreds of thousands of square kilometres becoming subject to burning in a three-degree scenario, with torched areas covering virtually the entire Amazon. Not surpris-ingly, repeatedly burned zones retain just a small fraction of their original carbon stocks. The rest ends up in the atmosphere, where it adds a further feedback to global warming. It seems almost callous to ask – given the irreplaceable value of all the plants and animals that will be extinguished with the loss of the Amazon – what the carbon implications of this catastrophic collapse will be. The Brazilian rain-forest is currently one of the largest living carbon reserves on the planet, storing 150–200 billion tonnes in its biomass and soils. Losing just half of this gigantic carbon store would be equivalent to a decade of humanity's fossil fuel emissions.

It is extraordinary – and utterly tragic – to think that this spectacular ecosystem, which is thought to have endured on Earth for at least 55 million years, could be largely gone in our lifetimes. After the loss of tropical coral reefs, which will already be ecologically functionally extinct in the three-degree world, the death of the Amazon will stand as the second great ecosystem collapse of planetary significance brought about by global climate heating. The process of ecological breakdown could be one of slow degradation, barely visible to the observer as an ever-increasing number of individual trees wither, die and topple in remote regions of the forest. More likely is a much more dramatic scenario, one that could destroy a significant proportion of the whole rainforest in the space of just a few days and weeks. Picture a future megadrought, the three-degree world equivalent of the once-in-a-century droughts already experienced in 2005, 2012 and 2016. Months without rainfall are exacerbated by searing temperatures, reducing the formerly swampy forest to a dry tinderbox over vast areas from Brazil to Colombia. In whatever way the spark comes, perhaps from lightning or the continuing destructive efforts of loggers or cattle ranchers, the resulting firestorm will be an event of planet-scale significance.

With tens or even hundreds of thousands of square kilometres simultaneously in flames – a conflagration equivalent in size to the state of Texas – vast quantities of smoke, barrelled up into the atmosphere by colossal convection-driven pyrocumulonimbus mushroom clouds, will punch through into the stratosphere and begin to circulate around the globe. This will dim the skies worldwide, briefly darkening the sun in an event analogous to a medium-sized volcanic eruption or a small nuclear winter. It will also deliver spectacular sunsets as the suspended smoke particles scatter the solar rays. All around the world, people will pause to witness the death of the Amazon, as what was once the largest and most biodiverse rainforest in the world circulates the globe in vaporised form as ash, smoke and dust. Over a couple of months this smear in the sky will fade, and the world's greatest terrestrial ecosystem will be gone for ever.

The permafrost feedback

The loss of the majority of the Amazon rainforest would not just be a tragedy for life on Earth, it would also be a significant positive feedback, adding another few tenths of a degree to global temperatures. With billions of tonnes of additional carbon being rapidly released due to warming, drought and fires in the Amazon and other rainforest ecosystems, it will become ever harder to stabilise world temperatures at three degrees. But this epic disaster is not even the largest positive feedback that keeps climate scientists awake at night. A far greater store of carbon currently lies locked up in the frozen soils of the Arctic. This could total well over a trillion tonnes, which for millennia has lain undisturbed in permafrost deposits in Siberia, northern Canada, Scandinavia and Alaska. The key question now is how rapidly it will thaw, over how wide an area, and how much additional carbon will spew into the atmosphere as a result.

Although most climate models do not include the permafrost carbon feedback in their future projections, scientists looking specifically at this problem conclude that each degree of global warming will thaw four million square kilometres of permafrost, according to a 2017 paper published in *Nature Climate Change*. For a three-degree planet, that means 12 million square kilometres thaw out – out of a current initial total of only 15 million, meaning that nearly three-quarters of the globe's inventory of permafrost will be turned to mush as temperatures rise to three degrees. This will release upwards of 100 billion tonnes of carbon by the end of the century – boosting global heating by a further two-tenths of a degree by 2100 and still more thereafter.

And it gets worse. Not all the thawing permafrost will be released as CO_2. Some will bubble out as methane, a gas with a global warming potential 30–40 times as powerful as CO_2. Huge quantities of methane lie trapped in unstable underwater deposits in the ocean shelves off Siberia, where sea temperatures have already risen by two degrees in recent decades. As scientists warned in a commentary piece in *Nature* in 2013: 'A 50-gigatonne reservoir of methane, stored in the form of hydrates, exists on the East Siberian Arctic Shelf. It is likely to be emitted as the seabed warms, either steadily over 50 years or suddenly.' Massive methane plumes have already been spotted, some more than a kilometre wide, by research ships north of Siberia. While there is no conclusive evidence yet that these methane plumes, dramatic as they may appear to observers, are yet a sign of any runaway positive feedback, no one doubts that the Arctic seafloor holds a massive inventory of methane. And it is not just the ocean. Large amounts of methane are also likely to be emitted from spreading lakes and ponds that are suddenly appearing all over the Arctic landscape as ice-rich permafrost thaws out.

Even without the methane wild card, the picture looks increasingly grim. Existing model projections for Arctic permafrost carbon melt have been called 'a vast underestimate'. The reason is straightforward – Arctic permafrost is currently collapsing much faster than the experts expected. Whereas models are designed to simulate permafrost thawing gradually from the top down, this is not always how the process takes place in the real world. 'Instead of a few centimetres of soil thawing each year, several metres of soil can become destabilized within days or weeks,' a team of scientists report in *Nature*. As thawed areas slump and collapse, the process of abrupt permafrost thawing has become visibly dramatic. Returning to field sites in Alaska the researchers found lands that were forested a year ago now covered in lakes, while once-clear rivers ran 'thick with sediment'. Whole hillsides turned suddenly to liquid, causing landslides that sometimes carried away sensitive scientific equipment. Once this abrupt thaw is even partially integrated into the models, scenarios for end-of-century carbon release increase by tens of billions of tonnes of carbon, with much of this extra input coming in the form of methane.

This abrupt thaw is being witnessed even in the highest latitudes of the terrestrial Arctic. Scientists from the University of Alaska working in the Arctic Canadian islands over the last ten years have been surprised to see what was formerly flat terrain collapse into troughs and ponds. Perhaps their most stunning observation is this: 'Observed maximum thaw depths at our sites are already exceeding those projected to occur by 2090' in a three-degree global warming model. At the risk of stating the obvious, if large areas of Arctic permafrost are melting 70 years and two degrees too soon, this clearly does not bode well for our existing expectations about permafrost carbon release. So instead of two-tenths of a degree, as scientists projected back in 2015, perhaps we are now looking at 0.3 or 0.4°C of additional global heating thanks to the Arctic permafrost emissions. Added to other positive feedbacks, such as the release of Amazonian carbon, and another few tens of billions of tonnes as the northern forests dry out and catch fire, plus potentially substantial releases from peatlands in the tropics, we could be seeing half a degree or more of additional warming by the end of the century.

An ice-free Arctic Ocean

And that is not all. A more direct potential positive feedback also lies in the Arctic, but not on land – instead this drastic acceleration of the warming process operates out in the ocean. Most studies agree that a three-degree world sees permanent summertime ice-free conditions in the Arctic Ocean, perhaps as soon as mid-century. While the average September becomes ice-free as early as 2045, August and October also see open water across the North Pole by about 2070. This means that the only permanent, all-year ice left in the Arctic will be small areas attached to the land masses of northern Greenland and the Canadian Arctic archipelago, and even they won't last long into the second half of the century.

The impact on the ecology of the Arctic will be disastrous, with polar bears forced to either starve on land or swim immense distances to chase rapidly drifting slushy ice floes. The remaining populations of bears – along with other ice-dependent animals like walrus, bowhead whales, numerous different species of seals, fish and seabirds – will be herded into a diminishing polar refuge in small, still-frozen areas for longer and longer periods of the year. With survival prospects dimming for each new generation of pups, calves, chicks and cubs, extinction in the wild looms for all Arctic species unfortunate enough to have evolved to be dependent on this vanishing sea ice habitat. After coral reefs and the Amazon, this is the third globally significant ecological collapse in our hotter world.

The effects of the loss of the Arctic ice cap ricochet around the planet as increasing climate chaos. With open water extending across virtually the entire northern polar ocean, huge amounts of heat are captured from the sun during the ice-free summer months (open water absorbs six times as much solar heat as sea ice). This energy is then released as warmth and moisture during the winter, transforming storm tracks across the mid and high latitudes, changing centres of high and low pressure, and even displacing the jet stream. Most importantly of all, this disappearance of white snow and ice changes the albedo and consequently the energy balance of the entire planet. With less solar radiation being reflected back into space by highly reflective polar ice, more of the Sun's heat is retained by the darker-coloured land and ocean and recirculated within the Earth system.

The magnitude of this additional heat is no mystery, because it is already being monitored by scientific instruments. Satellites orbiting the Earth above the North Pole can directly measure the energy budget at the top of the atmosphere over the newly ice-free areas that have already appeared in our one-degree world. Extrapolate this additional heat over the whole polar ocean – as scientists did in a *Geophysical Research Letters* paper published in June 2019 – and it is possible to generate a figure for the additional energy that will be absorbed by the whole planet in the event of a complete loss of Arctic sea ice. This adds up to about 0.7 watts per square metre of extra heat. That might not sound like much, but it yields an equivalent planetary heating effect to one trillion tonnes of CO_2 emissions, on top of the 2.4 trillion tonnes that have already been released by humans since the pre-industrial period. This in turn is equivalent to fast-forwarding global warming by about 25 years.

The scientists are not suggesting that this scenario will play out the instant the Arctic Ocean sees its first ice-free September. To fully absorb this amount of new solar heat, the Arctic needs to be ice-free all the way through from mid-March to the end of September, which most models do not simulate until global warming reaches five degrees or more. However, the scientists start by pointing out that the models are wrong on Arctic sea ice already, and that observed rates of melt are already double those predicted by existing simulations. This suggests that ice-free conditions could come earlier and last for longer in the year than is foreseen in conventional projections. And even half this amount of extra energy – equivalent to an additional 500 billion tonnes of CO_2 – would be disastrous.

Add these positive feedbacks together – the permafrost, the methane, the Amazonian carbon, the additional heat captured by the ice-free Arctic – and it is clear that entering the three-degree world risks pushing the global heating process beyond humanity's control. This could happen even in the event that we successfully reduce fossil fuel emissions substantially in future decades. Having said that, if we keep on increasing our carbon consumption in line with business-as-usual projections, another degree of global heating is virtually guaranteed, even without positive feedbacks. Maybe it is worth taking a look, therefore, at what the four-degree world has in store.

4°

Deadly heat

As we enter the four-degree world, global heating has radically altered the look of our planet. The European Alps have lost 90% of their ice; in the Himalayas only half remains. Other once-glaciated mountain ranges are now just bare rock. Ice shelves in the Antarctic are popping like corks out of a bottle, releasing an awakened West Antarctic Ice Sheet to surge and fragment into the warming oceans. Billions of tonnes of meltwater now sluice off the Greenland ice sheet every summer, forming torrents of mud and sediment that pour into the North Atlantic. Sea level rise of one to two metres is probably on the cards for the end of the century, displacing hundreds of millions of people from coastal areas, and leaving dozens of megacities hunkered behind fragile sea walls in fear of the next storm.

In the deep tropics and mid-latitudes, cataclysmic floods sweep away towns and villages alongside once-placid rivers, while in the parched sub-tropics and Mediterranean regions the transition to full-scale desert is under way. Wild plants and animals struggle to adapt to climate zones shifting at several kilometres per year, and species that fall behind the chaotic general exodus join the ever-lengthening extinction casualty list. For several years in the late 21st century the globe is blanketed in smoky haze as gigantic forest fires accelerate the catastrophic dieback of the Amazon rainforest, spelling a dramatic end for one of the Earth's great biomes. In the oceans tropical coral reefs are but a fading memory of our grandparents, and the last polar bears too are long dead.

Humans as a species are not facing extinction – not yet anyway. But advanced industrial civilisation, with its constantly increasing levels of material consumption, energy use and living standards – the system that we call modernity and that has brought us into this crisis by continuing to be utterly dependent on fossil fuels – this civilisation is tottering. Droughts and heatwaves scorch crops throughout the world's great breadbaskets, sending global commodity prices surging and forcing tens of millions of hungry people out onto the streets and across national borders. Formerly productive agricultural regions are suffering from encroaching desertification over vast areas, while cities once surrounded by lush countryside are now stranded inside an expanding ocean of shifting sand. New civil conflicts emerge as dark political forces are released in nations facing an influx of millions of refugees. In the high Arctic, the permafrost has melted, with billions of tonnes of CO_2 and methane released in a devastating positive feedback. The North Polar summertime ice is gone, and the relentless sun shines down into the darker open waters, changing the albedo of the planet and aiding the absorption of colossal amounts of additional solar energy.

In the four-degree world, the big story is heat. The US National Weather Service defines a 'heat index' – combining heat and humidity into a 'feels-like' temperature – of 40.6°C as 'dangerous'. In a four-degree world billions of people are experiencing 'dangerous' heat index conditions every year, encompassing most of the world's great megacities, from Tokyo to Shanghai to Rio de Janeiro to New York. Cities like Lagos and Delhi, which already face occasional dangerous heat in the current climate, suffer extreme conditions for almost the entire year. Global exposure to extreme heat increases 30-fold, while in Africa it increases by a factor of more than 100. It is not only the tropics; mid-latitude regions will be experiencing an additional 80–120 days of temperatures currently classed as 'heat-wave' conditions, while even sub-polar regions will experience 40–80 days of heatwave conditions each year. Extreme hotspots – experiencing rises in heat stress of over 6°C – appear in mid-latitude North America, the Mediterranean, the Sahel in Africa, and the rapidly desertifying deep interior of South America formerly occupied by the rainforest known as the Amazon.

One way to visualise the drastic heating of the climate – as we saw earlier – is to imagine where a city might move to in the current climate to experience the four-degree world. This time Washington DC, for example, will be experiencing the kind of climate that today is characteristic of Greenwood, Mississippi. Los Angeles moves south to nearly the tip of Baja California in Mexico; Tampa, Florida moves all the way to Central America; Portland, Oregon shifts to Sacramento in California; and Denver, Colorado relocates to northern Texas. Across the whole of North America it will be so hot that two-thirds of the continental United States will be setting new heat records every single year, with a 20-fold increase in the American population exposed to extreme heat. Average annual maximum temperatures that are currently only seen in hot, hyper-arid conditions such as the Mojave Desert and Death Valley of 43°C (110°F) become commonplace. In the four-degree world, virtually all of Texas, Oklahoma, Kansas, Missouri and Arkansas experience peak temperatures exceeding current Death Valley conditions every year. These states, including southern Arizona, Louisiana and south-eastern California, can expect more than eight weeks a year with temperatures above 37°C (100°F). New York's extreme heatwave of 2 August 2006, which caused blackouts and led to the deaths of an estimated 140 people, would be experienced for at least 20 days every single year. Even the interior of Alaska will see annual temperatures in excess of 35°C (95°F).

This extreme heat will kill increasingly large numbers of people. If historical heatwave mortality rates are used as a threshold by which to judge 'deadly heat' in the future climate, half the Earth's land area and nearly three-quarters of the entire global population will be exposed to deadly heat for more than 20 days per year in a four-degree world. New York will see deadly heat conditions for 50 days annually, while due to its location nearer the tropics Jakarta, Indonesia, will experience deadly heat for 365 days – the entire year – as will three-quarters of the island of Borneo, home to a current population of 19 million. It is difficult to exaggerate what this means; one 2018 study concluded that 'most regions within 30° latitude of the equator' may experience up to 250 days of extreme heat index, resulting in a 'radical transformation' of the tropics and sub-tropics, which would now spend much of the year in heatwave conditions.

Older people are particularly vulnerable to heat-related death. One study projects that the mortality risk associated with excessive heat stress for people aged 65 and over will increase as much as 20-fold across the Middle East and North Africa. Researchers have quantified the population-wide increases in mortality expected due to heat in the four-degree world: across the US a 500% increase in deaths is projected; Brazil sees an 850% increase; Australia 470%; while the Philippines sees a 1,300% increase in death rates and Colombia a devastating 2,000% increase in heat-related mortality.

There is some good news, however: in the four-degree world parts of the tropics will be so hot that disease-carrying mosquitoes will no longer be able to transmit pathogens. So while these diseases have all moved up into the mid-latitudes and areas that are currently safe from malaria, dengue, yellow fever and Zika, in the tropics at least the incidence of dengue and other vector-borne viral diseases should decline. When we have made our planet too hot even for mosquitoes, something really has gone seriously wrong.

Uninhabitable Earth

At four degrees a whole new process has begun to unfold, making substantial areas of the planet biologically uninhabitable for humans. While the increased mortality risk in today's heatwaves tends to be among older, very young and other vulnerable people, temperatures at four degrees of global heating are high enough to reach a critical threshold that will kill anyone, however fit and healthy, because of the laws of thermodynamics.

Like all other warm-blooded animals, humans sometimes need to be able to expel excessive heat in order to regulate our temperatures at a stable 37°C. We do that by sweating, thereby losing body heat via evaporative cooling. But that relies on the humidity of the air being sufficiently low that heat can still be lost as liquid sweat evaporates. Once both humidity and temperatures pass a critical level – defined at what scientists call a 'wet-bulb' temperature of 35°C – no amount of sweating will cool us down, and unless an external source of cooling can be found, death will inevitably result. It won't matter how good your physical condition is, or whether you find shade and water; if you try to survive for more than a couple of hours outside an artificial environment in these conditions you will die. Let's be clear. At four degrees we are beginning to turn parts of our once-temperate world into a lethal hothouse, hostile to virtually all life.

When scientists first proposed the existence of this critical wet-bulb temperature in a landmark 2010 study in *PNAS*, they noted reassuringly that nowhere on Earth was expected to exceed this threshold until the average global temperature rose by seven degrees or more. But that was before the dramatic events of July 2015, when one of the worst heatwaves ever recorded swept across the Middle East. Sea temperatures in the Gulf rose to 34°C, as hot as a bathtub, while blistering winds sweeping in from the surrounding deserts saw ambient temperatures in Basra, Iraq, and Omidiyeh, Iran, rise to between 48 and 51°C. One Iranian town, Bandar Mahshahr, saw the mercury rise to 46°C for a few hours with a relative humidity of 49%. This corresponds to a wet-bulb temperature of 34.6°C, just a few tenths of a degree below the critical level. The conclusion is stark. If the temperature can already approach this deadly threshold in the one-degree world, by the time we are living in the four-degree world large areas of the planet will see lethal hothouse conditions for long periods.

More recent model studies – which, given the unforeseen events of 2015, are still likely to be conservative – give an indication of what lies in store, and which areas are likely to be most seriously affected. As you might expect from the event already experienced, one epicentre is the Persian Gulf, with the liveability threshold exceeded regularly in the simulated four-degree world in Abu Dhabi, Dubai, Dhahran (Saudi Arabia) and Bandar Abbas (Iran). Kuwait City is less humid, so keeps a lower wet-bulb temperature, but still faces dry-bulb – normal thermometer measurements, in other words – summertime highs in excess of 60°C in this scenario. (For comparison, 60°C is higher than any temperature recorded so far on Earth. The current record is 54°C, measured in both Kuwait and Death Valley in 2013.) Much of the Arabian Peninsula, including the Muslim holy cities of Mecca and Jeddah, is similarly affected, endangering the safety of millions of religious pilgrims whose sacred Hajj rituals include praying outside over several days in the open air. There may be an irony of sorts that these same Gulf and Arabian states are the major source of the oil and gas whose emissions are now making these same countries intolerably hot – but that will be of little comfort.

It is not only the Middle East that will be transitioning into a biologically uninhabitable state in the four-degree world. Model simulations also project that substantial areas of South Asia will be reaching the critical 35°C wet-bulb temperature limit at the same time. One key study reports that 'the most intense hazard from extreme future heat waves is concentrated around densely populated regions of the Ganges and Indus river basins,' noting that this 'presents a serious and unique risk to South Asia, a region inhabited by about one-fifth of the global human population.' In a four-degree scenario, according to the models, wet-bulb temperature 'is likely to exceed the survivability threshold' in parts of north-eastern India and Bangladesh, and to approach the critical threshold over most of the rest of South Asia. Whole cities, such as Lucknow in Uttar Pradesh and Patna in Bihar, each with a current population of over two million, find themselves stranded beyond the survivability threshold.

Obviously no one is going to build an artificially cooled survival dome over the Indian subcontinent. Such a thing is not even remotely feasible. But the fact remains that these projected future conditions will not be able to support the continued permanent existence of large-scale human habitation in areas currently home to hundreds of millions of people. Patches of habitability may remain in highland areas, like oases in a desert, but in social and political terms India, Pakistan and Bangladesh as we know them will no longer exist, and close to a billion people will face a choice between risking death in each progressively hotter summer or becoming part of the world's burgeoning population of climate refugees.

And the refugee numbers could be astronomical, encompassing a significant fraction of the Earth's people. This is because the other of the world's great human population centres, China, will also be bumping up against the survivability threshold at around this same time. As the authors of another study explicitly state: 'Continuation of the current pattern of global emissions may limit habitability in the most populous region of the most populous country on Earth.' This threat is centred on the North China Plain, the 400,000-square kilometre region that was the cradle of ancient Chinese civilisation and now – inhabited by nearly half a billion people – is one of the most densely populated parts of the world. The authors tick off a list of cities, each with a current population in the millions, where conditions will eventually become unliveable: Weifang, Jining, Qingdao, Rizhao, Yantai, Shanghai and Hangzhou. These are not small towns;

Shanghai has a metropolitan population of 34 million people, while Hangzhou is home to 22 million.

China is a technologically advanced economy and its cities are some of the most modern in the world. It is perhaps conceivable that they could transform towards Gulf status, with their giant populations sustained artificially in a technosphere cocoon of air-conditioned high-rises and supplied by desalinated seawater piped in from the warming oceans. Today's Gulf cities like Doha and Dubai are already nearly impossible creations, like glass and steel mirages in the desert, sustained by their consumption of prodigious quantities of energy (mostly generated by burning oil and gas) for air conditioning and water desalination. Perhaps as their physical environments trend closer to outright uninhabitability, megacities from Shanghai to Delhi will be able to seal themselves off in artificial enclosures, like domed space stations on the hostile surface of Mars. But imagine the consequences of a power outage in such circumstances, with millions of people trapped inside glass and steel structures that rapidly transform into greenhouses or even solar ovens once the electricity goes down.

And heatwaves do not always come in calm conditions. One 2019 study looked at the potential for tropical cyclones, which threaten some of the world's most densely populated coastlines, to be followed immediately by deadly heat events. Imagine the scene: devastated coastal cities, with no power, and millions of people faced with the immediate loss of shelter, food and water, in situations of intense heat stress, and with tens or even hundreds of thousands of unburied corpses rotting in the streets. In the four-degree world, the study suggests, such catastrophes would become annual events. Some humans might dream of a future in which we become more and more symbiotic with machines, but what happens when – as E. M. Forster once asked – the machine stops? We might live in increasingly artificial environments, but sooner or later the realities of the physical and biological world will bring us back to Earth.

As the belt of uninhabitability extends around the planet – beginning in the Middle East, but then swallowing up most of India, Pakistan, Bangladesh and eastern China – the future for a substantial portion of the planet's human population looks bleak. With the global temperature at four degrees, humans now face a completely new situation, one where expanding, densely populated zones of the planet, which have sustained our civilisations for millennia, are now functionally unliveable for our species. We are making our world increasingly unsuitable for life, and yet – space stations and moon colonies aside – we have nowhere else to go.

Dust and fire

Brian Allen had only been in Arizona two weeks when the symptoms began. His family of three had moved to Phoenix in April 2018 to start a new life, but had had little time to enjoy the sun. 'As soon as he got the job here, he got sick,' recalled his lifelong partner Franique, whom he had been with for 13 years. 'He was experiencing headaches … and chills.' By the time Brian was admitted to ER he had even stopped recognising his family, including his young son Kal'el. He died on 2 June, less than two weeks after the headaches began. Franique does what she can to console their young son, but 'Kal'el just wants his daddy to come back.'

Neither Franique nor Brian had even heard of valley fever when they first went to Phoenix. But the likely source of the infection was clear. 'He was working and he was caught in a dust storm and he inhaled the fungus in the air and it went to his lungs,' says Franique in a matter of fact way. Valley fever is a fungal infection caused by airborne spores that are lifted out of the arid desert soils in dust and transmitted long distances before being breathed in and lodging in the lungs. Most cases are mild, involving – as Brian Allen at first experienced – fever, fatigue, headaches and chills. But on rarer occasions the more serious form of the disease, disseminated coccidioidomycosis, can occur as the fungus spreads beyond the lungs into the bones, liver, brain and heart. If the fungus causes pneumonia, meningitis or other complications, it can be fatal.

Although valley fever has been around for a long time, its incidence increased eightfold in endemic areas – Arizona, California, Nevada, New Mexico and Utah – between 1998 and 2011. Scientists report a strong correlation between dust events and outbreaks of the disease, especially in the 'Valley' area of metropolitan Phoenix where fungal coccidioidomycosis is at its most severe. This is a serious concern because perennial drought in the south-western United States is helping to drive an extraordinary increase in airborne dust, which blankets towns and cities every summer when the monsoon arrives. The average number of dust storms has risen by 240%, from 20 storms a year in the later 1980s to nearly 50 in the decade before 2011. With dramatic drying and warming predicted for the southern and western United States in a four-degree scenario, valley fever will spread rapidly throughout the whole region east of the Rockies, even pushing up to the Canadian border and encompassing 17 states.

The hot and dry trend in Arizona, Texas and Oklahoma inevitably raises memories of the Dust Bowl of the 1930s, when drought and poor land-use practices led to catastrophic dust storms and widespread human misery across the south-western US, forcing millions to abandon their failing farms and trek west into California. Even in today's one-degree world a new Dust Bowl may have already begun. As I reported in the first chapter, snowpack in the Sierra Nevada reached lows unprecedented in 500 years in April 2015 after California's warmest winter on record, while the drought between 2011 and 2015 was probably the worst for at least a millennium.

Whether or not the 'megadrought' era has begun already, it is a virtual certainty in the four-degree world. As one team of climate modellers, writing in *Science Advances* in 2016, reports: 'The probability of megadrought is close to 100% if Southwest temperatures rise by 5°C or more' regionally, as is predicted in a four-degree world. The landscape will change utterly as the region's characteristic pine and fir forests die from drought or are consumed by beetle infestations and fire. Megadroughts in the past have been linked with the collapse of pre-industrial civilisations like the Anasazi, Maya and Angkor. Now it is our own industrial civilisation that is on the line. In their *Science Advances* paper the researchers remind readers that 'an aggressive reduction in greenhouse gas emissions cuts megadrought risks nearly in half'. But in the four-degree world it is too late for that.

The drying trend is so profound that more than half the world's land surface will become classed as 'arid' in a four-degree scenario. According to one 2018 paper reporting the results of 27 climate models, the areas that lose their rainfall first are southern Europe, Central America, South America (especially the interior region of the former Amazon rainforest), southern Africa, coastal Australia and southern China. Limiting global warming to 1.5°C would most likely have saved them, but now the desertification process is well under way. As usual, poorer countries are hit hardest – more than three-quarters of the newly arid areas are in the developing world. But being located outside the suffocatingly hot subtropics is no guarantee of adequate rainfall; arid and hyper-arid areas appear even in Alaska, north-west Canada and Siberia. Whole countries are consumed, from Iraq to Botswana, with dryland areas expanding by 5.8 million square kilometres globally. As the authors of one multi-model study, published in *Nature Climate Change*, report, in the four-degree world the 'drylands dominate the global land surface'. The latest research suggests that an additional 1.9 billion people will live in drylands in a four-degree world as compared with a world where temperatures are kept below 1.5°C.

Even the higher mid-latitudes, where average rainfall rates might be expected to remain stable or even increase, become prone to increasingly frequent and severe drought episodes in the four-degree world. As a group of researchers wrote in the *International Journal of Climatology* in 2018: 'The whole European continent, with the exception of Iceland, will be affected by more frequent and severe extreme droughts.' While the Mediterranean area is most parched by drying, the whole of France, the British Isles and even Scandinavia and western Russia are badly affected. In the four-degree world, according to a 2019 paper in the journal *Global and Planetary Change*, an additional three billion people suffer water stress, with a third of the world's much-larger population no longer having access to sufficient fresh water. This study, which uses the very latest updated climate and hydrological models, rattles off a now-familiar list of the areas that are most affected: 'The Mediterranean region, the Amazon, Central and Central North America, Western South America, Southeast Asia, Australia and South Africa regions are expected to face increased exposure in short term meteorological drought.'

Not surprisingly, in all these areas, which include hydrological basins covering half the world's land surface, less water will flow in the rivers. In West Africa, rivers lose up to 40% of their current flow, subjecting the region's rapidly growing population to 'unprecedented water deficit'. With weather belts gradually shifting low-pressure areas towards the poles, the Indian monsoon loses nearly half its rainfall across the central Ganges plain, subjecting an additional 600 million people to drastic water scarcity in what was formerly one of the most fertile regions of the world. Globally, huge areas of what were once considered temperate lands become dry sub-tropical, complete with invading diseases, termites, massive ecological disruption and crop failure. There is even a higher chance of deadly Ebola outbreaks as a hotter, more humid equatorial band increases the range of its animal hosts in Africa.

Four degrees means that we will have literally set our world on fire. Models project an increase in gigantic wildfires as temperatures rise and drought grips croplands, grasslands and forests alike. People will die not just from heat and thirst, but directly from smoke inhalation; one study projects a doubling of premature deaths from fire-related particulate pollution in the United States by the end of the century.

The risk of 'very large fires' rises, according to a different study, by between 100 and 600% across the western United States, with fire risk also increasing around the Great Lakes and the east coast. Whole national parks will burn, and the fire risk to the Everglades in Florida rises by 500%.

At a global level the areas of highest future fire danger overlap, as one would expect, with those most affected by drought, 'with sharp increases projected for the European Mediterranean Basin and Levant, subtropical Southern Hemisphere (Atlantic coast of Brazil, southern Africa and central east coast of Australia) and southwestern USA and Mexico', with the area burned around the Mediterranean region more than doubling. Where fires get large enough, they will generate towering pyrocumulonimbus clouds, complete with day-long darkness, frequent lightning, fire tornados and black hail. As well as further fanning the flames with intense winds, these gigantic storm clouds inject smoke into the stratosphere, where it circulates the globe, analogous in impact – for the largest wildfire events – to a medium-sized volcanic eruption.

This is not idle conjecture: in August 2017 massive wildfires in the Pacific Northwest, across British Columbia and Washington State, sparked these towering clouds, injecting roughly the same amount of particulates into the upper atmosphere as the 2008 eruption of Kasatochi volcano in Alaska. The quantity of smoke was so great that it was observed in the stratosphere for eight months, and was studied by scientists on the basis that it might 'provide new insights into potential global climate impacts from nuclear war'. Unlike volcanic eruptions, however, which tend to cool the Earth by reflecting solar radiation, black-coloured soot particles from massive wildfires act to warm the atmosphere even further by absorbing solar heat – another positive feedback.

While, as discussed above, substantial areas of the Middle East, South Asia and eastern China become biologically uninhabitable in the four-degree world due to high wet-bulb temperatures, much larger areas – including virtually the entire subtropics – become less habitable due to drying, desertification and fire. Many of these areas have nurtured human settlements for thousands of years. Now we will have to abandon them as the tides of sand sweep ever further north and south, out of the deserts and towards the mid-latitudes of our overheating planet. Millions of heat refugees will be joined by millions more drought refugees and those burned out of villages, towns and cities as vast fires sweep across the landscape – the huddled masses of half of humanity on the move, seeking shelter and survival wherever they can.

Mountains of melt

In a hotter world, remaining cooler areas contract towards the poles and uphill in mountain regions. Four degrees of global heating is roughly equivalent to raising the freezing level in the world's highlands by 800 metres. This means that slopes, peaks and even entire mountain ranges that have been accustomed to receiving snow will now be getting only rain, and the snow that falls on the highest summits will melt earlier in the season. Snow will disappear from all but the topmost peaks of the Sierra Nevada, for example, with overall snowpack totals reducing by 80–90% by the later part of the century. The lost water from these mountains is estimated at five times the annual residential usage of San Francisco. With drastically reduced snowpack, the Sierra Nevada and other mountain ranges will no longer act as water towers that gradually release freshwater into streams and rivers through the spring and early summer. Instead, precipitation will run off more quickly in the winter, and spring droughts will lead to parched summers, with some streams and rivers in highland areas drying up entirely.

Mountain glaciers around the world face an even more drastic fate. Most of the world's upland glaciated area will now be in the melt zone, and mountain ranges whose dramatic peaks have been clothed in snow and ice for thousands of years will start transforming back to bare rock and rubble. I began my writing career reporting on the impacts of climate warming on the mountain glaciers of the Peruvian Andes, which have already shrunk by a quarter in the last few decades. Almost all these glaciers will be gone in a four-degree world, with only the very highest peaks in the tropical Andes still close to or just below freezing. With 92% of its glaciers gone, Peru would lose several cubic kilometres of previously stored freshwater, threatening the drinking-water supplies, livelihoods and agricultural production of millions of people in the country's highlands and arid coastal regions. Thawing glaciers also pose the risk of sudden disasters as chunks of ice collapse into new meltwater lakes, triggering floods and mudflows that can submerge whole towns and kill thousands of people in minutes. The entire Quelccaya Ice Cap in the east of the country would also be in the melt zone; this is currently the largest tropical ice cap in the world, and ice cores have been drilled in it by scientists studying thousands of years of climate variations. All this valuable data will be liquidated and gone in the four-degree world.

For 'High Mountain Asia' – combining the Hindu Kush, Himalaya, Karakoram and Tien Shan mountain ranges – the implications of the coming meltdown are even more serious. The freshwater runoff from the snow and ice in these ranges currently supports the livelihoods of over a billion people, but by the end of the century only a third of the original ice mass will remain, with 90% of the ice being lost in some mountain areas. The glaciated parts of these mountain ranges are already warming much faster than the global average, and this process will not just continue but accelerate over future decades. With so much snow and ice being lost, the volume of meltwater will increase steadily until 2050, before peaking and beginning a terminal decline. This will be the end of the Himalayas as they exist today; an area of ice currently so extensive that it is known as the 'third pole' will be largely consigned to history. The mountains will remain, but they will be naked and bleak.

All told, in the four-degree world all the planet's mountain ranges will shed enough ice to raise global sea levels by more than 20 centimetres. One 2019 study reported: 'The regions which lose more than 75% of their initial [ice] volume by the end of the century are Alaska, western Canada and the US, Iceland, Scandinavia, the Russian Arctic, central Europe, Caucasus, High Mountain Asia, low latitudes, southern Andes and New Zealand.' As with the disappearing Arctic sea ice, this transformation will slightly reduce the albedo of the planet, and with less bright-white snow and ice to reflect solar radiation, the warming process will accelerate. Viewed from outer space, the Earth would look a little less bright than before without its characteristic ice cover. But this process is still only just beginning, for unless global heating is curbed we are on course to eventually transform the Earth into an entirely ice-free state, for the first time in tens of millions of years. Ice is far more than just frozen water. It is the Earth's thermostat, and without it there is nothing to keep our planet cool.

Rising floods

The first sign of the impending disaster was a sudden rise in the level of the Meghna River in early July 1998. For several days monsoon rains had deluged the north-east of Bangladesh, sparking flash floods and landslides. Then, in the third week of July the level of the mighty Brahmaputra also began to climb, adding to the vast additional quantities of water now also flooding out of India via the Ganges. By late August and September, half the country of Bangladesh was submerged. At one point much of the capital Dhaka was underwater, and foreign embassies made emergency evacuation plans for their staff and families as troops, civil engineers and policemen worked through the night to plug more than a hundred breaches in a vital embankment around the city. People began to travel by boat rather than road, with rickshaw drivers finding new employment as ferrymen, taking stranded residents across the city's flooded streets. The death toll began to rise too, as food ran short and epidemics of diarrhoea swept through a population now forced to live and bathe for weeks in filthy water.

The 1998 floods were the worst in Bangladesh's recent history. They were also the longest. Water levels on major rivers were above the danger level for nearly 60 days. While flooding is an annual event in Bangladesh, and even beneficial – rivers bring fertile silt to heavily farmed floodplains – the extent and duration of the 1998 event caused enormous misery. In total 30 million people were affected and over a thousand died, from drowning, disease and even snakebites. More than 15,000 kilometres of roads were damaged, as were nearly 7,000 bridges. A million people were displaced, and two million tonnes of rice production lost as waters stagnated for two months in the fields, meaning farmers were unable to sow or harvest. A truly catastrophic outcome was only averted thanks to an international aid effort ensuring that food and medicines were able to reach people in time to avoid famine.

Bangladesh is particularly vulnerable to flooding. Over 80% of the country is classed as floodplain, and three major rivers – the Ganges, the Meghna and the Brahmaputra – converge within the nation's borders. The Brahmaputra is the fourth-largest river in the world, draining half a million square kilometres of China, India, Bhutan and Bangladesh, with an average downstream flow rate of 20,000 cubic metres a second – about ten times that of Niagara Falls. The three rivers have somewhat different seasonal patterns; discharge from the Brahmaputra usually starts rising in March due to snowmelt in the Himalayas, while the Ganges begins to surge in early June with the onset of the Indian monsoon. The monsoon rains also raise the levels of both the Meghna and the Brahmaputra as moisture-laden air masses track north from the Bay of Bengal and run into the mountains of north-east India. While normally the Brahmaputra flood peaks occur in July and August, the Ganges tends to peak somewhat later, in August and September. Sometimes the peaks can coincide, however, and this is what happened during the flood disaster of 1998, when the two enormous rivers peaked only two days apart.

In the four-degree world, Bangladesh faces an increasingly perilous future. Although the Indian monsoon might decline across the central plains of South Asia, colossal quantities of rainfall are forecast for the north-east. Flood flows with a 100-year return period in the current climate are projected to increase by 80% for the Meghna, 63% for the Brahmaputra and 54% for the Ganges, according to climate models. The three rivers are also more likely to synchronise their times of peak discharge, meaning that Bangladesh faces more catastrophic events as the floodwaters merge across the country at the same time. In addition, the impact of rising sea levels and storm surges from stronger cyclonic storms in the Bay of Bengal means that less water will be able to flow out to sea. If all these events combine, then Bangladesh faces a hotter future in which the majority of its coastal and inland territories may be simultaneously underwater for weeks or months of the year. Bangladesh is one of the most densely populated nations in the world, so this means that tens of millions of vulnerable people face regular or even near-permanent inundation.

Four degrees of global heating will add tremendous amounts of energy to the Earth's hydrological cycle, intensifying both droughts and floods. Even drier areas may find themselves subject to sudden intense downpours, with denuded hillsides less able to retain water and therefore subject to landslides, erosion and flash-flooding. At a global level, projections for flooding in a high-emissions, hotter future are 'remarkable', according to scientists writing in *Nature Climate Change*. The experts forecast increasing floods across large areas of south and east Asia, equatorial Africa and South America, even as flood frequency declines in drier areas such as the Mediterranean and western Eurasia. What is currently a once-in-a-century flood in the one-degree world will happen as often as once in a decade in the four-degree scenario, with 62 million people exposed to regular flooding around the world.

A 2017 paper in the journal *Earth's Future*, using the combined outputs of seven different climate models, reports that 'relative changes in population affected at 4°C warming are projected to exceed 1,000% in 15 countries in Central Europe, South Asia, South America and Japan.' The scientists again use the word 'remarkable', writing that 'a remarkable finding is the more than 20-fold increase in flood risk in India and Bangladesh at 4°C warming, which puts them in the first 3 countries by population affected.' The top ten, in descending order of population affected, are China, India, Bangladesh, Vietnam, Myanmar, Pakistan, Thailand, Egypt, Nigeria and Uzbekistan. Millions of people will be facing regular flood disasters in these countries, even as usable fresh water may become scarcer overall. This is because the biggest increase is in daily precipitation extremes, rather than the more gentle rainfall that can help nurture agricultural crops and recharge aquifers. These projections indicate a 'virtually certain' likelihood (another unusual finding, given that most model forecasts are characterised by high levels of uncertainty) of heavier maximum rainfall events across the whole land surface of the planet. Economic damages from flooding will rise by as much as 500% globally, while in Europe one million people will be affected annually, with flood damages totalling as much as €100 billion every year.

This heavier rainfall and worsening flooding will impact different places in different ways. With snow disappearing from the lower elevations of the world's mountain ranges, more precipitation comes as rain, raising river levels in winter. 'Rain-on-snow' events, where warm rain combines with sudden snowmelt to cause dramatic increases in runoff, rise by more than 50% in western North America, raising flood risk by up to 200% for the Sierra Nevada, the Colorado headwaters and the Canadian Rocky Mountains. 'Atmospheric rivers', long streams of water vapour high in the atmosphere that can cause prolonged and intense rainfall on the western sides of continents, become longer, wider and stronger in a four-degree scenario. From Scotland to Oregon, this means that days and weeks of downpours will lead to flooding on a scale never before experienced in the current climate.

Europe also faces the likelihood of increased 'compound flooding', where storm surges and heavy rainfall combine to inundate large areas of vulnerable coastline. According to a 2019 paper in *Science Advances* journal, 'hot spot' regions include the Bristol Channel and the coasts of Devon and Cornwall in the UK, as well as the Dutch and German North Sea coasts. Holland is particularly at risk of compound flooding as it also experiences the highest rates of relative sea level rise, tripling the likelihood of combined storm surge/river floods. The Norwegian coast around Bergen, already frequently battered by Atlantic cyclones, sees a fivefold increase in compound flooding in a four-degree scenario. With more of Norway's future winter precipitation coming as rain rather than snow, the picture may be even worse than the models currently project. Similar forecasts can be expected for other higher-latitude coastal areas around the world.

Some of the heaviest rainfall totals experienced anywhere come in thunderstorms and other smaller-scale convective precipitation events that cannot be realistically simulated by global climate models because their small size falls below the typical resolution of the models. This means that conventional forecasts probably under-represent changes in extreme rainfall. Once the models are down-scaled to a higher resolution over smaller geographical areas, daily and hourly precipitation extremes become much better represented – a vital step forward for future projections because much more of the Earth's rainfall is projected to come in these shorter, heavier bursts. These downscaled models show increases in extreme precipitation of as much as 400% across North American land regions, for instance. Much of this will come as rain and hail in so-called 'mesoscale convective systems' (MCSs), which generate the supercell thunderstorms that bring strong winds, large hail, flash floods and tornados across the Great Plains of the US every spring and summer. These are some of the most powerful storms on Earth, even in the current climate, and every year they cause more than $20 billion in economic damage, as well as hundreds of deaths.

MCSs are already on the increase, bringing more intense rainfall across the United States over the last half-century. In a four-degree future, a fivefold increase is projected for the biggest and most powerful MCSs across the central US; these break out from the Great Plains and begin to batter Canada and the north-east of the US. Imagine a supercell bearing down on Washington DC, Boston or New York – like a scene from a disaster movie, gigantic tornados could be weaving through the skyscrapers, shattering glass and bending steel as hailstones the size of baseballs pummel the city. The clouds turn inky black as the storm front advances, followed by a downpour so intense that streets become rivers within minutes. This is the reality of the hotter world; weather we have never seen before, in areas that are currently totally unprepared. These kinds of storms can blow up within minutes and are very hard to predict, giving little warning of just where and when they will strike. With a whole city under an afternoon tornado warning, do you still send your kids to school? Or do you hunker down in the basement as the skies darken and a gusty wind arises as if out of nowhere? These are life-and-death decisions, and they need to be made quickly.

Hurricane warning

The largest and most powerful convective storms on Earth are hurricanes. These tropical cyclones form over areas of warm ocean when groups of thunderstorms converge and begin to rotate. If conditions are favourable, an enormous vortex forms, causing intense rainfall and destructive winds surrounding a characteristic clear central eye only a few kilometres wide. Tropical cyclones are known as typhoons in the western Pacific and hurricanes in the eastern Pacific and Atlantic, and figuring out precisely how they will change in a warming world is a question that has long bedevilled researchers.

Conventional climate models have a resolution – often of 100-km by 100-km grid boxes – that is too low to accurately simulate hurricanes. This is unavoidable because a higher resolution model, effectively representing the world's weather minute by minute over the entire Earth's surface for several simulated decades at a time, would require impossible amounts of computational power. Models also have to simulate the Earth's climate in three dimensions, with grid cells stacked up vertically in the atmosphere and down into the depths of the oceans. In addition, they must also accurately simulate sea ice, continental ice sheets, mountains, clouds, vegetation and so on, often totalling over one million lines of code and needing to be run on the world's most powerful supercomputers. (The UK Met Office's three Cray XC40 supercomputers occupy the same space as a tennis court and can run 14,000 trillion arithmetic operations per second.) High-resolution atmosphere-only models that aim to better represent smaller-scale features like tropical cyclones have to neglect the ocean – but this means they can't properly simulate the way the strongest storms are supercharged by changing sea temperatures.

To address this conundrum, in 2015 scientists at the Global Fluid Dynamics Laboratory in Princeton, New Jersey, took an earlier 'coupled' ocean and atmosphere model and increased the atmospheric and land surface resolution to 25-km boxes, while saving computational resources by keeping the ocean component at a relatively low resolution. The result – which they termed the 'High-Resolution Forecast-Oriented Low Ocean Resolution' (HiFLOR) model – turned out to be surprisingly successful. Its control output of 300 simulated years of tropical cyclone occurrences looks strikingly similar to where these storms have been observed to occur in the real world. The higher resolution of the model also meant that it was much more successful than previous models in simulating the most intense Category 4 and 5 storms. The scientists further tested HiFLOR by running retrospective seasonal forecasts for 1997 and 1998, finding that the model did a remarkably good job in forecasting where the strongest storms did in fact appear each year.

Armed with these relatively successful test runs, the GFDL experts then ran HiFLOR in a high-CO_2 world to see what would happen to the number, geographical extent and intensity of tropical cyclones. They found that not only would the hotter future see more tropical cyclones overall – in contradiction to most earlier models, which tended to show a reduction in hurricanes – but that the increase would be greatest for the most intense storms, the Category 4 and 5 events that can cause major loss of life and property at landfall through flooding, wind damage and storm surges. Most striking of all, HiFLOR simulates an increase in the strongest storms that is so dramatic that it implies the need to add an additional 'Category 6' superstorm level to the current 1–5 categorisation of hurricane wind-speed. Taiwan and the Philippines would be most directly in the line of fire for these Category 6 monster typhoons, as would Hawaii and the south-eastern United States. Australia would also see an increase in strong storms, along with Madagascar. In virtually all hurricane-prone regions of the world, storms would be more likely to undergo the rapid intensification that can turn a minor tropical depression into a colossal superstorm in a matter of hours – all fuelled by dramatically higher sea temperatures in the four-degree world.

However, this is just one model. Other coupled models do not necessarily agree on what is in store. For example, a 2017 paper look-ing at the outputs of six different models for a four-degree scenario found that the global number of tropical cyclones overall fell by a third, with decreases also in the number of the strongest Category 4 and 5 storms. While Hawaii, Japan and Madagascar saw more of the most intense tropical cyclones, much of the rest of the tropics saw decreases. However, these models typically have lower resolution than HiFLOR, and may be missing what is happening at the smaller scale. One approach to try to avoid this pitfall and more accurately deduce the future changes in tropical cyclones is statistical downscaling, where the most intense (but much weaker) storms simulated in low-resolution climate models are assumed to represent the strongest Category 4 and 5 storms and counted accordingly. When scientists tried this in 2017, they found not only that 'very intense tropical cyclones increase in most regions of the Northern Hemisphere,' but that the pattern of change closely resembled the GFDL approach. Models also seem to agree that storms of the future, with more heat energy to fuel them, will bring higher rainfall totals, as Hurricane Harvey recently did in Texas. For example, one 2017 paper by tropical cyclone expert Kerry Emanuel estimated that hurricane rains in excess of 500 mm in Texas – currently classed as a once-in-a-century event – would happen every five years in a high-CO_2 future.

As well as the probable increase in the number of the strongest storms bringing heavier rainfall – and the potential for the emergence of Category 6 super-hurricanes – another area of concern is the possible widening geographic extent of tropical cyclones. These currently only form close to the tropics, as sea-surface temperatures typically need to be above about 26°C. As global heating increases, and ocean temperatures rise, the potential area over which hurricanes can form and intensify could expand further into the mid-latitudes, making more of the world's coastlines vulnerable to landfalling hurricanes. One place this already seems to be happening is the Arabian Sea, which saw tropical cyclones forming in the post-monsoon period for the first time ever in both 2014 and 2015.

Hurricane-like storms, dubbed 'medicanes', are also starting to occur in the Mediterranean, where summer sea-surface temperatures over wide areas now rise above the critical 26°C level. When researchers used the HiFLOR model to examine the occurrence of medicanes in a hotter future, they found that while fewer in number, the simulated storms lasted for longer and were able to develop a 'more robust tropical structure, increasing the likelihood of achieving hurricane intensity' and increasing their potential destructiveness. Tropical cyclones are also likely to be able to move closer to the poles in a hotter future, bringing hurricane-force winds to hitherto hurricane-free regions such as northern Europe. In some areas, as I mentioned in previous chapters, the intense rainfall brought by tropical cyclones is a welcome relief for arid lands. Unfortunately, parched Botswana and southern Africa are likely to see fewer rain-bearing storms in a hotter future.

All this assumes that the hurricanes of the future will be a reasonable approximation of the storms we are already familiar with today. But that isn't necessarily going to be the case. Scientists call events that are conceivable, but nevertheless highly unexpected, 'grey swan' events – as opposed to 'black swans', which always come as a complete surprise. While grey swans are 'unobserved and unanticipated [they] may nevertheless be predictable', Kerry Emanuel and his colleague Ning Lin suggested in a 2015 paper published in *Nature Climate Change*. To investigate this, they ran climate models more than 3,000 times to simulate the worst-possible but currently highly unlikely tropical cyclone and associated storm surge events. To their surprise, a classic grey swan did appear – a cyclone in the Persian Gulf, where extremely warm sea temperatures spawned a simulated superstorm with windspeeds of 115 metres per second. This is far more intense than the world's record most-extreme landfalling tropical cyclone, Supertyphoon Haiyan, which peaked with windspeeds of a mere 87 metres per second in November 2013. This simulated Gulf storm would not be a Category 4 or 5, nor even a 6 – it would be more like a Category 7, far off the scale of current storms.

Could this happen in reality? As Lin and Emanuel warn, we cannot know for sure, but rising sea temperatures can only raise the risk. Whatever the ins and outs of climate modelling, the basics are clear: hotter seas are like rocket fuel for stronger hurricanes and typhoons. As we saw in Chapter 1, tropical cyclones are already beginning to nudge into Category 6 territory in today's world. Add in several more degrees of global heating and all bets are off, even those based on the latest and most sophisticated climate models. My advice is simple: stay tuned to tropical weather forecasts, and if an evacuation is advised, obey it.

Harvest failure

Four degrees will see temperatures rise above the thermal tolerances of staple crops across virtually all the world's major food-producing areas. High temperatures of up to 39°C cause 'direct damage to enzymes, tissues or reproductive organs' of crop plants. Above these 'lethal thresholds', plants may simply be killed outright. Heatwaves in the four-degree world will see temperatures reach the high 40s Celsius in the mid-latitudes, and soar into the 50s in the sub-tropics. Once critical crop temperature thresholds are included in models, they simulate losses of nearly 50% of the US maize crop, with most of the current-day Corn Belt being knocked out of production.

When droughts are added into the picture, the future for food production looks even scarier. The authors of one recent paper analysed the US Dust Bowl of the 1930s and then factored in the temperature increases expected later this century from global warming. While the worst Dust Bowl years led to crop losses of up to a third between 1933 and 1939, add in four degrees of warming and the losses soar to 80% or more. Just the warming effect on its own would mean that a typical year would see yields equivalent to the terrible Dust Bowl year of 1936. The researchers warn in the paper's introduction that 'damages at these extremes are highly sensitive to temperature, worsening by ~25% with each degree centigrade of warming.' For four-degree temperature rises, losses could therefore be reaching 100%, obliterating the entire harvest. These conclusions hold not just for maize in the central Dust Bowl area, but for wheat, soy and other crops across the Great Plains and Midwestern states. Four degrees of global warming, in other words, turns virtually the entire area that produces crops in the US into a Dust Bowl state.

This matters not just for the livelihoods of US farmers or domestic food supplies for American consumers, but because the US is the breadbasket of the world. Maize yields in places like Iowa frequently set world records. The top four maize-exporting countries – the United States, Brazil, Argentina and Ukraine – account for 87% of global maize exports. Four degrees is projected to wipe out 139 million tonnes from their combined corn production – more than the current average global annual maize exports of 125 million. In other words, there will be no maize surplus in producer countries to be exported to hungry city dwellers in consumer countries. Factor in the expected rise in global population to 10 billion or so by mid-century and the consequences hardly bear thinking about.

And it gets worse. In the one-degree world, surpluses in one place tend to balance out deficits in another, and therefore even in bad years the world has enough food. (The fact that over 800 million people remain hungry is down to poverty, not a shortage of overall supply.) Synchronised harvest failures involving multiple regions are unknown in the modern world – they have simply never happened. As the authors of a 2018 paper in *PNAS* write: 'Collectively, the probability that these large-exporting countries will incur simultaneous production losses greater than 10% in any given year is virtually zero under present-day climate conditions.' In a four-degree world, however, this probability rises to 86%. The implications are not difficult to grasp, particularly because recent history gives us a clue. During the relatively minor 2006–8 food price crisis, Brazil, Argentina and Ukraine imposed export bans on maize to safeguard domestic supplies, reducing global export supply and further pushing up prices, with similar restrictive trade policies being implemented for rice and wheat. With synchronised crop production shocks across several of the world's major producer countries, global harvests would fall drastically short of demand for the first time in the modern era.

A similar concern applies to wheat, possibly the world's most vital crop in that it provides a fifth of all the calories consumed by the human species. The global wheat trade equals those of maize and rice combined. Wheat production is also concentrated in a small number of key areas: the top ten wheat-producing regions account for more than half of total production and nearly all global exports. Drought is already having an effect; in recent decades drought impacts on global wheat production have doubled. As global temperatures rise, however, water scarcity shocks begin to ricochet throughout the world's crucial wheat-producing areas. As an international group of scientists wrote in a 2019 paper:

> By the mid-21st century, severe water scarcity is most likely to occur in an almost continuous belt from the Iberian Peninsula in the west to Anatolia and Pakistan in the east. Significant increases in severe water scarcity will also very likely affect southeastern Ukraine, southern regions of Russia, and western parts of the United States and Mexico, as well as southwestern Australia and South Africa.

In an average year, by the time global temperatures hit four degrees, nearly two-thirds of the worldwide wheat-producing area will be gripped by drought. There is also a big increase in the risk that simultaneous drought-driven harvest failures strike multiple key wheat regions for three years in a row. Be in no doubt what this means. The world will run out of food.

This is another reason to be sceptical of broad average changes typically projected by crop production models: long-term averages disguise the variations that can happen on a daily, weekly or monthly basis. Yet as humans we need to eat every few hours, not every few years. It would only require a serious global food deficit to be sustained for a few months on just one occasion for stockpiles to be exhausted and a significant proportion of the world's population – beginning with the urban poor in developing countries – to begin to starve. And we are not just talking about the world trade in commodity crops. Studies have shown that horticultural production is also extremely sensitive to the warming climate, with yields of vegetables and legumes slashed by a third in a four-degree scenario. The livestock sector will be seriously affected; one-third of the global cereal harvest is currently used for livestock feed, and with the world's grazing lands desertifying and/or too hot for outdoors livestock rearing, animal production will similarly suffer drastic losses as cattle and other stock die from thirst and heat stress.

There is another possibility, of course. We could try to move crop production out of current breadbasket areas and towards the poles to keep step with global temperature rises. One study shows that three-quarters of the current-day boreal region will be crop-suitable in a roughly four-degree warming scenario. In the northern hemisphere, agriculture would shift into Arctic Canada, Alaska, Siberia and Scandinavia, with cultivable areas moving as much as 1,200 kilometres north of current croplands. But in reality, the feasibility of this is doubtful; it would require destroying most of the existing boreal forest, and ploughing up thawed permafrost and tundra areas to sow corn and wheat. All this would release millions of tonnes of additional CO_2, and require massive amounts of fertiliser. There is also the danger that droughts and heatwaves will be severe even in the Arctic by this stage, and that wildfires would also threaten food crops. Continental regions like Siberia will in particular be suffering extreme heatwaves, so only areas close to the Arctic Ocean are likely to remain reliably temperate for cultivation. Most northern polar land regions have thin, rocky soils with little prospect of yielding much harvest even under the most optimistic scenarios however. In the Southern Hemisphere the option of shifting crop-production zones by a thousand kilometres towards the poles is not available at all – the continents peter out at the higher latitudes and there is barely any new land to farm.

Perhaps the final option for humanity, faced with synchronous failures of major world food crops all around the world, would be to abandon farming altogether and produce food in indoor industrial systems using genetically engineered microbes and chemical feedstocks. Temperature, nutrients and humidity can be controlled in a closed cycle, and energy supplied from cleaner sources like solar, wind and nuclear. But the scalability is doubtful. Could we really provide for the calorific needs of 10 billion people by synthesising food in big vats? The scale of such an enterprise might be analogous to today's oil industry, with pipelines and gigantic 'food refineries' on the edge of every town. It is one thing to produce high-value niche outputs using synthetic biology; quite another to find the feedstocks and energy to replace most of the world's arable farming, which currently uses free solar energy and soil nutrients across millions of square kilometres. Having compromised the habitability of many of the world's cities, we will also have destroyed much of the world's cultivable land.

Failing that, it is anyone's guess how long modern civilisation could withstand food shocks of the magnitude predicted for the four-degree world. No model can forecast what the results will be. Will we intelligently plan a decades-long adaptation effort, sharing the burdens of heroic sacrifices and immense technological change fairly, in order to maintain at least the minimum necessary for everyone's daily calorific needs? Or will a sequence of collapses take place, with billions of people fleeing heat, drought and starvation, and the ensuing global disorder and conflict usher in a new dark age? It would be better not to conduct the experiment, and to continue farming on existing agricultural land. But at four degrees this will no longer be an option.

Mass extinction

It is difficult to overstate the extent of the dramatic transformation of our planet implied by four degrees of average temperature change. During the last glacial period, when massive ice sheets a mile thick covered much of North America, Scandinavia and the British Isles, global temperatures were only about four degrees lower than today. Sea levels were over a hundred metres below where they are now because so much water was locked up in the giant continental ice sheets. Deserts expanded and atmospheric dust circulated around the planet. Rainforests contracted to small refuges and permafrost reached as far south as London and Beijing. After the last ice age, rising temperatures ushered in the Holocene interglacial period, thawing the ice sheets and enabling the rise of complex human civilisations.

Over the last million years there have been many ice ages, their regular periodicity modulated by small changes in the Earth's orbit around the sun. Each warm interglacial period, however, was roughly similar to today's climate. Look at graphs of temperature swings and it looks like the Earth has guard-rails, beyond which the climate stabilises either in a cold glacial or a warm interglacial regime – it never gets hotter or colder than a certain level each time. If we add another four degrees to global temperatures while already in an inter-glacial, we will be busting right through the warm guard-rail, pushing the world into a hotter climate regime that has not been experienced on Earth for far longer back in geological time. Because there is no direct measure of temperatures millions of years ago, proxies must be used, such as changing seawater isotope ratios now preserved in the shells of fossil plankton. These all bring substantial uncertainties, but the latest research suggests that the last time global temperatures were four degrees higher than now was during the Oligocene and Miocene epochs, roughly 15–40 million years ago.

Global biomes and ecosystems did of course manage to adjust to the end of the last ice age, with tree lines advancing back towards the poles and new warm-loving vegetation invading the formerly frigid tundra areas such as southern Britain. We know, therefore, that nature can adapt to climate change, because it has done so numerous times in the past. Ice ages had a periodicity of about 100,000 years, so life learned to adjust to many rounds of warming and cooling. Rainforests recolonised large areas of the Amazon basin and West Africa once rainfall returned to its warmer and moister interglacial patterns. Given that four degrees of warming after the last ice age did not seem to cause many species to go extinct, perhaps this is a hopeful sign for an additional four degrees of climate warming now?

Unfortunately, there is little chance of such a happy outcome this time round. For a start, the sheer speed of the temperature rise will be unprecedented. As we make the transition into a four-degree world this century, global warming will be taking place 65 times faster than the average rate of warming at the end of the last glacial period. Turning the geological clock back to the Oligocene means that we are bringing back into existence a climate that has not been experienced on Earth for tens of millions of years, well beyond the evolutionary experience of many plants and animals alive today. Any adaptation of nature is also vastly more difficult in a world that has been profoundly altered by human activity. So while ice age species had a largely wild planet and 5,000 years in which to adapt to the warmer Holocene, nature has now just a few decades and a world whose ecosystems are already fragmented and degraded by human activity.

Under such circumstances, mass extinction is a virtual certainty. Species are already being wiped out by humans, but climate breakdown will be the greatest threat so far, driving at least a sixth of all species over the edge in a four-degree world. Whole climate zones will be wiped off the map, with as much as half the Earth's terrestrial surface experiencing what scientists call either 'novel' or 'disappearing' climates by the end of the century. Sadly, there is a lot of overlap between these disappearing climates and global biodiversity hotspots. Tropical mountains and the poleward sides of major continents are especially affected. These include the Colombian and Peruvian Andes, Central America, the African Rift mountains, the Zambian and Angolan Highlands, Cape Province in South Africa, south-east

Australia, portions of the Himalayas, the Indonesian and Philippine archipelagos and much of the circum-Arctic. All the endemic species of these regions will most likely disappear along with their climates – they will have no suitable habitat left on Earth.

This process will not be pretty. The Pacific chinook salmon, for example, has a precise water temperature thermal limit of 24.5°C, above which the fish suffer cardiac failure; their hearts stop working because there is insufficient oxygen in warmer water to fuel their muscles. In a four-degree future, therefore, researchers predict a 98% chance of 'catastrophic loss' of chinooks by the end of the century. Virtually the entire Mediterranean ecosystem will also disappear, to be largely replaced by desert. The 417 national parks in the US are especially vulnerable and are already warming at twice the average rate even in today's one-degree climate. In a four-degree scenario, their current climate envelopes will be located hundreds of kilometres further north. Yellowstone might be somewhere in the northern Canadian Rockies, while California's Yosemite Valley will have moved in climatic terms into Washington State. It may be that 'assisted migration' – airlifting grizzlies, wolves, elk and so on to new homes – can help, but trees cannot be so easily transplanted. Still less can we pack up and transport entire ecosystems. And species will not be shifting to a new stable state even by 2100; rapid change is the new normal, and will continue for many centuries to come.

Even if species do not go extinct globally, between one-third and two-thirds of species will be rendered extinct in their current local habitats. As Arctic becomes boreal, boreal becomes temperate, temperate becomes sub-tropical, sub-tropical becomes tropical, and tropical becomes lethally hot, ecosystems will be restructured on a gigantic scale across the entire planet. Nowhere is left untouched. While Mediterranean-type ecosystems dry out, boreal forests burn or convert to temperate woodlands. Tropical forests are particularly vulnerable. As we saw in previous chapters, the Brazilian Amazon rainforest is likely to shift almost entirely into savannah-type dry shrubland in a four-degree scenario, with even semi-desert emerging in some eastern areas. This region will be the epicentre of the future mass extinction, with the near-total loss of a forest that currently includes species of at least 40,000 different plants, 427 mammals, 1,294 birds, 378 reptiles, 427 amphibians and around 3,000 fishes. This is a substantial fraction of the Earth's entire stock of biodiversity – it will be as if a meteor of a similar dimension to the one that wiped out the dinosaurs has hit the western half of Brazil.

This catastrophic biological wipeout includes the oceans. Already in the one-degree world – as I discussed earlier – 'marine heatwaves' are transforming oceanic ecosystems, bringing tropical fish into temperate kelp forests, destroying coral reefs and triggering mass die-offs of seabirds. While marine heatwave risk has already doubled in the current climate, scientists estimate that in the four-degree world the probability of occurrence will increase 41-fold, while marine heatwaves will last on average for 112 days and cover an area 21 times larger than today. A 1-in-100-days event is projected to become a 1-in-3-days event in this scenario, spelling disaster for oceanic species across the planet, especially those adapted to colder waters in the polar oceans, and those already living in tropical waters, which will simply become too hot to support most lifeforms. One study projects that in a four-degree world sea temperatures will be above the thermal tolerance threshold of 100% of species in many tropical marine ecoregions.

Current 'marine protected areas' will be devastated by ocean warming, just as nature reserves and national parks are affected on land. There is also a considerable overlap between 'hotspots' of marine biodiversity and the areas already most strongly affected by oceanic warming. Not only does the heating of seawater affect species directly, but warmer water also holds less oxygen. And it is not just the tropics that suffer. In the Southern Ocean, declining krill supplies imperil the future of blue, fin, right and humpback whales, species that have only recently begun to recover from the devastation of commercial whaling. All substantial tropical coral reef structures will be long dead.

Surface waters will be absorbing more CO_2 from our carbon-rich atmosphere, acidifying the oceans. The Southern Ocean is one of the regions affected most – and earliest – with 90% of its area 'undersaturated' with calcium carbonate by the end of the century, meaning it is too acidic to support shell-building organisms, including many species of phytoplankton, which are the basis of the marine food chain. Ocean acidification will also dissolve coral structures wherever they appear, and continue to degrade older reefs. Toxic algae will proliferate in the carbon-rich oceans, killing fish and causing poisonous algal blooms across extensive areas of coastal shelf. The oceans gradually lose their ability to sequester carbon in the depths, because voracious algae occupying surface waters recycle it before it can sink down to the seafloor. This process, which keeps an additional two billion tonnes of carbon per decade in the atmosphere by the end of the century, is yet another neglected positive feedback on climate change.

As on land, there may be refugia, and perhaps humans will be able to help support migration and speed adaptation. But four degrees will be causing such devastation to human societies that in all likelihood we will be in no state to come to the aid of the natural world. Our best way to help will always be to reduce carbon emissions sufficiently in today's world to avoid a four-degree outcome ever coming to pass. If we continue to burn carbon along business-as-usual lines we will bequeath a planet that is steadily less hospitable to life as it heats up beyond the heat tolerance ability of many species. This will be the worst mass extinction since the end of the Cretaceous, 65 million years ago. The difference is that this time the 'meteor' was visible decades in advance, but we simply turned away as it loomed ever larger in the sky.

Climate breakdown in the Atlantic

Not for nothing is the rather benign term 'climate change' now being replaced with the rather more dramatic 'climate breakdown'. Weather patterns in a four-degree world will be barely recognisable from the ones we are familiar with today. The onset of meteorological summer, for example, will advance by 20 days, coming on 25 March of the calendar year. Winter remains the same, meaning that there will be a much longer hot period in every year. It would be a mistake to expect climate changes to be gradual and linear however. Between the first and second two degrees of a four-degree warming scenario, one modelling study shows stratospheric winds reversing direction from an easterly to a westerly flow, altering the position of the jet stream, and the location of the North Atlantic storm track. One of the drivers of this flip may be the final disappearance of sea ice in critical areas of the Arctic at two degrees, which changes the heat balance of the polar atmosphere in ways never before experienced.

The biggest weather shift of all, however, might come not in the Atlantic or the Arctic but in the Pacific. Models suggest that a four-degree world would see a doubling in the occurrence of strong El Niño events. During extreme El Niños, in the words of the authors of a 2014 paper in *Nature Climate Change*, a 'massive reorganisation of atmospheric convection takes place', displacing rainfall belts by as much as 1,000 kilometres and triggering weather chaos around the world. During past events, such as the 1997–98 mega-El Niño, catastrophic floods occurred in South America in normally arid areas, marine life was devastated in coastal areas across the world, and 23,000 lives were lost in weather-related disasters, which also caused economic damage of $35–45 billion.

El Niño's opposite number La Niña, which occurs when the eastern tropical Pacific switches into a cold phase, is also expected to increase in frequency by 75%. Moreover, extreme La Niñas often follow extreme El Niños, with less and less time for calmer, neutral conditions. When this sequence of events occurred in 1998–99, the south-western United States experienced one of its worst-ever droughts, flash flooding and landslides killed up to 50,000 people in Venezuela, storms and floods displaced 200 million in China, and half of Bangladesh was submerged by flooding. La Niña can also favour an intense North Atlantic hurricane season, which in 1998 saw the formation of Hurricane Mitch, one of the deadliest and strongest storms on historical record, claiming more than 11,000 lives as it struck Honduras and Nicaragua in Central America. This Pacific see-saw, between extreme El Niños closely followed by equally devas-tating La Niñas, is an example of what 'climate breakdown' will look like in reality, as extreme weather modes flip from one state to the other in close succession. The precise trigger may be in the Pacific, but the effects are truly global, with impacts everywhere from drought and flood in Australia to the strength of the Indian monsoon.

El Niño and La Niña are opposite phases of Pacific Ocean surface sea temperatures and wind patterns. The greatest ocean current of all, however, which redistributes vast quantities of heat between the Southern and Northern Hemispheres, is the 'Atlantic Meridional Overturning Circulation' (AMOC, of which the well-known Gulf Stream is a part). I discussed in the first chapter possible impacts of climate warming occurring today, which may have already driven a slowing down of this great current in our one-degree world. In a four-degree scenario some models show a complete collapse in AMOC, causing a large cooling hole across the entire North Atlantic, from Newfoundland to Scandinavia, in the otherwise worldwide pattern of extreme temperature rise. With four degrees of global heat-ing there is no prospect of a new ice age in Europe, as was once feared. Instead, along with a general moderating of regional temperature rise comes a massive shift in atmospheric circulation, with 'less precipita-tion in the northern hemisphere midlatitudes; large changes in precipitation in the tropics and a strengthening of the North Atlantic storm track'. This would have knock-on effects on everything from flooding to crop production. The impacts ricochet around the world, affecting Africa, the Amazon, the Indian monsoon and even El Niño.

Perhaps the greatest surprise from a weaker or collapsed AMOC would be a dramatic increase in the rate of sea level rise on the eastern seaboard of North America. An inkling of this came in 2009–10, when tide gauges north of New York City recorded a jump of 12 centimetres in the rate of sea level rise during this two-year period, apparently as a result of a 30% temporary reduction in the strength of AMOC. Scientists studying the event compared it to a storm surge – but without the storm, which nevertheless 'caused persistent and widespread coastal flooding even without weather processes'. They added that in terms of beach erosion, the 2009–10 sea-level-rise event 'is almost as significant as some hurricane events'. The amount temporarily lost from North Atlantic circulation was 5 Sv, equivalent to 20 times the flow of the River Amazon.

Had these higher sea levels been combined with extreme weather such as a real hurricane, the impacts would have been disastrous along much of the US east coast. This time, however, AMOC recovered and sea levels fell back. But the respite will not continue for long. Whatever happens to the North Atlantic current, in the four-degree world the great polar ice sheets will be melting rapidly away, pouring trillions of tonnes of additional water into the global oceans and raising sea levels at a rate that is more rapid than anything seen for thousands of years. At four degrees, Greenland is toast – the total disappearance of the ice sheet is only a matter of time, with the meltdown eventually delivering seven metres of sea level rise. But the greatest contribution to the rising oceans now comes from the opposite pole, where the sleeping giant that is Antarctica has begun to wake from its million-year slumber.

Apocalpyse in the Antarctic

As it emerges from millions of years in deep freeze, the Antarctica of the four-degree world is already looking very different from the ice-clad continent of the 20th century. Already many of the familiar names of ice shelves possess only historical resonance; the Larsen C, Venable, Crosson, Dotson and Thwaites ice shelves have all collapsed. With the ice shelves gone, gigantic glaciers are surging out of the centre of the West Antarctic Ice Sheet and into the oceans. The Ronne and Ross ice shelves, the greatest of all, are now covered in dark-blue meltwater pools, and gigantic waterfalls thunder off their thawing surfaces into the warming waters of the Southern Ocean. In most summers, virtually the entire West Antarctic surface is in the melt zone, and gigantic rivers pour through meltwater canyons for enormous distances before suddenly plunging into the unseen dark depths of the ice sheet.

West Antarctic melt is now irreversible. Like Greenland, the whole ice sheet is condemned to disappear over many centuries of relentlessly accelerating melt. Sea levels are rising at over a centimetre a year, comparable to the fastest rates at the end of the last ice age, when much larger Northern Hemisphere ice sheets were retreating. Summer sea ice around the whole of Antarctica has vanished, leaving the edges of the East Antarctic's glaciers in direct contact with the warming ocean. Towering cliffs have formed where the sea meets the ice sheet; periods of calm are punctuated by gigantic roars as huge sections of ice break off and plunge into the sea. Each time this happens, tsunamis tens of metres high surge onto surrounding coastlines and out into the open ocean, like a regular distress call from the embattled ice sheet to the wider world. Armadas of icebergs now litter the Southern Ocean as far as the tips of South America and even New Zealand. The fragile Antarctic ecosystem has been torn apart – all the krill have gone, as have penguins, whales and seals, while invasive plants have begun to turn the coastal sections of the formerly bare Antarctic Peninsula an unfamiliar shade of green.

Over the very long term, four degrees of global heating sets our planet on the course for an eventual ice-free state. Take a 10,000-year perspective and a high-emissions scenario, and all the ice in Greenland and the West Antarctic melts away, as does the vast majority of the ice in the East Antarctic, leaving only a residual smaller ice cap centred around the geographical South Pole. All this melting ice yields 30–40 metres of sea level rise, enough to dramatically transform the coastal geography of our planet, with rates of rise somewhere between two to four metres per century. This would submerge all coastal megacities, while countries varying from Guyana to the Netherlands to Bangladesh to Vietnam would lose half or more of their populated territories. Needless to say, all low-lying island states would disappear. In today's population terms, about two billion people would have to move, affecting a quarter to a third of the global population. Virtually everybody would be affected if you consider the need to construct new cities to harbour coastal migrants, together with the ongoing challenges of large-scale relocation and land abandonment.

Given the dislocations that are already affecting the four-degree world, from loss of food production to extreme heat and river flooding, adapting to the challenge of multi-metre sea level rise looks exceedingly difficult, even over the shorter term. Considering just the US, a four-degree scenario by 2100 means 25 cities with populations of more than 100,000 facing inundation, with more than 30 million people displaced, the majority coming from low-lying Florida. All of New Orleans would be flooded, as would substantial portions of New York City, Boston, Honolulu, Tampa and Miami in Florida, and Long Beach and Sacramento in California. The population displacement suggested by these projections means that far more than just coastal communities are affected. As scientist Mathew Hauer put it in a 2017 paper, 'unmitigated sea-level rise is expected to reshape the US population distribution, potentially stressing landlocked areas unprepared to accommodate this wave of coastal migrants.' Some of this dislocation can be avoided with coastal protection infrastructure, but the cost will be enormous – upwards of $130 billion just for Miami, and trillions of dollars for the entire country.

Europe, with its 100,000-kilometre-long coastline and densely populated coastal regions, is just as seriously affected. Annual damage costs in the one-degree world of around €1.25 billion are expected to rise by two to three orders of magnitude, reaching €93–961 billion per year by the end of the century. The number of people annually exposed to coastal flooding rises from 0.1 million currently to 3.6 million, with the UK worst hit, followed by France and Italy. Even in today's one-degree world, the Dutch are spending €1.2–1.6 billion per year on their Delta Programme, while storm-surge gates have been installed to protect Venice and London. To prevent inundation in the four-degree world, huge lengths of coastline would need to be protected, costing tens to hundreds of billions of euros per year. Surrounded by dikes and fortifications, coastal cities may become completely disconnected from their hinterlands, ending up as densely populated islands stranded well below sea level and surrounded on all sides by rapidly rising waters.

For this reason, coastal protection efforts come with a long-term health warning. As stated by a scientific team writing in *Nature Climate Change* in 2018: 'Structural measures are very effective in protecting our coasts, but the upsurge in the intensity and frequency of extreme sea levels projected for the coming decades increases the risk of cataclysmic losses in the event of defence failure.' In other words, if a future storm surge succeeded in breaching the defences of a city that was now a couple of metres below sea level, tens of thousands could drown in the ensuing disaster, and the death toll could be even higher if a larger area of coastline was suddenly inundated. Successive failures might ultimately lead to the abandonment of cities entirely – living in such areas would be like living under a dam wall, continually threatened by imminent catastrophic failure. In the longer term, over many centuries, none of today's coastal cities will be viable, so the question will be when to abandon them, and how much to spend on fortifications in the meantime.

As a team of scientists wrote in 2016, humanity 'will have a very limited time after midcentury to adapt to sea level rises unprecedented since the dawn of the Bronze Age'. In the best-case four-degree scenario, New York can expect the waters to rise by 1.09 metres, Guangzhou can expect 0.91 m and Lagos 0.9 m by the end of the century. More likely, with the rate of melt in the last decade from the polar ice sheets already far outstripping model projections, the rate of sea level rise will be more extreme, in which case New York can expect a hefty 2.2m rise, and both Guangzhou and Lagos 1.9m. Each time scientists consider the issue, the worst-case scenario is raised; in 2014 the 'upper limit' of 21st-century sea level rise was given as 1.8 m, with only a 5% chance of a higher rate than that. By 2017 this had been revised upwards, with the same 'upper limit' (with a 5% chance of being exceeded) now raised to nearly 3 m (292 cm, to be exact). This is because ice-sheet models have now been upgraded to include the potential for rapid ice-shelf breakup, as increasingly seen in the real world around Antarctica.

Globally, people displaced will number in the hundreds of millions, with 1.7 million square kilometres of land lost from the world's coasts in the event of a two-metre rise in sea levels, equivalent to the combined surface area of Germany, the UK, France and Sweden – all submerged beneath the waves. The latest data, including both ice-sheet instability and land elevation, projects 1.7 million people displaced for each centimetre of global sea level rise, with 480 million people currently living on land vulnerable to annual flooding by 2100 in a four-degree scenario. As a scientific team writing in *Nature Communications* journal in October 2019 warned: 'Continued high emissions with Antarctic instability could entail land currently home to roughly one-third of Bangladesh's and Vietnam's populations permanently falling below the high-tide line.'

Putting a cost on all this is almost a futile exercise, but economic models suggest annual coastal flood damage costs of $27 trillion per year for a sea level rise of 1.8 metres. What proportion of GDP this represents depends on what level of economic growth – if any – takes place during the 21st century. Conventional models tend to assume that economic growth will continue for ever, and that therefore costs even in the tens of trillions of dollars per year still represent only a small percentage of overall GDP. The latest estimate, published in 2018, for annual damage caused by a 1.8-metre rise in sea levels is 2.8% of global GDP in 2100.

Feel free not to take these numbers too seriously. We are not going into a business-as-usual world. With four degrees of heating, massive shocks to society will be taking place, threatening or even destroying modern industrial civilisation because of mass starvation, flooding, and the loss of large areas of the tropics and sub-tropics to extreme heat and drought. For such a world, academic assumptions about everlasting economic growth are surely absurd. In reality, societies that no longer exist in the way that we know them today will not be spending hundreds of billions per year on complex engineering projects to fortify coastal cities. Large-scale abandonment of the coast may come sooner than we expect in such a scenario, with hundreds of millions of people moving inland, adding further to migrant flows of millions more fleeing from areas too hot or too dry to support large-scale human habitation. Crowded into diminishing refuges, and with little surplus to support large numbers of climate refugees, the survival prospects of a significant proportion of humanity begin to look bleak.

The Arctic carbon bomb

Planet Earth has now entered the endgame, and four degrees is unlikely to be our final destination. By this stage large-scale feedbacks have kicked in, threatening to turn the heating process into an unstoppable upwards spiral. The epicentre of this is in the Arctic, where the entirety of the circumpolar permafrost region is now in the melt zone. That means 15 million square kilometres of collapsing ground, with sudden craters opening up in the middle of forests, lakes filling or draining away in a matter of hours, and millions of tonnes of methane bubbling up out of the thawing mush that was once the frozen Arctic. Methane is roughly 30 times as potent a global warming gas as CO_2, and methane released from warming wetlands around the world will by now be on course to raise world temperatures by another couple of tenths of a degree. Although boreal forests are marching northwards into the tundra, millions of trees are lost to insect outbreaks and lightning-ignited fires each year, meaning that this globe-girdling forest zone also becomes a net emitter of carbon.

How bad could it get? The latest estimates suggest that around 1.5 trillion tonnes of carbon lie entombed in the ground of the far north, about three times more than humans have so far emitted since the beginning of the Industrial Revolution. Standard climate models project that less than a tenth of this will be lost to the atmosphere by the end of the century, but on-the-ground research suggests that 'this feedback to climate change may be occurring faster than previously thought.' This is because scientific experiments measuring the loss of soil carbon from thawed ground – which used a standard fixed depth – did not take into account how much the ground subsided as the ice melted out, and so probably missed the loss of large quantities of carbon. Hence erroneous conclusions, from measurements in Greenland, Alaska and elsewhere, were drawn that no soil carbon was being lost, even after a decade or more of melting. Based on these flawed measurements, standard projections to date have been that only 5–15% of permafrost carbon will be lost by the end of the century, totalling less than 100 billion tonnes of carbon, equivalent to about a decade of current human emissions.

However, the August 2019 paper, published in the journal *Nature Geoscience*, found that when ground subsidence was corrected for in the experiments, 5% of carbon was being lost from the top half-metre of ground *per year*, with a quarter of the carbon stock lost within just five years. The conventional scenario projects less than 0.2°C additional warming by 2100 from the permafrost carbon feedback, but with much greater rates of melt and resulting carbon loss this figure certainly needs to be revised upwards. With at least half the total Arctic carbon stock in the top three metres of soils, and with a substantial proportion of this carbon emitted as methane, my back-of-the-envelope calculation suggests that we could be in for between 0.5 and 1 additional degrees Celsius of global heating thanks to an accelerated permafrost carbon feedback in a four-degree world. Add in that extra global-warming boost, and by the end of the century we will be knocking on the door of an even hotter era – the super-greenhouse world of five degrees.

5°

Heat shock

At five degrees, humanity has lost control of global temperatures, which are now spiralling relentlessly upwards. Food production is decimated, and large areas of the planet are too hot for humans to inhabit. All ice sheets are doomed to vanish, and vast quantities of additional carbon are pouring into the atmosphere from thawed Arctic permafrost and burning forests. Unless something can be done to reverse the upwards spiral, runaway global warming could transform our planet into a wasteland of lifeless rocky continents surrounded by stagnant oceans. It is almost game over.

The entire tropical belt and much of the sub-tropics of Planet Earth are subject to year-round temperatures that would today be classed as 'deadly heat'. The highest temperatures are found in North Africa, the Middle East and South Asia. As I outlined in the previous chapter, when wet-bulb temperatures pass the critical threshold of 35°C, humans can no longer survive outside for any significant period of time. In this kind of humid extreme heat, all other warm-blooded animals will also die unless they can find a cooler refuge – that includes livestock, wildlife, everything. Wet-bulb thresholds aside, ambient temperature extremes of 60°C are now commonplace everywhere from Riyadh to Karachi. The arid sub-tropics have become a kind of global Death Valley, where lack of water and intense heat kill all plant and animal life. Apart from microbes and bacteria, vast areas of the surface of the planet are gradually becoming sterilised by heat shock.

These places include regions that are home to as much as half the current human population, including East and South Asia, Central America, the southern half of the US and much of Africa. The fate of the Indian monsoon is unknown in such a scenario – a total failure is possible, but so is a further intensification, with colossal downpours eroding the remaining soil from fields and hillsides left bare by drought and fire. In the deep tropics there will be no winter relief, as year-round heatwaves – punctuated by flash floods – denude the land surface. In Africa, a quarter of cities will experience dangerous heat conditions for 200 days every year, with extremes so hazardous that venturing outside for more than a few minutes at a time is impossible without protection. All transport, agriculture and other human activities requiring outside labour cease, triggering famine and economic collapse.

Global food production will be pushed over the limit in such a scenario, with most of the world's breadbaskets too hot or dry to yield any significant harvest. Synchronous harvest failures over multiple years mean that global trade in food ends entirely, and most countries have to attempt some form of self-sufficiency to feed their populations. It is likely that the majority of such attempts will fail. The human species has never experienced a situation where we are unable to gather or grow food over most of our habitual range. What kinds of economies can persist under such a scenario? How can ten billion people avoid mass starvation when world harvests fail completely? Climate models cannot shed much light on this future because it involves social, economic and political scenarios for which human civilisation has no historical precedent. You cannot add a line of code into a climate model to represent the response of a country's political system to ten million climate refugees on its borders. Even with all its complexity and approximations, atmospheric physics is always going to be much easier to understand and predict than human responses to climate impacts.

It is technically conceivable, as I suggested earlier, that energy-hungry industrial growth will be so successful that humanity is able to build and maintain artificial environments within which we might both live and produce food indefinitely, irrespective of lethally high outside temperatures, using feedstocks such as CO_2 harvested from the air, nuclear power-originated hydrogen and desalinated seawater. This scenario is perhaps reminiscent of futuristic ideas about colonising new planets with space stations, but instead of venturing into new worlds to set up habitable zones, we would be being forced to deploy space-age technology at home in order to continue to live on our own planet. In the 20th century, science fiction writers fantasised about living on Venus. Now we will have brought Venus home to Earth.

And how many people, realistically, could be supported and sheltered under such air-conditioned techno-domes? Surely not the entire global population. Ten billion people take up a lot of space, and feeding them artificially would be a colossal challenge, as would finding the energy required to keep such environments cool. The only realistic concentrated energy option, unless we are to continue burning yet more fossil fuel, is nuclear. This is, however, so feared by so many people – irrationally, in my view – that it is unlikely to be accepted on the scale necessary for such an endeavour. A more pessimistic scenario might be a kind of global apartheid, where the rich are able to sequester themselves away from a collapsing biosphere behind fortified barriers or on remote islands, while the majority of the human population starves outside. This sounds like something out of a zombie movie, and would surely be intolerable to our modern morality. How many of us would really be prepared to machine-gun starving families of climate refugees massed outside the gates of cooling life-preserving compounds reserved for the super-rich? Who knows – but perhaps it is not really so unthinkable, given that we tolerate the current extreme economic inequality in which, according to the charity Oxfam, eight billionaires own the same amount of wealth as the poorest half of the global population. As I write, 850 million people are malnourished due to lack of food, while the super-rich criss-cross the world in private jets and mega-yachts, each with a staff of hundreds. We all acquiesce in this ongoing moral outrage as if it were the natural state of affairs.

Climate apartheid could therefore be seen as merely an extension of our current extreme inequality, not a new paradigm. Every time I watch the news and see migrants trying to get from North Africa to Europe drown in their dozens – hundreds even – in the Mediterranean, I see the future for millions of climate refugees. While some good people do their best to help, many more turn away in disgust and vote for far-right parties that make a political virtue of demonising the downtrodden, the different and the desperate. It is no accident that these same proto-fascist parties, now in or close to power in many countries, typically also deny or downplay climate change. They are in the business of blaming victims to gain power, and telling lies is second nature to them because they do not believe that the truth matters or even exists. As *Yale Environment 360* reported in October 2019: 'Right-wing populist parties now on the rise across Europe are elevating opposition to climate action into a new culture war issue, American-style.'

How exactly the socio-political collapse might happen, or how post-collapse human societies might evolve, goes too far into the realms of speculation for me to say anything useful about it. I will leave such musings to dystopian fiction authors and Hollywood disaster movie scriptwriters. Suffice to say that most cities will lie dead and abandoned; current superpowers and long-fought-over national borders will largely cease to exist; the human population will be drastically reduced; and much of the remaining life on Earth will be eliminated. Perhaps the end will be dramatic, shrouded in the smoke of war as the survivors battle it out for what is left of our planet's vanishing resources and living space. Or perhaps it will be slow, and civilisation will die a death by a thousand cuts, as democracy fades away, barriers and borders rise, while the heat keeps on rising and fatal impacts multiply year on year. One local famine becomes regional and then global, 'failed states' multiply, and societies and nations that have survived for thousands of years totter and collapse. Darkness falls gradually as the lights over whole regions flicker and go out.

Climate refuges

As I will outline in the next chapter, at very intense levels of warming the likelihood increases that a runaway greenhouse effect will take place that ultimately sterilises the biosphere. At five degrees this has not yet happened, and substantial areas of the planet's surface do remain tolerably habitable. They are just not the same regions that humans currently generally live in. Nor are they spacious or resource-rich enough to be able to support ten billion desperate people. They are, however, of sufficient extent to mean that some humans should be able to survive in the numbers needed to avoid the outright extinction of our species, which I think is unlikely even with the catastrophic heat-related impacts expected in the five-degree world.

So where might these refuges be? For clues we need to look both at the aggregated outputs of climate models and extrapolations based on the planet's current geographic and climatic zones. In general, areas on the higher-latitude western margins of continents, particularly when their geographies include mountain ranges, should be both wet and cool enough to support humans. For example, while the interior of Alaska will see a continental climate with 35°C heatwaves in the summer months and parching droughts, the southern coast of the state continues to enjoy a temperate climate regime. High mountain ranges – from Denali in the north to Mount Logan, just over the border in Canada – will still see snow even in the five-degree world, and catch sufficient precipitation generally on the maritime westerlies to keep this whole area temperate and well-watered. Further down the North American coast, the western side of the Rockies should also retain high precipitation levels and equable temperatures, through British Columbia and Washington State, and even as far as Oregon. Further south than that, however, California will be baking into dust, with the Sierra Nevada scorched brown and snowless.

In South America the Andean mountains are high enough to stay cool, even as the final remnants of their glaciers disappear. Depending on the fate of the Amazon to the east, sufficient rainfall may still arrive, even in tropical areas. A better bet lies further south and west, in Chilean Patagonia and down into Tierra del Fuego, where westerly storm systems will continue to dump large amounts of precipitation in a latitude high enough to remain in the cool zone. If humanity is well organised, we might consider establishing plantations of tropical rainforest plants in these latitudes to prevent them going extinct globally, perhaps with a view to re-establishing these species in their old ranges once the Earth's temperature can be reduced back to safe levels a few centuries hence. (This could be a kind of global biosphere preserve – a sort of Noah's Ark for the global warming extinction.) The Antarctic Peninsula might be a better bet, however. At this stage it will be fully habitable, and well supplied with freshwater both from precipitation and the year-round melting of its remaining glaciers. Perhaps this will be one of the exclusive locations where the super-rich flee for safety. Flotillas of climate refugees putting out onto the stormy Southern Ocean are unlikely to pose much threat to their Antarctic fastnesses.

Continue to virtually spin the globe searching for habitable places, and the next likely spot that jumps out is the South Island of New Zealand. The Southern Alps will have lost all their ice, but should still attract enough rain to keep the rivers flowing throughout most of the year. Moreover, the location of this small landmass far away from the over-populated conflict zones of Africa, Europe and Asia might also perhaps prove attractive. New Zealand may, however, be pushed to more immediately attend to the needs of millions of displaced Australians, whose own continent is now too hot to support large-scale human habitation in all but a few small coastal fringes in the very south, in Tasmania and perhaps in the Blue Mountains. What vegetation does persist in Australia burns repeatedly in immense fires, leaving just a few weedy generalist heat- and fire-tolerant species to proliferate. Large-scale agriculture is now a distant memory.

In the tropics, highlands do exist that promise tolerable temperatures even as the lowlands below them are baked out of existence. The spine of New Guinea has a range of peaks high enough to still catch the rain and provide sustenance for a few hundred thousand people. The wettest place on Earth, in the foothills of the Himalayas in eastern India, is another such location – although residents will need to relocate a couple of thousand metres higher up the mountain slopes to escape the rising heat. Altitude rather than latitude may also save western parts of China and the Tibetan Plateau, although the latter is already highly arid and unlikely to receive much more precipitation. There will still be snowfall on the highest Himalayan peaks, although even the largest glaciers and icefields will all be melting fast year-round and will eventually disappear entirely. The problem with highlands as refuges, however, is that by definition they contain very limited flat space and can support little in the way of agriculture. Russia and Siberia will still be cool in winter, but in the summer months their refuge potential is limited. Temperatures will regularly climb into the 40s and 50s Celsius, sparking immense wildfires in what remains of the boreal forest. Around the circum-polar shores of the Arctic Ocean there may also be suitable habitat, but the response of the planetary hydrological cycle to the year-round disappearance of sea ice is a wild card for these regions. Storms might possibly migrate up from the mid-latitudes as the jet stream goes haywire, but on the other hand the area might well remain marooned under dry high-pressure systems for much of the year. Climate models have little useful light to shed on such an epochal shift.

As usual Africa looks likely to suffer more than anywhere. Located almost entirely in the tropics and the sub-tropics, the continent will be experiencing some of the highest temperatures ever seen on Earth. Highs into the mid-60s Celsius occur regularly in North Africa in the five-degree world, and rainfall has virtually ceased across many land areas. Highland zones are small and located far in the continent's interior, such as the Rwenzori mountains and the Ethiopian highlands, endangering their supplies of precipitation. The tropical convergence zone, which currently supplies most of Africa's rainfall, may intensify and further fluctuate, but with temperatures too high in lowland areas to support forests and agriculture it will bring little relief from the scorching sun. The obvious injustice that Africa has done little to contribute to the stock of greenhouse gases that have now heated the planet to such extremes is of no concern to the morally impervious gods of climate physics.

What of Europe? The Iberian Peninsula, much of France, Italy, Greece and the rest of the Mediterranean are now transitioning into full-scale deserts, despite the arrival every few years of medicane tropical cyclones that bring devastating floods. Temperatures in northern Europe reach the 50s Celsius now in summer, with deadly heat conditions for weeks at a time even up to the Arctic Circle. Small tolerable areas exist in the Pyrenees, Alps and British mountains, while Scandinavia still has a relatively equable climate – albeit one uncomfortably shared by 100 million refugees from southern Europe and the Middle East. The margins of Greenland can now also support substantial human populations, helpfully supplied by constant meltwater from thawing ice, and kept cool both by their high latitude and the nearby presence of what remains of the Greenland ice sheet. Perhaps Greenland might be purchased from Denmark by a coalition of African nations in order to host a refugee population that keeps the memory of the old continent alive.

And that is pretty much it. At five degrees we are seeing humanity clinging on in only small refuges, surrounded on all sides by spreading deserts, forests in flame and rising seas. We will have lost nine-tenths of our habitable planetary space, including most of our lowlands and virtually all land outside the higher latitudes. The rest of our planet is a silent cemetery, suitable for the dead but no longer with much to offer the living.

Ice-free Antarctic

In a five-degree world, with much of the planet's surface now uninhabitable, continued sea level rise is perhaps the least of humanity's worries. All the same, it is worth noting that massive ongoing melt from both Greenland and the Antarctic ice sheets could raise ocean levels by as much as three metres by the end of the century. This would of course inundate all low-lying islands, and substantial areas of coastline and deltas in larger countries, further cramping what is left of the Earth's habitable space. As I mentioned in the previous chapter, recent scientific assessments taking into account more rapid melting of the polar ice sheets now give a potential upper value on sea level rise that is more than twice the worst-case scenario considered by the IPCC in its 2013 report. The ten countries that lose most land in absolute terms are of course some of the largest: China, Russia, the US, Canada, Brazil, Vietnam, Australia, India, Indonesia and Mexico. About 800 million people are directly flooded out of their homes (this is assuming that they have not already been displaced by food shortages or heat shocks), with about two million square kilometres of land inundated. All coastal megacities either have to be defended at enormous cost or permanently evacuated. In Asia alone the list includes Jakarta, Manila, Ho Chi Minh City, Bangkok, Guangzhou, Hong Kong, Mumbai, Kuala Lumpur, Tokyo and Shanghai.

The only areas protected from sea level rise are those regions that lose so much ice so quickly that the Earth's crust rebounds underneath them and raises the level of the land, reducing the rate of relative sea-level rise around Greenland, parts of the Canadian Arctic,

Alaska, Antarctica and possibly Scandinavia. Some of these areas overlap with the probable remaining habitable 'refuges' I suggested earlier, making these locations doubly desirable. Assuming conventional rates of economic growth, models project that about 5% of humanity would be flooded annually, reducing global GDP by about a tenth. However, these kinds of business-as-usual figures generated by economic models do not hold much real-world value, as I discussed earlier. In any case, the maximum rate of sea level rise by the end of the 21st century would be 2–4 centimetres per year. This is roughly a tenfold acceleration over the rate the oceans are currently rising in our one-degree world.

Over a few hundred years, the Greenland ice sheet will be reduced to a rump, with all ice eliminated within a millennium. This will deliver its full amount of water into the global oceans, equivalent to a sea level rise of 7.28 metres. From the Antarctic, whose entire surface will eventually be inside the melt zone in a five-degree scenario, about 12–15 metres of sea level rise is expected by the year 2500, with the West Antarctic Ice Sheet having fully collapsed within 250 years from now. The seas could rise by 7.5 metres as soon as 2200 in a five-degree world, according to the latest assessments. Scientists have calculated that the combustion of the planet's entire stock of fossil fuels would be enough to eliminate the entire Antarctic ice sheet over about 10,000 years, yielding the full complement of more than 50 metres of sea level rise. However, burning ten trillion tonnes of carbon would be quite a feat (we have so far burned 0.63 trillion), and it is likely that the direct heating impacts would destroy industrial civilisation's capacity to combust fossil fuels on a large scale long before all the accessible oil, coal and gas can be dug up and burned by our presumably very foolish descendants.

The thawing of ice in Antarctica will also produce new areas of ice-free land, beginning with the Antarctic Peninsula and extending further around the continent as the melt accelerates. Plants will colonise the newly available areas, which will be amply supplied with freshwater from melting glaciers further inland. While Antarctica currently has only two vascular plants – Antarctic pearlwort (*Colobanthus quitensis*) and Antarctic hair grass (*Deschampsia antarctica*) – many more, including woody shrubs, can be expected to colonise the continent later this century as more than 17,000 square kilometres of new land appears from beneath the ice. While insects and other animal species may find their way to these new promised lands, many iconic animals currently on Antarctica such as emperor and Adélie penguins will find their habitat eliminated as sea ice disappears. Ice-free land areas will also open on Greenland, in Arctic Canada and the Pacific coast of Alaska. However, furnished with only poor soils or just bare rock, none of these regions hold much prospect for replacing agricultural production lost elsewhere, though they will at least remain tolerably cool.

These new ice-free lands, however, represent only a tiny fraction of what is lost to the rising oceans. The net impact of melting ice is a planetary-scale loss of land of dramatic proportions. With many metres of sea level rise now on the cards, those members of future generations who survive civilisational collapse will inhabit a planet with radically different coastlines. In the past, coasts have always been a relatively stable feature of our planet's geography. With sea levels rising by centimetres per year for centuries and millennia to come, coastlines in the hotter future will shift constantly inland as new areas are inundated.

Perhaps traces of our cities will remain on the seabed as concrete and glass mausoleums inhabited by jellyfish, algae and other heat-tolerant remnant marine species. It is likely that some of our larger and most valuable settlements, especially those outside the tropical extreme heat zone, will persist for longer, trapped behind their prison-like sea walls and surrounded by rising oceans. But coastal protection measures can only delay the inevitable. One day, with the next mega-storm or Category 6 hurricane, the dykes will be breached and the seas will rush in. The apocalypse of climate breakdown comes not once but many times over, as each successive city faces its own Day Zero, when the countdown stops and the future arrives as a wall of water three storeys high.

Hyperthermal hothouses

As we enter the five-degree world, we have now made the planet hotter than at any point for over 50 million years. The closest geological analogue for our new super-greenhouse climate is a 'hyperthermal' event that took place at the boundary of the Palaeocene and Eocene epochs, about 56 million years ago, when the planet's temperature rose between five and nine degrees alongside CO_2 levels of 1,000–2,000 ppm. The Palaeocene–Eocene Thermal Maximum (PETM) has long provoked interest among climate scientists because it closely parallels the world we will be heading into if we continue to rapidly increase our consumption of fossil fuels. This was an inhospitable and violent world, barely recognisable from the Earth humans have always known.

If you want to stand right at the PETM boundary one of the best places to do so sits part way up a dusty valley on the Spanish side of the Pyrenean foothills. Just outside the pretty stone village of Arén, you cross a concrete bridge off the main highway, over a small river that marks the border between the provinces of Aragon and Catalunya. Travel up an unremarkable valley on an asphalt road that later gives way to a gravel track. The valley floor has some tilled land but the hillsides are all scrub, with reddish eroded soils and only a few trees. The whole area has a badlands feel, a bit like the old Wild West. As you scramble up the dusty red hillside on foot, you are climbing through soils deposited during the last few million years of the Palaeocene. Appearing near the top is a long, prominent formation that stretches for a kilometre in both directions, a linear outcrop made of welded stones, pebbles and even boulders. This is the Claret Conglomerate, a deposit several metres thick that sits exactly at the

Palaeocene–Eocene Thermal Maximum. This tough rock layer offers tantalising clues as to the true nature of the Earth's last extreme greenhouse event.

The base of the Claret Conglomerate coincides with the spike in atmospheric CO_2 that marked the ascent into hyperthermal conditions of the PETM. Its pebbly structure, with rounded stones of different sizes, shows that it was deposited in a braided river channel, while the width and depth of the channel, and the size of the stones, betray what geologists term a 'high-energy' environment. In other words, this material was deposited during large-scale flood events that cut huge channels in the landscape and left them full of polished rocks. Pollen records from the time show that overall rainfall declined, meaning that the PETM was hotter and drier than the preceding period. As a result, vegetation became increasingly sparse, making the overall landscape more susceptible to erosion when heavy precipitation events hit.

In a 2018 paper in the journal *Scientific Reports*, scientists point out that this combination of a more arid climate punctuated by intermittent floods would 'have enhanced wholesale denudation of the entire landscape', washing huge quantities of material into the sea. All told, they conclude that water discharge increased by between 1.35 and 14 times during the early phase of the PETM. 'These results support hypotheses that extreme rainfall events and associated risks of flooding increase with global warming at similar, but potentially much higher, magnitudes than currently predicted,' they add. In other words, this relatively recent geological evidence suggests that rainfall episodes, even in a drier overall climate, may become much more extreme than they have been conventionally projected in higher-warming scenarios.

PETM-aged sediments are also found elsewhere in Spain, and the rocks in these regions tell a similar tale. Far to the south, about 50 kilometres inland from the tourist traps of the Costa del Sol, sits another nondescript valley surrounded by olive groves and drab, arid hillsides. Here the PETM sections were laid down in a shallow marine environment on the northern shores of the now-vanished Tethys Ocean. The sediments contain plant-derived remains from the nearby land surfaces, part of a mixture of debris that was washed into the ocean in dramatic fashion by epic floods within the context of an otherwise highly arid climate. These flood deposits are intersected with finer sediments, which the experts suggest were probably deposited on the sea surface by dust storms. After becoming denuded of most of its vegetation, it seems as if the land was scoured alternately by dust storms and floods, which removed most of the soil in a climate that remained hostile for thousands of years. These deposits were all located at a similar latitude 55 million years ago, so the Spanish PETM remains provide a plausible glimpse into the future for the Mediterranean region as our climate once again moves into an extreme greenhouse regime.

There are other rock formations around the world that also have a story to tell about the extreme climate of the PETM. Geological evidence from the Bighorn Basin in Wyoming shows a similar picture to the Spanish sections: intense drying as the planet's climate heated up, with the whole area then intermittently swept by heavy rainfall from a resurgent monsoon. All these regions suggest that the land surface was devastated and denuded by a deadly sequence of desertification and extreme floods. One can only imagine the intensity of the heatwaves that accompanied them.

Arctic rainforests

Faddeyevsky Island must be one of the least hospitable places in the world. This wind-blasted patch of tundra and permafrost lies off the northern Arctic coast of Siberia, which together with Belkovsky Island and other small land fragments comprise the New Siberian Islands. Human visitors in the past were often in search of the valuable ivory in mammoth tusks that are occasionally found protruding from exposed thawing permafrost along the crumbling cliffs. The most notable visitors today are walruses, which haul themselves out of the sea onto Belkovsky Island's frozen shingle beaches to rest from their foraging expeditions out on the Arctic Ocean seafloor. The islands are so far north that they are fully consumed by polar darkness between November and February. Winter temperatures plunge as low as -45°C, while summer temperatures barely make it above zero. Some years the islands stay locked in sea ice throughout the brief summer months, while the wind is relentless and low clouds shedding occasional flurries of snow obscure the sun for weeks at a time.

In the early Eocene the New Siberian Islands were roughly at their current 72°N latitude, so might be expected to have experienced a similarly cold polar climate. But the Eocene, especially during the PETM, was vastly different. In fact, the region was almost subtropical. Annual mean air temperatures ranged between about 16 and 21°C, with summertime averages of 25–28°C. Warm-season high temperatures would presumably have been in the mid to high 30s. Even during the polar night, temperatures stayed well above freezing, with a wintertime average of 6–14°C. Scientists drilling sediment cores on Faddeyevsky Island have examined pollen from the PETM, and discovered that the predominant vegetation of the time was not lichen or mossy tundra like today, but mangroves. Amazingly, these trees thrived in lush coastal swamps of the sort only found today in the warm climates of eastern Australia, southern China and Taiwan. Alongside these unlikely mangroves grew evergreen deciduous forests and palms, an extraordinary finding for a high-Arctic landmass that was then, as now, shrouded in months of polar darkness.

Other Arctic fieldwork has shown similarly startling results. At Eureka Sound in the Canadian Arctic, which at 80°N is even closer to the North Pole than the New Siberian Islands, researchers found evidence of the same sort of warm, swampy early Eocene conditions, revealing 'a forested landscape analogous to the swamp-cypress and broadleaved floodplain forests of the modern southeastern United States'. Summer temperatures were at 20°C or above, winter lows barely touched freezing, and there was plentiful rainfall, although with so much biomass around and frequent thunderstorms there were probably also regular wildfires. These swamps were inhabited by alligators, turtles and fish, as well as a type of giant salamander, two species of lizard and a boa constrictor snake. There were also numerous mammals, including primates, tapirs, rhinoceros-like ungulates and the hippo-resembling *Coryphodon*.

It seems amazing that this thriving high-Arctic rainforest ecological community existed throughout months of polar twilight and night. During the winter the herbivorous animals probably ate evergreen foliage, branches, seeds and fungi. The ice-free, warm and brackish Arctic Ocean was covered at times with mats of *Azolla*, a type of small floating fern a bit like pond duckweed. Remains of plankton found in cores drilled in sea sediments under the Arctic Ocean suggest a PETM sea-surface temperature at a Mediterranean-like 23°C right across the North Pole itself. These sediments also contain 55-million-year-old fossil pollen from palm trees, cycads and relatives of the African baobab. These unlikely Arctic rainforests are mirrored best by ecological zones today occurring 5,000 kilometres further south.

Near-tropical Eocene warmth was also found at the opposite pole, on Antarctica. Along the coastal setting of Wilkes Land there were similar thriving rainforests of palms and other warmth-loving species. As with the Arctic, winters in the Antarctic coastal lowlands remained frost-free despite months of darkness, with temperatures rarely falling below a mild 10°C. There was no ice anywhere on the continent, not even at the actual South Pole, and the interior was most likely occupied by cooler, more temperate woodlands. The Southern Ocean was balmy enough for warm-water plankton to thrive, and the high sea temperatures also generated plentiful rainfall – of a metre per year or more – to support the Antarctic coastal rainforests. All this palaeoclimatic evidence adds up to what scientists writing in *Nature* termed 'drastic polar amplification of warming' during the real-world Eocene greenhouse experiment more than 50 million years ago. In other words, as we enter the five-degree world, the poles may get a lot hotter than most people currently expect.

Anoxic oceans

Polar rainforests aside, it would be wrong to get the impression that the early Eocene hothouse was some kind of primordial Eden. With the poles basking in improbable sub-tropical conditions, the actual tropics must have been intolerably hot. Tropical sea-surface temperatures during the PETM probably exceeded 40°C, much hotter than the highest sea temperatures found in today's world. The low-latitude oceans were so hot that they were almost lifeless; this level of extreme heat lies far above the thermal tolerance threshold of any plankton species, meaning that oceanic plankton were displaced to much higher latitudes and consequently virtually disappear from the PETM tropical sedimentary record. Scientists examining a PETM seabed core drilled off the coast of modern-day Nigeria found a 'maximum recorded absolute sea-surface temperature of 37°C, about 8°C warmer than any open ocean at present'. They point out that temperature values above 36°C 'are considered uninhabitable for most marine eukaryotic [higher] organisms today'. Not surprisingly, therefore, the Nigerian core shows little sign of life; the experts accordingly term it a 'heat-induced marine plankton dead zone'.

Also absent are coral reefs, which were eradicated from the global oceans during the extreme heat of the PETM and other hyperthermal events during the early Eocene. As a result this period is considered as one of the five great 'reef crises' to have occurred over the last 400 million years. Having been displaced to the cooler mid-latitudes during the early stages of the PETM global heating event, coral reefs later disappeared altogether as ocean temperatures rose too high everywhere in their range. The cause may well have been the same heat-related coral-bleaching effect that is being seen on modern-day reefs such as Australia's Great Barrier Reef and in the Maldives. Without a food supply from their symbiotic zooxanthellate algae, corals were unable to secrete the large carbonate shells from which reef colonies are built. Most corals did not go entirely extinct at the species level, however, possibly because some small refuges in cooler or deeper areas remained habitable or because individual coral animals could drift through the oceans without their external skeletons. These lonely survivors were condemned to a solitary, nomadic life in inhospitable seas. Just a few individuals occasionally formed small colonies in muddy algal mats in some coastal locations, a far cry from the thriving and ecologically diverse reefs that existed in cooler eras.

And heat was not the only issue. As is again happening today, during the PETM the oceans turned rapidly more acidic. With higher levels of CO_2 in the atmosphere, more of the gas dissolves in the oceans, reducing their pH and the resulting carbonate saturation state of seawater. This makes it harder for marine organisms – like corals, but also calcifying plankton and many others – to build shells. At its extremes, ocean acidification means that carbonates begin to dissolve, threatening the survival of all calcifying organisms across the global ocean. PETM rock samples from Maryland and New Jersey show tiny fossils, deposited in what would then have been a shallow marine environment, with clear evidence of significant chemical dissolution. This ocean acidification took place worldwide and lasted tens of thousands of years. The estimated degree of acidification during PETM was a decrease in pH of 0.15–0.3, less than the 0.4 pH decrease predicted for the end of the twenty-first century due to human emissions. Ocean chemistry acts to buffer acidification over longer periods of time, and – severe and dramatic as it was – the PETM took place much more slowly than our currently unfolding hyperthermal. As a result, acidification probably had less impact on marine plankton than outright extreme heat.

With water temperatures so high, the PETM oceans also began to haemorrhage oxygen, leading to widespread anoxia. With hotter, less dense water spreading on top of the oceans, currents stopped moving surface oxygen to the depths. Over substantial areas the shortage of oxygen was so extreme that marine bacteria began to produce hydrogen sulphide, poisoning higher organisms. The thermal stratification of the ocean surface during the hotter early Eocene also encouraged the growth of harmful algal blooms, which produced neurotoxins that killed most other lifeforms. All these environmental stresses led to a mass extinction of deep-sea plankton that was the most severe for 100 million years during the PETM. All told, the extreme climate would have collapsed the marine food chain, wiping out multicellular organisms from most of the Earth's seas. Needless to say, this does not provide a happy model for our hotter future.

A two-degree tipping point?

So where did the PETM hothouse come from? Obviously there were no humans 55 million years ago burning coal in power stations and oil in cars. Scientists are not entirely sure about the source of the sudden and massive pulse of carbon, but there are several leading hypotheses. PETM-dated rocks all have a clear isotopic carbon signature, showing that vast amounts of CO_2 – perhaps accompanied by methane – were released very rapidly into the atmosphere once some unknown trigger was pulled. How this process worked, where the carbon came from, and whether some kind of similar tipping point could be triggered today by human activities are critically important questions for our own hotter future.

Some of the additional carbon originated from the Earth itself. Travel to the north-west of Scotland, and on numerous islands – including Skye, Eigg and Rum – you can see remnants of a vast volcanic episode that tore apart the North Atlantic region between 54 and 61 million years ago. Over long periods of time, these eruptions piled up blankets of lava that today also form the characteristic layered mountains of eastern Greenland and the Faroe Islands. In the process, colossal amounts of CO_2 were degassed from the erupting magma, driving a gradual rise in the planet's temperature beginning about 57 million years ago. Scientists are still debating how much carbon was released during the formation of this 'North Atlantic Igneous Province' (NAIP) and how much this drove an enhanced greenhouse effect. Estimates for carbon emissions during the second phase of the eruptions, between 55 and 56 million years ago, total somewhere between 18 and 40 trillion tonnes. This is a colossal amount by any standard, but it would have been released slowly, limiting the climatic greenhouse impact. Moreover, the isotopic signature of the carbon in PETM rocks does not clearly match a volcanic source. Something else was also probably going on.

There are two leading candidates for non-volcanic carbon sources. These, singly or combined, could have been released much more dramatically into the atmosphere after a climate tipping point was crossed following slow temperature rises driven by solar orbital changes and volcanism. The first is methane. Today, vast quantities of methane lie locked up as ice-like hydrates in shallow seafloor sediments, anchored in place by low temperatures. It was probably little different at the end of the Palaeocene. As the oceans gradually warmed, larger and larger amounts of methane hydrate would have begun to turn back into gas, bubbling into the oceans and bumping up the atmospheric concentrations of methane. Against a background of slow volcanic-driven warming, methane hydrate release is therefore a strong candidate for causing at least some of the PETM temperature spike.

The other leading contender was proposed by Robert DeConto and colleagues in a much-cited 2012 paper in *Nature*. They began by restating that the 'PETM is characterized by a massive input of carbon, ocean acidification and an increase of global temperature of about 5°C within a few thousand years'. They then suggested that gradual background warming forced the Earth over a threshold that led to the sudden release, not of oceanic methane hydrates but of enormous amounts of CO_2 from melting permafrost in polar regions. Crossing this threshold could have triggered the release of as much as three trillion tonnes of carbon from these sources, DeConto and colleagues calculated. The guilty permafrost was not only in the Arctic, but also in the interior of the Antarctic continent, which lacked any ice sheets but was probably still cold enough for tundra and peat to form carbon-rich permafrost over vast areas, as seen in Siberia and Arctic Canada today. The theory remains controversial, not least because no evidence of Palaeocene-aged permafrost carbon has ever been found in Antarctica. The dispute may never be resolved, given that almost the entire continent today sits under kilometres of ice, making investigations of its bedrock challenging to say the least.

Whatever the relative contributions of thawing peat, bubbling methane hydrates or something else, the current scientific consensus is that not only was the PETM a sudden and extreme greenhouse episode, but that its onset was also triggered quite rapidly by the crossing of some kind of climatic threshold or tipping point. Scientists looking at sedimentary records have found characteristic statistical signatures suggesting that the Earth system was becoming destabilised by gradual warming just prior to the crossing of this tipping point. As Joost Frieling and colleagues wrote in April 2019, whatever the specific sources of the additional carbon, all the evidence 'strongly suggests a scenario of positive feedbacks'. Most alarming of all is the likely magnitude of the pre-existing long-term temperature rise that is thought to have triggered the geologically sudden catastrophe of the PETM – an estimated two degrees of global warming. Frieling and his co-authors pointed out that 'these results … may warrant reconsideration of the political assignment of 2°C warming as a safe future scenario.'

Similar positive feedback cascades, albeit with less profound heating than for the PETM, are observed in other later hyperthermal events in the Eocene. For example, the Eocene Thermal Maximum 2, which took place only a couple of million years after the PETM, also saw devastating sub-tropical droughts, hot oceans and between two and four degrees of rapid global warming. A third hyperthermal, another million years later, saw a similar process unfolding. This potential two-degree tipping point was not just a geological one-off.

While the PETM may be the best analogue in the geological record for our current greenhouse event, it is still not a perfect one. The reason is not that the PETM world – with its anoxic oceans, denuded landscapes and ice-free poles – is too extreme an example of what we may be heading into, but that it is not extreme enough. Admittedly, larger amounts of carbon overall were released during the entire 170,000-year evolution of the event (humanity would have to burn all known fossil fuel reserves to come close). However, the rate of release of carbon today is at least an order of magnitude faster than anything seen even during the height of the Palaeocene–Eocene Thermal Maximum. In fact, the initial carbon pulse, which at its maximum rates of release still totalled less than a billion tonnes a year, probably took at least 4,000 years to play out. Today we are pumping ten billion tonnes of carbon a year into the atmosphere, making our current emissions at least ten times faster than those that triggered the world's worst greenhouse event of the last 60 million years.

This matters because we are vastly overwhelming the Earth's capacity to re-absorb our emitted carbon, and such rapid releases will therefore also worsen ocean acidification as compared with the PETM. Indeed, scientists calculate that if we are foolish enough to continue increasing our emissions for decades to come, we could approach a PETM-style total accumulation of several trillion tonnes of atmospheric carbon in as little as 140 years. Needless to say, geologically unprecedented rapid carbon emissions will consequently lead to geologically unprecedented rapid temperature rises. Five degrees over a century will be a faster and more profound rise in planetary temperature than at any time since the end of the dinosaurs. This is not a road that we should head down lightly.

Life and death at five degrees

At five degrees we are approaching the end of life on Earth as we know it. The poles are in meltdown, and complex human societies have long since passed the point of collapse. For the natural world, the impacts are if anything even more devastating. Moving 5,000 kilometres towards the poles, as would be required for species to track the shift in climate zones implied by the PETM world, requires a 'climate velocity' of about 62 kilometres a year, or 170 metres a day. It goes without saying that few plants can broadcast seeds and reproduce themselves sufficiently quickly to move at such a speed. Moreover, you cannot just roll up a rainforest like a piece of carpet and transport it thousands of kilometres to the north or south. Ecosystems are incredibly complex, with interconnections, mutualities and dependencies at every level in the food chain. Predator–prey relationships, the dependencies of plants on insect pollinators and on fruit and seed dispersers, the fungi and micro-organisms that enable plants to thrive – all this complex web will be fragmented and torn apart. The PETM avoided a major land-based mass extinction because species were able to shift over many millennia across an entirely wild planet. This time the Earth will not be so lucky.

There are a few species models that aim to estimate directly the impacts of five degrees on wild species. In March 2018 Rachel Warren and colleagues published a paper in *Nature* mainly comparing the biodiversity impacts of 1.5 versus 2°C of warming, but also examining the effects of higher levels of global heating. Their model results show a linear relationship between degrees of warming and biodiversity impacts that is likely to be conservative given the wholesale unravelling of ecosystems implied by rapid climate change, as the authors themselves point out. Even so, Warren and colleagues' results show that insects, plants, mammals, birds, reptiles and amphibians lose between half and two-thirds of their climatic range in a 4.5°C warming scenario. This is surely a mass extinction by any other name.

Returning to a geological perspective, in 2017 Daniel Rothman published a paper in *Science* with the ominous title 'Thresholds of catastrophe in the Earth system'. As he explains, five times during the Phanerozoic (the past 542 million years) the planet has been struck by mass extinctions that killed more than three-quarters of marine animal species, and many more on land. Rothman writes: 'Each of these events is associated with a significant change in the Earth's carbon cycle.' However, there were many other times when big carbon-cycle events – identifiable because of a sudden change in isotopic ratios – did not lead to mass extinctions. Examining 31 different carbon events over the last half-billion years, Rothman hypothesises that 'perturbations of Earth's carbon cycle lead to mass extinction if they exceed either a critical rate at long time scales or a critical size at short time scales.' Almost all the palaeoclimatic data – despite its numerous uncertainties and deficiencies – supports Rothman's case that either releasing carbon too rapidly over a long time or too voluminously over a short time means the inevitable crossing of a catastrophe threshold. The most worrying aspect of this conclusion is that by releasing a vast store of carbon in a geological instant, humanity is currently on course to doing both things. Indeed, Rothman concludes, we will have consequently crashed through the catastrophe threshold within just a few decades from now in all but the most moderate of emissions scenarios.

While the PETM example almost certainly underestimates the scale of the wipeout of life to come this century, one of the Big Five mass extinctions does closely parallel the future with unchecked human greenhouse gas emissions and runaway positive feedbacks. This disaster occurred at the end of the Permian period, 251.94 million years ago. It was the worst mass extinction of all time, eliminating 90% of life on Earth. And it took place alongside a sudden global temperature rise of six degrees.

6°

Catastrophic failure

A temperature increase of six degrees within the space of a century would be such an extreme shock to the Earth that it is difficult to make any confident predictions about what might result. Although six degrees has been within the upper bounds of what is considered possible by probabilistic climate model projections for at least the last three IPCC reports, I have found that researchers are reluctant to talk about it, and to my knowledge almost no papers have been published reporting on any efforts to try to understand or model a six-degree future world in detail.

This rather odd gap might be because climatologists are human after all, and the scientists would prefer not to think about worst-case scenarios when there is clearly still time to hope for the best and focus on more moderate outcomes. It might also be that many experts consider the unrestrained carbon emissions and positive feedbacks necessary to raise the Earth's temperature by six degrees as highly unlikely, and they do not want to risk the career damage and lost grant-funding opportunities that might come with being branded an 'alarmist' or a 'doomsayer'. Another factor is that most climate models, on most runs, do not heat up to six degrees by 2100 even in the highest emissions scenarios, making this world hard to simulate on computers and therefore difficult to discuss in a sufficiently informed way. Climate sceptics often accuse scientists of being overly pessimistic in their assessments; in my view, the reverse is probably true.

Having said all that, given that a six-degree outcome has been considered plausible by the IPCC for over 15 years, one might have expected the climate community to have put some real effort into examining and modelling this world. By way of analogy, there are many far less likely outcomes that experts spend an inordinate amount of time trying to figure out and therefore avoid. For example, the chances of a plane crash for each individual flight are considerably less than one in a million, and yet airline safety experts spend millions of dollars trying to reduce the odds still further. Nuclear power stations cost many additional billions to build because multiple redundant safety systems aim to keep the odds of catastrophic failure down to infinitesimal odds. Yet the chances of a six-degree outcome for our planet are far higher than either of these and the impacts obviously incalculably worse.

No one should doubt that six degrees of global heating would represent a catastrophic failure of the Earth system. Nor should anyone doubt that the chances of it happening are much greater than one in a million. I wouldn't bet on the odds, but my view is that the chances lie somewhere between one in ten and one in a hundred. If I am right, that makes six degrees at least as likely as the lower temperature scenario of 1.5°C – a subject on which the IPCC has published a whole weighty report citing thousands of papers. I would personally not board an aircraft with a 1–10% chance of crashing, but in the case of the planet we are all on board together and have no other choice. Although we do not know the precise risks of a fatal disaster, a collision course of some sort has already been set.

In my research for this book I did find a couple of relatively recent publications looking at what the title of one terms 'very high greenhouse gas emission scenarios'. This paper was written by Ben Sanderson and colleagues in 2011, and published in the open-source journal *Environmental Research Letters*. What is most interesting about this study is not so much the specifics of their model-derived planet – although this reaches 5.1°C above the 1990 average global temperature by 2100 – but that the paper sheds light on the relative likelihood of the very high emissions scenarios needed to drive worst-case global heating outcomes. Using the numbers presented in these scenarios, we can judge for ourselves how plausible they seem.

The first input selected by Sanderson et al. is that the global population rises to 15 billion by 2100. This is at the very top end of the UN population projections, and has a big impact because each person is assumed to have relatively high carbon emissions (perhaps like the average Australian or Qatari today). Sanderson and colleagues also assume that the carbon intensity of energy increases as the global economy grows, rather than staying relatively constant as it has in recent decades. With virtually all new energy coming from coal, annual carbon emissions by the end of the century top 100 billion tonnes, ten times their current rate. If this sounds highly improbable, Sanderson and his co-authors remind their readers, 'one could interpret the CO_2 concentration pathway in this scenario as one achieved not by anthropogenic emissions alone, but by anthropogenic emissions plus an unforeseen feedback' – such as rapid emissions from thawing permafrost, a collapsing Amazon rainforest, or the albedo effect of vanishing polar ice. Either way, add all these factors together, and a six-degree world is the result.

So how plausible is this overall scenario? Certainly there are worrying signs of positive feedbacks already emerging in the Earth system, as I have outlined in this book. But will humanity really increase its coal consumption throughout the 21st century? Since this 2011 paper was written there have unfortunately been some new grounds for pessimism. One point to note is that technological improvements do not necessarily make human society more sustainable. Consider the shale oil and gas revolution, which has in less than a decade transformed the United States from a declining energy producer back into the world's largest extractor of fossil fuels, overtaking even the oil behemoth Saudi Arabia. In 2011 no one saw this coming, energy modellers included. Indeed, just a few years earlier, 'peak oil' was all the rage, and fossil fuels were supposed to be running out. Coal is admittedly declining in both the US and Europe, but continues to increase in China, India, Indonesia and many other large developing countries, and may well do so for years or even decades to come.

There are also political reasons for increased pessimism. When I wrote the first *Six Degrees*, I did not imagine that the governing political party in the world's most powerful nation (the US Republican Party) would adopt overt climate denialism as one of its core philosophies. Indeed the prospect would have seemed absurd. I assumed that climate denialism was just a flash-in-the-pan response to heavy political spending by fossil fuel companies. Nor did I expect that this bizarre phenomenon of science denialism would be accompanied by conspiracy theorising and broad-ranging assaults on the very concept of truth throughout the political system, including at the level of the presidency. If the trend towards populism continues throughout the world, overt denial of climate change may become consistently more prominent over future decades, even alongside worsening impacts of climate chaos. Humanity in aggregate, therefore, may not be as clever as many of us like to think. The proverbial boiling frog was at least just a passive and ignorant victim; we would be active and enthusiastic participants in our own demise.

Intriguingly, Sanderson and colleagues' six-degree-modelled world probably underestimates the climate impacts of the scenario it simulates. For example, the loss of Arctic sea ice is currently running about 40 years ahead of schedule in the real world as compared with the model they use. With a modelled temperature rise of about 12°C, the Arctic is ice-free by 2100, but only just. Southern Europe, Central America, the Southern Andes, the northern Middle East, Southern Australia and oceanic subtropical regions lose 30–80% of their rainfall, but precipitation increases of 50–200% are seen in polar and sub-polar regions, and across parts of the equator. Sea levels rise by 33 cm due to thermal expansion, but ice-sheet melt is not included in the model, nor are carbon cycle feedbacks such as tropical forest collapse, the oxidation of carbon in soils, or permafrost melt. As with most models in most scenarios, there is no sign of tipping points or catastrophic feedbacks.

A second paper, published in 2016 in *Nature Climate Change*, is not so much about the specific impacts of six degrees of warming as whether the linear relationship between cumulative CO_2 and global heating holds up under an illustrative scenario of very high emissions, totalling 5 trillion tonnes by 2300. (It does.) The various models used in the study yield temperature rises of 6.4 to 9.5°C within three centuries, with a mean warming of 8.2°C by 2300. Warming of this magnitude triggers significant 'Arctic amplification', with average temperature rises there of 14.7 to 19.5°C. Precipitation in polar regions also rises by 200%, and by a factor of four in the tropical Pacific, with 'decreases exceeding a factor of two over parts of Australia, the Mediterranean, southern Africa and the Amazon, and decreases exceeding a factor of three over parts of central America and North Africa.' The paper's closing sentence states that 'such climate changes, if realised, would have extremely profound impacts on ecosystems, human health, agriculture, economies and other sectors,' thereby winning my personal prize for scientific understatement.

There are one or two other studies that look at some of the specifics of high-end warming. For example, as I mentioned previously, a model assuming the consumption of all fossil fuels in less than 500 years projects the melting of the entire Antarctic Ice Sheet over about ten millennia. There is also the 2010 paper from *PNAS* that first raised the danger of wet-bulb temperature thresholds rising above the threshold of human survivability. This paper envisaged a planetary-scale loss of habitable space taking place with 7°C of average global warming. But as we have seen in previous chapters, later work has shown that this large-scale habitability threshold is likely to be crossed much earlier, at three or four degrees. On a different topic, a paper by tropical cyclone specialists including world expert Kerry Emanuel investigates simulated possible changes in hurricanes in a world with 8 to 32-times-higher CO_2 than currently. The scientists find, perhaps not surprisingly, that intense storms increase (though only by 50%) and that even some areas of the Arctic Ocean become hot enough to support tropical cyclones.

But – really – that's about it. I do not pretend to have conducted a fully rigorous and comprehensive literature review for this book, and doubtless I have missed some important papers. But my point stands: compared with the policy- and funding-driven attention that has been lavished on arguably equally unlikely 1.5-degree scenarios – generating hundreds upon hundreds of scientific papers, all painstakingly assessed by the IPCC in its 2018 report on the subject – the state of the science on the impacts of higher-end warming is woeful. In my view, the IPCC must urgently address this gap. A future special report on the impacts of high-end warming scenarios is long overdue – at least 15 years overdue, in fact. I suspect that this august scientific body is running scared of being called 'alarmist', but there is no reason why climate experts should be bullied into maintaining the current culture of complacency and reticence. The IPCC needs to properly consider high-end warming scenarios, tell us what their impacts would be on human society and the Earth system, and give a reasonably quantified assessment of their likelihood given different emissions trajectories. That is not 'alarmist' – it is responsible, and well within the IPCC's official mandate.

In the meantime, if we want to get any additional insight into the possibilities of a six-degree world, we have to return to the geological and palaeoclimatic literature. Fortunately, research is thriving in these disciplines, and large numbers of studies have been published about past extreme greenhouse episodes in Earth history. If we want to understand the future, therefore, our best option is to better understand the past.

The Cretaceous super-greenhouse

The geological record demonstrates unequivocally that the Earth has been in super-greenhouse episodes several times in the past. During the early Eocene, 49–54 million years ago (just after the PETM discussed in Chapter 5), global temperatures averaged around 29°C, nearly 15°C higher than the pre-industrial temperature of 14.4°C. The PETM itself was probably a couple of degrees warmer still. But earlier time periods during the Cretaceous, famous as the latter part of the age of the dinosaurs, were possibly even hotter than that. The Cretaceous Thermal Maximum, for example, was potentially the hottest the globe has been since the evolution of complex life began half a billion years ago. It saw sea-surface temperatures at high southern latitudes around 6°C warmer even than the PETM. That might imply global average temperatures in the region of 20°C warmer than in the pre-industrial period. This was a world where the ocean was as warm as 27°C in the sub-Antarctic, and champosaurs (a crocodile-like reptile) snapped their way around the high Arctic. As with other super-greenhouse episodes, the likely driver was the eruption of so-called 'large igneous provinces', gigantic emplacements of magma that de-gassed prodigious quantities of CO_2 as they spilled out from the Earth's mantle over many tens of thousands of years.

So why fret about what is by comparison but a minor six-degree rise this century? Clearly, if the world has previously been twenty degrees hotter, we can emit a lot more CO_2 without needing to worry about entering some unknown danger zone, right? On closer examination, however, the Cretaceous super-greenhouses were not exactly idyllic. They are typically characterised by super-heated, oxygen-starved, dead oceans; hence their alternative name – 'ocean anoxic events'. Taking place about 94 million years ago, the Cretaceous Thermal Maximum also has another name: 'Ocean Anoxic Event 2' (OAE 2). It devastated marine ecosystems, notably leading to the extinction of ichthyosaurs, fish-shaped seagoing reptiles that had dominated the oceans as apex predators for tens of millions of years. Lasting for 900,000 years, OAE 2 left a layer of black shale in Cretaceous rocks, evidence of huge amounts of organic carbon burial in oxygen-starved, sulfidic oceans. Ocean Anoxic Event 1a, which occurred somewhere between 119–120 million years ago, was not much better. It too saw oxygen-starved, super-heated oceans lasting for about a million years, leaving the characteristic black shale marker in both Atlantic and Pacific sediments. In many areas carbonate plankton fossils deposited during OAE 1a are malformed or absent entirely, suggesting a severe bout of ocean acidification.

Nor was life in the Cretaceous super-greenhouse necessarily much easier on land. Perennial sub-tropical high-pressure systems led to the development of globe-girdling, hyper-arid deserts throughout mid- to low-latitude continents. Desert dune systems are preserved in sandstones in modern-day China, showing wadi-type channels carved by occasional flash floods that scoured through otherwise desertified and denuded landscapes. There was no ice anywhere on the planet, and trees grew right up to the highest Arctic and Antarctic land areas. However, these high-latitude forests were not safe from the heat and were frequently struck by enormous polar wildfires that left thick deposits of fossil charcoal. Fossils also show clear evidence that coniferous trees evolved seed adaptations to a relentlessly high-fire world. We should not compare the Cretaceous too literally with today; back then, oxygen levels were higher, making wildfires more likely, and the continents were configured differently. Even so, the ice-free super-greenhouse world, with hyper-arid sub-tropics and extreme warmth at the poles, is consistent both with the PETM and expectations from computer models.

But the most important issue facing us today in comparing our own future with the hothouse worlds of the Cretaceous is not so much the magnitude of warming as the rate at which it occurs. Geological evidence from ocean sediments suggests that the initial carbon release triggering OAE 1a took a minimum of 30,000 years to play out. OAE 2 was probably similar, with carbon being released over a period of up to 100,000 years, according to modelling reconstructions based on isotope data. And as we saw earlier, while the PETM carbon release pulse took place over as little as 4,000 years, this rate is still an order of magnitude slower than our ongoing human greenhouse gas emissions. In fact, there is only one warming event over the last 100 million years that comes close to our 21st-century carbon pulse in terms of its abruptness in changing the climate. This was when a gigantic asteroid crashed into the planet 65 million years ago, causing the world's most famous mass extinction.

Unluckily for life at the time, the globe had already been heating up for hundreds of thousands of years before the asteroid collision that would end the age of the non-avian dinosaurs. Massive volcanism following the eruption of another large igneous province – this time the Deccan Traps in eastern India – had already raised CO_2 levels by 400–500 ppm and pushed up global temperatures by several degrees. The warming climate destabilised ecosytems, causing the extinction of marine fauna, although the direct effects of volcanism – acid rains or toxic emissions – may also have been a contributing factor. When it came, the asteroid that ended the Cretaceous was so large that it vaporised a three-kilometre-thick layer of carbonate rock under the shallow ocean impact site at Chicxulub in Mexico, ejecting much of this into the atmosphere as CO_2. The total amount of CO_2 released has been estimated at about 425 billion tonnes, only about a quarter of human emissions so far, although it may have been considerably higher. The carbon was also accompanied by large amounts of ejected sulphur, so the subsequent greenhouse warming was preceded by a sulphate aerosol-driven nuclear winter. This forced global temperatures down by at least 26°C, with the world's surface left largely below freezing for somewhere between three and sixteen years, followed by a gradual 30-year recovery. As the sulphate sunshield cleared, temperatures shot up by two degrees above pre-impact levels thanks to the additional CO_2 now in the atmosphere.

This climatic see-saw aggravated the initial extinction pulse by turning the oceans anoxic over large areas. The oceans were also hit by a bout of extreme ocean acidification, thanks to the sudden CO_2 increase in the atmosphere, which destroyed plankton and cut marine productivity in half at a stroke.

One aspect of the end-Cretaceous mass extinction might serve as a particularly useful cautionary tale for humanity. The scenario of a sulphate winter flipping into a sudden greenhouse is perhaps analogous to what might happen if a stratospheric aerosol-spraying geo-engineering programme suddenly ceases for some reason, perhaps because of worldwide conflict or some other form of social or political collapse. At that point all the hidden climate forcing from the accumulating CO_2 will suddenly come into play, pushing up global temperatures by several degrees in a matter of years. This would deliver a climatic shock to the Earth not dissimilar to that of the end-Cretaceous asteroid, perhaps triggering massive positive feedbacks or destabilising the planetary system in unforeseen ways. Although this would be a fascinating area for climate modellers to look into, we should probably not try it in the real world.

The end-Permian wipeout

There is only one occasion over the last half-billion years when the planet's self-regulatory climatic thermostat has come close to failing completely. This event was a true apocalypse, one that wiped out 90% of species and arguably came within a whisker of entirely eradicating life on Earth. Few experts now doubt that intense and sustained global heating played a central role, accompanied by a combination of other environmental crises that added together comprised the main 'kill mechanisms' driving the world's worst-ever mass extinction. Although the end-Permian wipeout took place 251 million years ago, some of these kill mechanisms seem eerily familiar today. History never repeats itself exactly, and the planet is very different now from the world as it approached the Permian–Triassic boundary. But written in the geological sediments laid down at that time, which outcrop all over the world from China to Italy, is a critical warning about how unstoppable greenhouse gas emissions once drove a worldwide catastrophe – and could potentially do so again.

Life was thriving at the end of the Permian. The Earth was dominated by a gigantic supercontinent, Pangaea, with the rest of the planet's surface covered by the globe-girdling Panthalassic Ocean. Although the interior of Pangaea probably saw seasonal climate extremes, the equatorial regions supported lush tropical forests dominated by ferns and conifers. (Flowering plants, or angiosperms, were not to evolve for another 100 million years.) These forests buzzed with insect life. Large herbivores included para-reptiles like pareiasaurs – stocky animals with armoured backs and spiny heads. Top predators included gorgonopsian therapsids, mammalian ancestors looking like sabre-toothed bears, while reptilian archosauromorphs scampered noisily around in the undergrowth. In some ways the late Permian biomes were not unlike today's; tundra ecosystems probably fringed the poles (although large ice sheets were absent), with boreal forests in the higher latitudes and sub-tropical deserts on either side of the equator. In the oceans, trilobites and ammonites – still some of the most commonly found fossils – moved through the depths, alongside sharks, rays and numerous species of bony fish.

All this was to disappear in a geologically unprecedented cataclysm. Although not as instantaneously dramatic as the later asteroid strike that ended the Cretaceous, the end-Permian mass extinction still ranks as the worst in the entire history of the Earth. And the animals alive then would have had similarly little warning of their impending doom. Those living in Siberia might have witnessed immense fountains of lava towering into the smoky sky, while around their feet gigantic fissures would have torn the land apart as if ripping open the fiery gates of hell. As a multi-million-year super-eruption gathered pace, magma flooded out from chasms in the ground and began to pile up in layers, each hundreds of metres thick. The first sign of the chaos to come was probably an accelerating bout of global warming, as the monster volcanoes released prodigious quantities of CO_2 from deep within the Earth's mantle. This climate warming would have dried out Pangaea further and begun to drive species on land and in the seas away from an overheating equator. But it was still only the beginning.

Kill mechanisms

For a long time scientists were divided about what exactly drove the mass extinction at the end of the Permian. It has long been agreed that the eruption of the Siberian Traps basalt must have led to the emission of prodigious amounts of CO_2. Over the course of the eruptions so much magma reached the surface that in places it built up into layers as much as six kilometres thick. In addition to gigantic volcanic episodes, some have suggested kill mechanisms such as another asteroid strike or even deadly cosmic rays from a nearby supernova. The most likely answer, it turns out, lies much closer to home, and can still be seen with the naked eye in the form of small craters that are scattered all over southern Siberia.

What happened was that during a particularly deadly final phase of the eruptions, magma stopped pouring out onto the surface but instead intruded as underground horizontal sills over tens of thousands of square kilometres of Siberia. There, in an epic misfortune for life at the end of the Permian, this magma encountered and burned through thick layers of sedimentary carbon. In precise terms, the magma hit coal, so these already epic Siberian volcanoes began to burn fossil fuels. No wonder many scientists see this episode as a direct warning from the distant past about the future of humanity.

The gases from this colossal bout of sub-surface coal combustion then vented up into the atmosphere through giant pipes hundreds of metres deep, leaving craters often more than a kilometre in diameter where they exploded. At least 250 of these vertical pipes have been discovered in aerial surveys over vast areas of southern Siberia, and boreholes confirm that they emerged in exactly those areas where magmatic intrusions hit carbon-bearing shales and coal. The explosions would have been pretty dramatic to witness; studies show that with basalt intruding into coal seams, the whole mixture liquefies and vents to the surface, where the coal ignites in the presence of oxygen with sufficient force to blow the resulting plume right into the stratosphere. The whole vent would then drain like a massive volcano in just a matter of days, leaving a scorched and burned area around the crater. It would have been an incredible spectacle – the whole place must have looked like Mordor. In the process, millions of tonnes of methane, CO_2 and other gases were vented into the upper atmosphere during each blow-out. As Darcy Ogden and Norman Sleep write in *PNAS*: 'The hot (approximately 500°C) mixture of basalt, volatiles, coke, and solid coal would combust as it is exposed to oxygen at the surface, rapidly releasing fly ash, CO_2, sulfate, basaltic ash, and other potentially harmful products into the atmosphere.'

Although the main end-Permian mass-extinction episode is generally thought to have played out over about a period of 100,000–200,000 years, Ogden and Sleep point out that 'acceleration of extinction by massive coal-basalt eruption is particularly attractive because it has the virtue of changing the environment within a generation time of many of the organisms that became extinct'. In other words, huge numbers of animals and plants could be killed within days to years, preventing them from reproducing and leading to widespread species extinctions. As they write: 'Large injections of dust, CO_2 and methane into the atmosphere may have generated a highly unstable climate, driving extinctions of land biota,' especially when combined with acidification and anoxia in the surrounding oceans. All told, these pipes would have released trillions of tonnes of carbon into the atmosphere, driving global temperatures to unheard-of extremes.

Just how widespread the direct impact of these explosive eruptions would have been was illustrated by the discovery of traces of fly ash from coal combustion in end-Permian sediments in faraway Canada. Due to the high latitude and predominant westerly winds of the shallow-sea deposition zone, this fly ash would have had to travel 20,000 kilometres around the world from its probable combustion and release site in Siberia. This confirms that the eruption plumes must have reached as high as 20 kilometres into the atmosphere, sufficient to penetrate the stratosphere, where gases and particulates would have been able to circumnavigate the globe. The scientists who discovered the Canadian fly ash deposits wrote in *Nature Geoscience* that these 'megascale eruptions may have formed interhemispheric ash clouds, allowing for global coal ash distribution'. Intriguingly, the deposits recovered from the site 'show a strong resemblance to modern fly ash collected from coal-fired power plants'.

In a further eerie resemblance to another modern-day environmental problem associated with coal burning, several of the same researchers also discovered a worldwide layer of toxic mercury in marine sediments from the same era. Other studies have also found malformed pollen grains across the Permian–Triassic boundary, similar to the mutations found today 'on heavily polluted industrial sites'. Overall, mercury and other poisonous elements could have formed a toxic sludge that choked the life out of the seas, particularly if combined with extreme heat and oceanic oxygen starvation. Crucially, the fly ash and mercury deposition episodes exactly match carbon isotope spikes, showing that these tell-tale remnants of coal combustion were released at the same time as vast quantities of CO_2.

Another coal-related modern problem is acid rain. This too could have been a contributory end-Permian kill mechanism, because the Siberian volcanoes vented colossal amounts of sulphur into the atmosphere during their biggest eruptions. According to one study, across most of the Northern Hemisphere between the equator and 60°N the annual averaged acidity of precipitation would have fallen to pH 2–3, 'similar to undiluted lemon juice'. A ten-times larger eruption would have reduced the annual average rainfall pH to 2, or even lower during extremes. In other words, much of the terrestrial biosphere was being drenched with concentrated sulphuric acid, deadly to most forms of life. Anything below a pH of 4 is lethal to fish, while lower than 3 is lethal to amphibians. Plants are stunted and killed at 2. After a dousing of acid with a pH of 1, nothing would survive.

A further suspect in the warming-driven mass extinction is a familiar killer, one that I spent a lot of time examining in the first *Six Degrees*: methane hydrate. The case for the prosecution was put forward most recently by Uwe Brand and co-authors writing in the journal *Paleoworld* in 2016; they gave their paper the unambiguous title 'Methane hydrate: killer cause of Earth's greatest mass extinction'. Brand and colleagues make the case that most life survived the initial bout of slow global warming resulting from the Siberian Traps volcanic emissions, but that this in turn triggered the release of methane from polar permafrost and hydrates in sediments under shallow ocean shelves. This methane hydrate emission was geologically very rapid, 'lasting several years to thousands of years', thereby driving global warming that 'reached levels lethal to most life on land and in the oceans', they assert, concluding: 'Global warming triggered by the massive release of CO_2 may be catastrophic, but the release of methane from hydrate may be apocalyptic.' However, this thesis is by no means universally accepted, with another group of scholars recently concluding that 'any potential gas hydrate release would have had only a minor contributing impact to the runaway greenhouse during the Latest Permian extinction.' The prosecution has made a strong case, but the jury is still out.

The massive Siberian Traps eruptions did not, however, only generate CO_2, methane and sulphur. As well as combusting coal seams, the magma intruded into sedimentary rocks containing salt and other evaporites. At subsurface temperatures of hundreds of degrees Celsius, these would have been vaporised, leading to surface emissions of methyl chloride and methyl bromide, both potent destroyers of atmospheric ozone. In volcanic plumes, these chemicals might have been conducted straight into the stratosphere in sufficient quantities to either significantly reduce or even temporarily destroy the Earth's ozone layer. If this is indeed what happened, it would have had dramatic impacts. An 85% reduction in stratospheric ozone equates to as much as a 4,900% increase in mutation-causing UVB radiation, according to one calculation. Scientists testing modern conifers under high UVB radiation have found that trees are effectively sterilised because the radiation makes them produce malformed pollen. Similarly mutated pollen grains have been found fossilised in sediments right across the Permian–Triassic boundary, suggesting that this ozone loss might well have been another kill mechanism driving the mass extinction.

Combined with drought driven by extreme global warming, bouts of acid rain and intense ultraviolet radiation could have eventually stripped the land of its vegetation across much of the planet's surface. Denuded hillsides were then vulnerable to intense downpours, which scoured the soil away, leaving whole continents barren and lifeless. This did not necessarily occur in a single episode; palaeontologists collecting fossils at the Permian–Triassic boundary in South Africa have catalogued three distinct extinction pulses, each lasting a few tens of thousands of years, although shorter periods during each extinction pulse would have been truly catastrophic. They note: 'At the boundary, torrential monsoon driven rainstorms led to sheet flows that scoured devegetated flood plains.' In the southern hemisphere, straightforward global warming was most likely the main culprit rather than acid rain, toxic mercury or anything else. 'The rapidity of the onset of drought conditions led to a breakdown of the terrestrial ecosystem which adversely affected the vertebrate communities from the bottom to the top of the food chain,' the fossil experts working in South Africa conclude.

As the end-Permian kill mechanisms took their deadly toll, world-wide ecological collapse spread around the planet. Virtually all the Earth's forests died. After the extinction boundary there is a world-wide 'coal gap', with no known coal being deposited anywhere until the middle Triassic, ten million years later. Coal results from the fossilisation of peat formed in swamp forests, and this long absence of coal in the geological record shows that peat-forming ecosystems on land were virtually eradicated. It was not until new plant forms evolved to fill this ecological niche that coal began to be produced again, and even then the first Triassic coal layers are thin and sparse. There is also a 'tetrapod gap' in the fossil record, suggesting that four-legged animals were displaced from large areas of the globe. Writing in *Science* in 2012, Yadong Sun and colleagues described how in their view 'lethally hot temperatures' drove both plants and animals out of Pangaea's equatorial zones. Temperatures were so high that photosynthesis failed, and animals would have died from drought and heatstroke. As a result, there are almost no land animal fossils from this period anywhere on the globe across a broad equatorial latitudinal belt from 30°N to 40°S, right up until the middle Triassic.

The Permian tropical forests might not simply have given way gradually. Lying right at the extinction boundary in a number of sedimentary records from different locations is a band of soot and charcoal. This tells of a fiery fate for the doomed forests, which burned down in a series of conflagrations without parallel in the modern world. As a team of researchers, led by the Chinese scientist Shu-zhong Shen, wrote in *Science*:

> The widespread distributions of fire-derived products suggest
> that dramatic global warming and increasing aridity reached a
> climax coincident with the marine extinction, rapidly turned
> the ever-wet [rainforest] biome into a seasonally dry climate,
> and increased forest fire that was immediately followed by

catastrophic soil erosion and fungal virulence due to rapid deforestation.

As terrestrial ecosystems were scrubbed from the land in a catastrophic bout of soil erosion, the oceans filled with dead and dying plants and animals. Sediments deposited at this time contain a huge amount of terrestrial organic debris. The nutrients from these rafts of biological matter caused eutrophication as algal blooms stripped the water of its oxygen. As time passed and global warming continued to spike, the oceans deoxygenated right down to the depths, with widespread marine anoxia and high temperatures combining to kill off the vast majority of oceanic life. As a team of researchers wrote in a 2018 paper for *Science*: 'The combined physiological stresses of ocean warming and O_2 loss can account for more than half the magnitude of the "Great Dying".' These two factors would have acted together at different levels in the ocean in what one group of researchers termed a 'double whammy', where 'a combination of lethally warm, shallow waters and anoxic deep waters ... acted to severely restrict the habitable area to a narrow mid-water refuge zone.' Isotopic proxy records demonstrate clearly that the entire Panthalassic and Tethys oceans – comprising almost all the oceanic space on Earth – were anoxic.

Blast from the past

So just how sudden and rapid was the end-Permian global temperature rise that denuded the land and turned the world's oceans into stagnant ponds? Oxygen isotope ratios in fossilised therapsid tusks suggest that temperatures in the Karoo region of South Africa jumped initially by 4–6°C at the Permian–Triassic boundary. Other records from China, at the exact boundary layer, imply rises of 4–8°C, while sea-surface temperatures recorded in two sediment samples 40 kilometres apart in Iran show a dramatic increase of seven and ten degrees at the extinction horizon. The peak of the destruction took place over something like 90,000 years, with the whole extinction interval lasting about 200,000 years. Although temperatures rose even higher over the subsequent hundreds of thousands of years of the early Triassic, the initial temperature rise associated with the end-Permian mass extinction is still considered to be in the region of the six degrees from which the first *Six Degrees* took its title and this current edition its subtitle.

It is worth pausing at this point to make an explicit comparison with modern-day global warming caused by human activity. Scientists estimate that, all told, the gigantic eruptions that tore Siberia apart 251 million years ago were degassing as much as two billion tonnes of CO_2 per year into the Permian atmosphere. With possible contributions from other positive feedbacks such as methane hydrates, the geological record shows that this rate of emissions was enough to overwhelm the Earth's capacity to sequester carbon, leading to an extreme greenhouse event and the associated destruction of the majority of life on Earth. Although the total volume of human emissions so far is still a lot less than was vented into the atmosphere over the duration of the end-Permian extinction, our current carbon releases are taking place at least an order of magnitude faster.

This is an extraordinary conclusion, so let me repeat it: the combined efforts of human beings to dig up and burn fossil fuels to power our global industrialised economy is taking place at least ten times faster than the catastrophic carbon release that drove the world's worst-ever mass extinction. My verdict after surveying the palaeoclimatic literature is that our current releases of carbon are very likely unprecedented throughout the entire Phanerozoic. At no point since complex life appeared on Earth has so much carbon been released as quickly as we are releasing it now.

This means that in reality there is no episode in the planet's geological history that truly mirrors what we are doing now in terms of the speed and volume of our greenhouse gas emissions. We are therefore conducting a genuine first-time experiment with our planet; a bit like the Soviet nuclear engineers in Chernobyl, we are shutting down the safety systems and turning up the heat simultaneously to see what happens. And like the Soviet reactor operators at Chernobyl, we are probably in for a nasty surprise.

Hell on Earth

So what would the end-Permian mass extinction look like in a world that included human civilisation? While the end-Permian event unfolded over tens of millennia, we have already seen most of the postulated impacts – bouts of acid rain, toxic pollution, a worldwide layer of mercury poisoning the seas, ocean acidification, spreading dead zones and a diminished ozone layer, among others – within just the last century as a result of human activities. Some of these, particularly the problems of acid rain and ozone depletion, are currently in recovery mode, but this was also the case at the end of the Permian; initial crises led to longer recoveries, followed by yet another crisis and a further depletion of life.

Superimpose what palaeoclimatic science tells us about conditions at the Permian–Triassic boundary onto Earth today and we can try to visualise at least some of the scenes. Imagine all the world's forests burning simultaneously, from the Arctic to the equator. Night fails to fall, as the world is lit by flames. When the smoke clears away, all that is left of the world's once-teeming tropical forests and snow-covered boreal woodlands is a layer of soot and charcoal spread thickly on the bare ground. Imagine all the resulting dead and dying plant remains being washed into the oceans by monsoons of biblical intensity. The layers of wood and debris combine with the carcasses of animals to form floating mats that wash up with the dead tides along the world's shorelines. The heat is so extreme that only a few animals can survive, hidden in burrows from the fierce daytime sun, or cowering in cooler nooks and crannies along rocky watercourses. Ecosystems and food webs cease to exist in any functional sense. In the daily battle for survival, the big winners are those that feast on the dead – detriti-vores, bacteria and fungi.

Still the greenhouse gets worse. Each year is hotter than the last. At the surface the equatorial oceans are so hot that nothing can survive, because the water temperatures are above the heat tolerance thresholds of any multi-cellular organisms. The deep oceans, filled with layer upon layer of carbon-rich rubble, are fully anoxic, as our brief Anthropocene era is immortalised as a layer of black sludge, heavy metals and plastic. The marine food chain has collapsed, helped by intense acidification. Most fish are dead, as are whales, dolphins and seabirds. Their skeletons settle in the sludge layer and are quickly buried. At the higher latitudes, jellyfish proliferate, along with blooms of toxic blue-green algae. Within the abyssal ocean depths, bacteria produce poisonous hydrogen sulphide, some of which vents into the atmosphere and attacks the ozone layer. Right up to the poles, the remaining land plants have their spores and pollen mutated as the DNA of surviving life is bombarded by intense ultraviolet radiation.

On either side of the equator, regular rainfall has virtually ceased, over vast globe-girdling bands of perennial drought. The desert zones extend throughout all the continental interiors, right up into northern Europe, central Russia and Canada. In coastal areas abandoned human cities are engulfed in the rising oceans, while across most of the land the rubble of humanity's built environment is swept over by sand. Huge rainstorms sometimes plough through, but often the heat is so intense that most precipitation evaporates before it reaches the ground. When bigger monsoonal floods arrive, they are the great leveller. With no roots to hold riverbanks together, braided water-courses scour the landscape, pulverising and devouring our abandoned cities with their acidic waters. Soils that once fed ten billion humans are blown away into vast dust clouds or washed into the sea. Perhaps no one will even notice when the shallow Arctic coastal shelves begin to bubble, then foam, then be torn apart by violent subsea eruptions as long-buried methane hydrates stir back into life.

This veil of death descends not for days, weeks or years, but for centuries upon centuries, monotonous millennia that follow each other through each successive overheated eon as the traces left by our civilisation's brief flowering are ground into broken fossils and dust. There will be survivors of course, including perhaps some hardy humans huddled into Arctic and Antarctic refuges. After all, even the end-Permian mass extinction didn't kill everything. Humans might be the next *Lystrosaurus*, the hardy, bull-headed therapsid that somehow made it through the Permian–Triassic boundary and for the subsequent ten or so million years mostly had the planet to itself. Humans will not be the first casualties of the mass extinction – more likely we will be among the last, clinging on until the bitter end.

The Venus effect

So what's the worst that can happen? To address that question, look westwards just after sunset. The bright star lingering for an hour or two a few degrees above the horizon is Venus, Earth's evil twin. Venus was once probably habitable, just like our planet. It is almost the same size as Earth, is composed of much the same elemental material, and probably began with a similar amount of liquid water. But as everyone knows, Venus today is unbearably hot. Surface temperatures average 460°C, high enough to melt lead. Largely, of course, this is because Venus orbits closer to the sun, at a distance of 0.723 astronomical units (AU: the Earth is 1). At this orbit Venus receives 90% more solar radiation than Earth. But this is not the whole answer. Venus's 460°C is a lot more than 90% higher than Earth's average of 15°C. What actually happened was that at some point in its early history Venus suffered a runaway greenhouse effect, which killed the planet for ever.

Here's how things probably unfolded. In the first billion years after the formation of the solar system, when the sun was fainter, Venus may have had oceans. But about 3.5 billion years ago a tipping point was crossed when the increase in heat from the sun began to evap-orate more and more water into the Venusian atmosphere. Water, like CO_2 and methane, is a greenhouse gas. This led to a runaway positive feedback, where more water vapour led to higher temperatures, evap-orating yet more water. Eventually Venus's oceans may even have boiled, putting most of the planet's inventory of water into a heavy atmosphere largely composed of steam. There it might have stayed, slowly cooking the surface, except that free H_2O at the top of the atmosphere is vulnerable. Intense ultraviolet radiation from the sun bombards the topmost water molecules, detaching the lighter hydro-gen atoms, which are then swept away into space via the solar wind. Venus could have lost all its water in less than ten million years, with the steam greenhouse being replaced by one composed of CO_2; today the planet has just 0.001% as much water as Earth. Its atmosphere is nearly a hundred times as heavy as ours, however, and is composed of 96% CO_2.

The contrast with Earth could not be more stark. Our planet actu-ally lies perilously close to the inner edge of the theoretical habitable zone that exists around a main sequence star like the sun – one esti-mate is that the Earth would be vulnerable to a runaway greenhouse at just 0.97 to 0.99 AUs. We have therefore always been at risk of getting too hot, but negative feedbacks have so far been able to keep our atmosphere at a tolerable temperature for billions of years. Water is still an important greenhouse gas, but the thermal structure of the lower atmosphere, which gets colder with height and thereby condenses gaseous water out as rain, mostly keeps the water liquid at ground level in the oceans. Meanwhile the very top of the atmos-phere, 100 kilometres above the surface, is so dry that very little hydrogen is lost to space, keeping our oceans safe from being stripped away by solar wind. (Our magnetic field helps with that too, some-thing else that Venus lacks.) The first life evolved in the oceans as long ago as 3.5 billion years, flourishing into incredible diversity over the last 500 million years.

For us, CO_2 is the dominant greenhouse gas, and water vapour is a feedback rather than a driver. So as carbon heats our atmosphere, more water evaporates from the seas, causing more warming than would be expected from the CO_2 alone. But over millions of years carbon never builds up into the atmosphere past critical levels because higher temperatures enhance precipitation and speed up silicate rock weathering, thereby drawing down carbon. Carbon is never depleted entirely from the atmosphere because its rate of drawdown is roughly balanced by emissions from volcanoes. Here is another difference between us and Venus; we have a geological carbon cycle thanks to plate tectonics, whereby plates move around and subduct sedimentary carbon back into the mantle, where it is liquefied and eventually re-emitted as a gas from volcanoes. There seems to be no plate tectonics on Venus, probably due to the absence of liquid water (which helps to lubricate plate subduction) and the fact that surface temperatures are now too hot for the process to operate.

Life is an essential part of this long-term carbon cycle on Earth, helping to keep the planet in a habitable state for itself, much as James Lovelock's Gaia theory predicts. In the seas, plankton and other calcifying organisms sequester carbon in seafloor sediments and calcium carbonate rocks, removing large quantities of CO_2 from the atmosphere and helping prevent a runaway greenhouse. But this carbon is not lost for ever; subducted under continental plates, it will eventually be degassed through volcanic eruptions – and the cycle begins again. As I explained earlier, life has also sequestered excess carbon during super-hot ocean anoxic events as black shales and oil deposits, and tropical forests built up layer upon layer of peat, which in similarly anoxic conditions was eventually hardened into coal. Either way, life operates negative feedbacks that help keep the Earth system in temperate balance in addition to the non-biological chemical weathering processes.

Of course, it has not always been plain sailing. Earth has strayed into the danger zones, both hot and cold, before. Feedbacks can operate both ways; if CO_2 falls too low, then ice and snow build up at the poles, reflecting incoming solar radiation and cooling the planet further. At various points in the Earth's early history, this process went so far as to create 'Snowball Earth' events, where glaciers reached right across the tropical oceans. The Earth was saved from a permanent icy fate by the carbon cycle; with all land buried under ice, weathering and CO_2 drawdown stopped, but emissions continued from volcanoes. So levels of CO_2 then built up until they were high enough to generate a sufficiently strong greenhouse effect to melt Snowball Earth. The Earth had a near escape from another global glaciation during the early Permian, 297–298 million years ago, when thriving forests sequestered so much carbon in coal deposits that atmospheric CO_2 fell to the perilously low level of 100 ppm. (It was probably saved because falling temperatures killed the forests.) At the opposite end of the spectrum, as we saw earlier on, at various points short-circuits in the carbon cycle have led to extreme greenhouse conditions and associated mass extinctions of life, such as at the end of the Permian, and more recently during the PETM.

But balance somehow always returned, at least over geological timescales. The question we are facing today is: could humans emit so much carbon so quickly – via the direct method of burning fossil fuels, augmented by positive feedbacks such as permafrost melt and methane hydrate release – that we trigger a surprise runaway greenhouse and render the biosphere completely extinct? In simpler terms, could we actually turn the Earth into a second Venus? Modelling experiments show that bumping up CO_2 is pretty much the same in terms of the planet's surface temperature as shifting the Earth's orbit closer to the sun; each added increment of carbon pushes us closer to the inner edge of the solar system's habitability zone. Think about that: every time you start your car engine, or board an aircraft, you are dragging this whole planet a few centimetres closer to the orbit of Venus.

So how far would we have to collectively shift our orbit to boil away Earth's oceans and sterilise the surface of the planet entirely?

Clearly we have some margin for error because the temperature of the planet has probably been more than 10°C higher than now at various points during the Earth's geological history, and we are still here to tell the story. But this margin for error is shrinking, because the sun is heating up – by 1% every 110 million years – as it moves through its life as a main sequence star. All else remaining equal, scientists calculate that the Earth will 'enter a catastrophic thermal runaway when the solar constant becomes 6% brighter than the present day', which 'will occur in ~650 million years'. However, 'moist greenhouse conditions' – where the oceans don't completely boil, but do evaporate in an enhanced greenhouse effect that means most of the planet's water will be lost to space – could come much earlier, in a mere ~170 million years. However, all else is not remaining equal; doubling CO_2 is roughly equivalent to increasing the solar constant by 2%.

Does that meant therefore mean that raising CO_2 by four to six times might push us close enough to trigger a 'catastrophic thermal runaway'? The truth is that no one knows for sure where the threshold lies. A 2014 study, with an updated model, concluded that 'the Earth will remain safe from both water loss and thermal runaway limits to habitability even for a 15.5% increase in solar constant.' Another study, however, concluded that while anthropogenic carbon emissions 'are probably insufficient' to trigger a full-scale transition to Venus, 'the runaway greenhouse may be much easier to initiate than previously thought.' A third paper, published in 2015, calculated that an increase in solar radiation of 12% would trigger an 'abrupt shift into a hotter climatic regime' with average global surface temperatures of 60°C. Although this doesn't turn us into Venus, it does mark the transition to 'moist greenhouse' conditions, which would eventually strip the Earth of its water and sterilise the surface.

Another study, published in 2014, found that increasing CO_2 to 12 times pre-industrial levels (roughly about 3,300 ppm) triggered 'an abrupt transition to a surface temperature >500K' in one model. Translating Kelvin into Celsius gives us an average Earth temperature of 226°C, more than enough to bring our oceans to the boil and extinct the biosphere. Burning five trillion tonnes of carbon – which experts calculate as 'the lower end of the range of estimates of the total fossil fuel resource' – would take us to about 2,000 ppm, so most of the way there. Add in some unconventional fossil fuels, and a slug of methane hydrates, and 3,300 ppm is certainly an achievable target for a suicidal species bent on destroying its home planet.

The authors of this and several other studies warn that their results are not to be taken too literally. Their models are simple, and miss out important atmospheric processes, in particular the complex effects of clouds. Clouds both cool and heat the planet at different levels and thicknesses. For example, high-level cirrus clouds mostly enhance the greenhouse effect, while low-level stratus clouds reflect much more heat than they trap. All told, clouds are thought to have strongly negative effects, helping to keep the planet safe from flipping into a runaway greenhouse regime.

There is one study, however – published in the journal *Nature Geoscience* in 2019 – that suggests the world's most important cooling-type stratus clouds might be susceptible to dissipation with rising CO_2. The clouds in question are the persistent stratocumulus sheets that shade a fifth of the world's tropical oceans, and are particularly prevalent in eastern parts of the Pacific off the coasts of Peru and California. These bright, low-level clouds act a bit like ice, reflecting 30–60% of the solar radiation that hits them straight back into space. But unlike ice – which lies almost entirely near the poles, and therefore receives much less direct sunshine – their tropical location means that their cooling effect is globally hugely important. Worryingly, the study's authors report that 'when a CO_2 threshold is crossed at around 1,200 ppm, the stratocumulus decks abruptly become unstable and break up into scattered cumulus clouds'. According to the model, this cloud breakup has such an enormous impact on the Earth's radiative budget that global surface temperatures rise by 8°C, in addition to the warming already added by the higher levels of CO_2. The researchers suggest that this process may have happened during the Eocene and other hot climates in the geological past. If so, it would be the mother of all positive feedbacks.

Looking to the future, we could see CO_2 levels rising to 1,200 ppm as soon as the end of this century if high emissions pathways are pursued. With today's hotter sun, one can imagine a scenario where this stratocumulus effect – added to methane meltdown and other feedbacks – pushes the Earth over a threshold and puts us on the path to an eventual runaway greenhouse state. The risk of this is very difficult to quantify, but one thing is certain; the more we keep on burning fossil fuels, the closer we must get to this dreadful final tipping point, wherever it may lie. In refusing to cut back on our carbon emissions, we are imperilling the existence not just of our species but of the entire planet – perhaps the only one in the history of the whole universe that has nurtured and brought forth life in all its magnificent beauty and diversity.

7
The Endgame

What's in half a degree?

It is not yet too late to avoid the worst, but we do not have much time. Scientists now know with extraordinary precision which carbon emissions budgets will lead to which temperature outcomes. While there is always some uncertainty, there is no big mystery and no room for excuses. There can be no looking back and saying, 'I didn't know.' Let's be clear: demands for absolute certainty are a delaying tactic, nothing more. It is up to us, as a planet and as a species, to determine where we end up, and how hot it gets in years to come. We can still save ourselves, but we must make an explicit choice to do so, and quickly.

At Paris in 2015 world leaders agreed to 'pursue efforts' to keep the rise in global temperatures below 1.5°C. After signing the agreement with great fanfare, they returned home and quietly continued with business as usual: growing the economy, building more fossil-fuelled power plants, expanding road networks for ever more oil-guzzling cars and SUVs, and drilling or fracking for the required oil and gas over larger and larger areas. Never mind all the warm words at UN meetings, all the tearful autocued waffle about 'future generations looking us in the eyes', the pats on the head for teenaged climate activists and suchlike. It is the hard stuff in the real world that matters: tarmac, pipelines, refineries, gas turbines, petrol engines and coal boilers. This is where the carbon hits the atmosphere. This is where the future is decided.

If we are concerned with avoiding increasing degrees of climate chaos and catastrophe, looking specifically at carbon-emitting infrastructure is a good place to start. For example, the average design lifetime of cars and light trucks is 15 years. So a car with a diesel engine, sold onto the market in 2025, can be expected to continue emitting CO_2 until at least 2040. Most fossil fuel plants have an even longer lifetime; coal and gas power stations might be expected to operate for 40 years at a minimum, in terms of the operational lifetime expected by those who have funded the capital costs of their construction. That means new ones built today will still be in service in 2060, adding up to thousands of point sources, each pouring out millions of tonnes of CO_2 for four more decades. Add all this up and it is clear that despite the Paris targets, enough carbon-emitting infrastructure is planned or already operational to blow right through the temperature targets that world leaders supposedly signed up to in 2015. Our leaders promised us heaven, but their actual policies will deliver us into hell.

Let's look at the precise numbers, which are readily available thanks to an international group of scientists who calculated – in a paper published in *Nature* in August 2019 – the 'committed emissions' from existing infrastructure. All the world's currently operational coal and gas electricity-generating power plants, if working to the end of their 40-year average lifetimes, will emit an additional 358 Gt CO_2 (Gt = gigatonnes, or billions of tonnes), if we take January 2018 as a starting point. Another 162 Gt can be expected to be emitted by industrial infrastructure, while a further 64 Gt will come from the transportation sector (mainly on-road vehicles). Residential infrastructure will emit 42 Gt and commercial 18 Gt CO_2. Add in residual amounts from other smaller sectors and the total committed emissions from infrastructure that is already built and running is 658 Gt CO_2.

But there is even more carbon in the pipeline, as it were. At the end of 2018 over 1,000 gigawatts-worth of additional fossil-fuelled electrical power generation capacity was planned, permitted or already under construction around the world. A fifth of this is in China, with most of the rest in other growing developing nations like India and Indonesia. If these plants are built and operated to the end of their design lifetimes, an additional 188 Gt CO_2 will enter the atmosphere. Add this to the 658 Gt from existing infrastructure, and the total of committed emissions from existing and planned fossil infrastructure is 846 Gt of CO_2. This is an under-estimate of the overall greenhouse gas total by the way, because it does not include emissions from deforestation, agriculture and other forms of future land-use change. (Nor does it include feedbacks: more on that later.)

Now, according to the IPCC, keeping to the Paris target of staying below 1.5°C above pre-industrial levels with a 66% probability would mean emitting no more than 420 Gt CO_2 over the foreseeable future. So our 846 Gt is double the permissible cumulative carbon emissions required to stay under the Paris temperature target. There is so little budget left, in fact, that achieving 1.5°C in effect means the world would have to hit net-zero emissions within less than 20 years.

So what can realistically be done? First, we can save 188 Gt by going back and cancelling all power plants that are planned, permitted or under construction. That means ceasing work on all power-plant building sites that are constructing coal-, oil- or gas-fired units – right now. Park the diggers and walk away, then tear up the plans for those that have not yet started construction and rescind all permits for those still in the planning stage. These are not UN-level decisions, by the way – they will have to be taken in national capitals from Beijing to Berlin. We also need to stop selling cars and trucks straight away – anything with an internal combustion engine in fact – as well as home boilers, aircraft and shipping, cement kilns, blast furnaces and other industrial infrastructure. All of it must be cancelled, whatever the implications for jobs and the economy.

A note of caution here. This cannot and must not be done in a way that freezes current international energy inequalities. It is hardly fair to expect India and Bangladesh to cancel planned coal plants when their citizens barely have access to reliable electricity at all, especially when this must be done to make up for the fact that the prodigiously overconsuming rich world has already used up all the atmospheric carbon space. So stopping future carbon emissions from developing countries who have not yet built fossil-fuelled power plants must be part of a programme to deliver access to modern energy across the whole of the developing world – but with the proviso that this must come from clean, non-carbon sources. This is a political reality as much as a moral concern; any carbon-reduction programme that is widely perceived as fundamentally unjust is doomed to fail.

But even if we succeed in cancelling all these sources of future emissions, we are still 200 Gt over budget for the 1.5°C target, if we want a 66% chance of staying under it. If we are prepared to accept only a 50% probability of staying at 1.5°C – gambling the planet for somewhat worse odds, in other words – we can go for a total budget of 580 Gt of CO_2. But even then we are still more than 100 Gt over the target (and more, if we include land-use change). The only way to retain even a 50:50 chance of a 1.5°C outcome, therefore, is to do something about future emissions from existing infrastructure – by closing it down early. That means mandatory premature shut-downs for coal power plants in particular, as well as closing heavy industry, and taking petrol and diesel trucks off the roads before they reach the end of their lifetimes. And it means scrapping jet aircraft and switching from flying to other less energy-intensive modes of transport until someone comes up with carbon-neutral air travel.

Be under no illusions, this will be politically a very bitter pill to swallow. All the owners of these assets – the companies, the pension funds, the investment houses and so on, as well as private individuals when it comes to residential and transport property like cars and trucks – will find themselves with valueless or 'stranded' assets. It would be the biggest markdown of human infrastructure ever, potentially involving scrapping or destroying buildings, vehicles and industrial plants on a scale unknown outside the damage inflicted by a world war. In the process we will need to start the process of decommissioning the entire fossil fuel industry, shutting down oil exploration activities and coal mining expansion, closing refineries, boarding up mines and so on. We would in effect be choosing something we have never been able to bring ourselves to do before on any scale. We would be deciding to leave fossil fuels in the ground.

If you think this is too much of a tall order – because miners will protest at the loss of their jobs, oil companies will sponsor political parties to oppose necessary legislation, truckers will block the roads and so on – then we have only one remaining option. We must be honest and let go of the 1.5°C target – at least in the sense of expecting it to be a reasonably realistic outcome. (There might still be a small percentage chance of reaching it, although this diminishes all the time. For example, if we allow an 840 Gt CO_2 emissions budget, the chance of staying below 1.5°C falls to 30%.) This means being prepared to accept the additional climate damages that predictably arise between 1.5 and 2°C if we miss the former target. So let's recall, in a brief summary of earlier chapters, what these damages are likely to be.

For starters, the Arctic sea-ice tipping point is thought to lie somewhere between these two warming levels. Keep global heating below 1.5°C, and the Arctic will probably retain at least some of its ice cover, and thereby its important role in cooling the Northern Hemisphere. Allow temperatures to hit two degrees, on the other hand, and every couple of years virtually the entire North Polar ocean will be ice free. That isn't just bad news for the polar bears; it also means that vast quantities of additional solar radiation will be absorbed by the darker ocean surface and recirculated into the Earth system, fast-forwarding the global heating process by a decade or more. Two degrees rather than 1.5°C also means allowing an additional two million square kilometres of Arctic permafrost to melt, thereby releasing several tens of billion tonnes'-worth of additional CO_2 and methane into an already destabilised atmosphere. In effect, these two positive feedbacks illustrate that by allowing the temperature to rise by two degrees we raise the risks of a greater temperature outcome, to 3°C – and perhaps more.

In its 2018 special report the IPCC states that dropping the 1.5°C target and allowing two degrees 'may initiate irreversible loss of the West Antarctic Ice Sheet and marine ice sheet instability'. Scientists also believe that Greenland has a tipping point for self-sustained irreversible melt of 1.8°C regional warming. Because warming is amplified at high latitudes, the global two-degree target is clearly well above this regional danger threshold, and even 1.5°C may be too much. Crossing all these ice-sheet tipping points will lead up to a much faster rate of sea level rise in a two-degree world, sufficient to displace an additional ten million people as compared with a 1.5°C target. Two degrees puts 136 coastal megacities at risk of flooding, with $1.4 trillion of damage every single year by 2100. Dropping the 1.5°C target also means half a million additional cases of dengue fever in Latin America, and another half a million extra deaths from malnutrition as soon as mid-century. This is because allowing two degrees of warming leads to larger net reductions of maize, rice, wheat and other major staple crops across much of the world, seriously jeopardising our ability to feed the projected global population of 9.5 billion and raising the risk of mass starvation.

Half a degree also makes a huge difference in the numbers of people exposed to extreme heat. Ditching the 1.5°C target means an additional 1.7 billion people exposed to severe heat waves, 420 million more exposed to extreme heat waves and 65 million more to exceptional – meaning deadly – heat conditions. And it's not just people that are affected. Ditching the 1.5°C target means doubling the numbers of insects, plants and vertebrates that lose more than half of their climatic range. While coral reefs decline by 70–90% even with 1.5°C warming, by the time warming reaches 2°C more than 99% of reefs will have been killed. Half a degree in the case of corals therefore makes the difference between some remaining reefs and the global extinction of an entire ecosystem.

Of course, all this death and destruction may well be worth it in order to keep the power plants humming along and the cars and trucks rolling for a few more years. This is a political decision and a moral judgement. We just need to be clear how the balance of costs and benefits stacks up on both sides. In favour of keeping the 1.5°C target is the probability of saving a few million lives. In favour of dropping it is the possibility of saving a few trillion dollars. It's a tough choice, I admit.

Two degrees and above

Let's say for the sake of argument that we have accepted that 1.5°C is out of reach and we need to aim for a 2°C target. This gives us a larger budget of remaining carbon emissions, which means that we can continue to operate existing infrastructure without scrapping power plants and cars early. It also means that we can allow infrastructure in planning and under construction to proceed. However, the committed emissions from all the resulting fossil fuel consumption will add up, as we saw earlier, to 846 Gt of CO_2. This is the majority of the remaining two-degree budget, of 1,170 Gt of CO_2, for a two-thirds chance of keeping temperatures from exceeding this target. Moreover, achieving two degrees still means that we would have to cut global fossil fuel emissions by 6% per year, starting now, and hit net carbon neutrality on a global scale by mid-century.

I am not suggesting that world governments have no plans at all for tackling climate change. Under the UN climate convention process, countries have been invited to submit 'nationally determined contributions' (NDCs), which in effect summarise each national target for greenhouse gas emissions action. NDCs have no legal force; unlike the Kyoto targets they replace, they are voluntary national targets and not part of any legally binding treaty. So far, 184 parties to the Climate Convention – almost every country in the world – have submitted NDCs. That's the good news. The bad news is that the combined NDCs only shave about 0.3°C off the expected global heating outcome, reducing it from 3.2°C to about 2.9°C by the end of the century. The NDCs are supposed to be tightened up in years to come, but the majority of nations at the time of writing have not produced plans to do so, and some – the United States in particular – are going backwards, weakening existing emissions targets and putting forward plans to burn more coal, oil and gas indefinitely.

So the world, even in terms of its paper targets, is choosing not a two-degree outcome, but a three-degree one. Once again, a quick summary of resulting climate impacts is in order. This means accepting that we will making the planet warmer than it has been for three million years, in effect taking the Earth back to the Pliocene. This was an epoch when the Arctic was an estimated 19°C hotter than today, with no ice anywhere across the North Pole and treelines 2,000 kilometres further north. The Greenland ice sheet was reduced to a small remnant, and the West Antarctic Ice sheet collapsed, leading to sea levels between 10 and 20 metres higher than today. This meltdown will take many centuries to fully play out, but even as soon as 2100 three degrees could mean sea level rise as high as 1.7 metres, displacing hundreds of millions of people. Combined with increased extreme weather events, even moderate sea level rise would see New York facing damage equivalent to three Hurricane Sandys per year, put 136 UNESCO World Heritage Sites at risk and flood 2,500 square kilometres of Bangladesh's densely populated coastal zone.

Then there's the rising heat. Three degrees puts vast areas of South Asia – and a significant fraction of the world's human population – into the 'extremely dangerous' heat zone. In Africa, cities face a 20- to 50-fold increase in 'dangerous' heat conditions. US cities can expect annual heatwave death tolls in the thousands for extreme events in this hotter climate regime. In total, a third of the global land area – and more than half the human population – will be exposed to temperature and humidity conditions that exceed the 'deadly' threshold for more than 20 days a year, with 50 million people exposed to temperatures above what scientists call 'the survivability threshold'. Mediterranean areas begin to transition into full-scale deserts and wildfire risk triples, while 'drylands' expand to cover half the global land surface, presenting a billion people with a severe decrease in water resources as drought magnitudes increase by as much as 500% across the Americas, Africa, Asia and Australia.

Rising heat and declining rainfall mean the world will move into major structural food deficit at three degrees. Smallholder farmers across Africa and South Asia are wiped out by drought and heat, eliminating the livelihoods of a billion people. Temperatures cross critical thresholds in all major food-production regions, drastically reducing yields for the world's key staple food crops. Even higher latitudes like Canada see crops scorched by intense heat. Precise outcomes depend on the ability of crops to adapt and farming zones to shift, but even so there is a heightened risk that famine will kill millions in developing countries, triggering major refugee flows and presenting an existential challenge to human civilisation on a global scale. In the Himalayas glacier mass declines by 50%, reducing freshwater and further harming food production. In the Andes and European Alps more than 90% of the snow and ice disappears. In the higher latitudes and tropics too much water is an increasing problem, with 200 million people affected by river flooding each year and resulting global damages rising by more than 1,000%.

The effects of climate breakdown on nature are even more disastrous. A half of insects, a quarter of mammals, 44% of plants and a fifth of birds will lose more than half their climatic range by the end of the century with a global temperature rise of three degrees. In North America, two-thirds of bird species face extinction. With coral reefs already gone, marine heatwaves take a deadly toll on remaining oceanic ecosystems from Australian kelp forests to Antarctic krill. There is no longer any such thing as an 'invasive species' because every species on Earth has to move alongside climate zones shifting at several kilometres per year. Those that fail to keep up are wiped out, contributing to an emerging mass extinction of geological significance.

Then there are the three-degree tipping points. Unless deforestation is dramatically curbed, global heating of three degrees pushes the Amazon into full-scale collapse, with colossal firestorms eliminating the Earth's most biodiverse terrestrial habitat and pouring tens of billions of tonnes of additional carbon into the atmosphere from burning wood and peat. Three degrees also thaws out 12 million square kilometres of Arctic permafrost, comprising three-quarters of the global total, releasing both CO_2 and unknown quantities of methane. These two feedbacks add perhaps an additional 0.5°C to global heating, though this is uncertain. Meanwhile, the complete loss of summertime Arctic sea ice adds a further boost to temperatures equivalent to a trillion tonnes of additional CO_2, fast-forwarding global heating by as much as 25 years.

Hitting four degrees

Despite all that, three degrees is actually in some ways a best-case scenario. If we ignore what governments say they are going to do and look at their actual policies – all the plans for new roads and airports, the billions spent on exploring for new fossil fuels, the vast expansion of coal-based electricity in China and elsewhere – the temperature outcome for the planet is even worse, with a 50:50 chance of reaching about 3.2°C by the end of the century, although there is a smaller chance that this rise could be as high as 4.3°C. Under current policies we will pass the 1.5°C target in 2035 and 2°C in 2053 on our merry way to this four-degree world.

Once again, let's reprise what is therefore in store. At four degrees the planet has become suffocatingly hot. Cities in the tropics bake in year-round 'extreme' heat, while southern states of the US experience temperature and drought conditions currently only seen in Death Valley. Gripped by 'megadroughts', these states are swept by intense dust storms that strip away remaining cultivable soils. Worldwide heat mortality increases by 500–2,000%. Temperatures are so high in the Gulf region that for much of the year it is biologically uninhabit-able, meaning humans are unable to move around outside and must stay within artificially cooled environments. Temperatures and humidity also cross the survivability threshold in parts of South Asia, imperilling continued human habitation in areas currently home to hundreds of millions of people. The uninhabitability belt also extends to eastern China, adding hundreds of millions more to the world's burgeoning total of climate refugees. Two of the cradles of human civilisation – South Asia and the North China plain – have now been rendered biologically intolerable for our species and all other warm-blooded animals.

Southern Europe, Central America, much of Brazil, southern Africa, coastal Australia and southern China are now in the hyper-arid belt and undergoing severe desertification. Dryland areas domi-nate the global land surface, engulfing nearly six million square kilometres in spreading deserts and bringing near-perennial drought to virtually all continental areas outside the higher latitudes. In the United States wildfires incinerate whole forests, turning entire towns into embers and ash, with fire risk increasing by more than 500% across much of the country. The largest conflagrations generate pyro-cumulonimbus clouds with fire tornados and black hail, pushing particulates into the stratosphere and covering the Earth in a layer of ash and dust similar to the impacts of a small nuclear war. Most of the world's mountain ranges are now deglaciated, with even the Himalayas losing 75–90% of their ice. This further diminishes fresh-water supplies and reduces the potential of agricultural production to move uphill in areas where lowland temperatures are now too hot to grow crops. With little remaining snowfall, heavier precipitation surges out of mountain ranges, causing devastating flash floods that submerge whole cities in a matter of hours. Coastal areas are pummelled by Category 6 superstorms, with tropical cyclones also battering areas such as western Europe and the Mediterranean that have previously been outside the hurricane belt.

Across the breadbaskets of the world, temperatures are so hot that crops cannot survive – lethal heatwaves damage the enzymes and tissues of plants, reducing harvests often down to zero. In the US the Corn Belt becomes a new Dust Bowl. With no surplus to trade because of synchronous regional harvest failures, commodity markets for major staple crops like maize, wheat and soybeans collapse. In the Northern Hemisphere suitable cropping areas are now 1,200 kilometres closer to the pole, including much of Siberia and Arctic Canada. Structural famine is now a central part of the human experience for the first time since the Middle Ages. Billions of people flee heat, drought and food shortages, rendering political boundaries obsolete and adding further stress to any remaining centres of complex civilisation. In the oceans, acidification and toxic algal blooms affect most of the world's coastlines, which are already transforming due to rapidly rising sea levels. With most of Antarctica now in the melt zone, and Greenland thawing rapidly for much of the year, the oceans could rise by close to three metres by the end of the century. This displaces another billion people.

With much of the planet's surface having entered new climatic regimes outside the evolutionary experience of plants and animals, this becomes the worst mass extinction since the end of the dinosaurs 65 million years ago. With a trillion tonnes of carbon now in the Arctic thaw zone, the permafrost feedback kicks into top gear, adding as much as another degree to global temperatures.

Towards six degrees

According to the latest Climate Action Tracker report, 'for the current policies projection, there is a 10–25% chance that warming could exceed 4°C by the end of the century.' This is without considering the impacts of feedbacks like Arctic permafrost melt and the collapse of the Amazon rainforest. Add these in, and we perhaps face an escalating risk of pushing planetary temperatures into the five-degree zone before the end of the century with current policies, never mind future emissions increases. The IPCC's fossil-intensive development scenario, termed 'RCP 8.5', sees CO_2 emissions continuing to rise right up until the end of the century, thanks largely to a sixfold increase in coal use. While the average temperature outcome is 4.3°C, the possible range extends as high as 5.4°C, well into my six-degree world. Many have questioned the plausibility of this scenario; will we still be increasing our coal consumption in half a century's time? Hopefully not – but this scenario could also be seen as one where we are unlucky with positive feedbacks in the Arctic and elsewhere, which could deliver the required additional carbon by indirect means. Moreover, at the time of writing, global emissions are still tracking closer to RCP 8.5 than to any of the other IPCC scenarios, with no sign of any imminent peak.

According to the Climate Action Tracker there is therefore as much as a 1-in-4 chance that current government policies deliver us into the early stages of the five-degree world. This is a planet where all the tropics and sub-tropical regions are subjected to year-round 'deadly heat', with large areas – formerly the centres of human civilisation – biologically uninhabitable due to high temperatures. Global food production is decimated, with agriculture only possible in diminishing zones of habitability in the highest latitudes and on continental margins. Surviving humans are crammed into 'refuges' in areas such as Greenland and the Antarctic Peninsula. Much of our planet is a wasteland of rocky continents surrounded by hot, stagnant oceans. Global temperatures are the highest they have been since the early Eocene, 50 million years ago. All the ice on the planet is now doomed to vanish, yielding eventual sea level rises of tens of metres. Hurricanes of unimaginable ferocity scour the world's coastlines, even reaching as high as the polar regions. Natural species that have survived thus far find their climatic zones as much as 5,000 kilometres away from current locations. As wildlife is wiped out by the searing heat, those humans that survive inhabit an eerie, silent world.

Six degrees sees the greatest mass extinction ever on Earth, greater even than the end-Permian catastrophe that destroyed 90% of species alive at the time. As I write, human carbon emissions are at least ten times more rapid than those that triggered the end-Permian cataclysm. In fact, we are probably putting carbon into the atmosphere at a rate that is unprecedented in all of geological time since complex life evolved. Warming at this level imperils even the survival of humans as a species. With most of the rest of life having already gone, plant debris combined with the rotting carcasses of animals form floating mats that wash up along the dead shorelines of oxygen-depleted oceans. Over the longer term, heating this extreme raises the prospect of a runaway greenhouse effect that evaporates the oceans and sterilises the biosphere, turning the Earth into Venus a billion years too soon.

Choose life

If all this sounds overwhelming, remember one thing: we are not yet doomed. If global emissions ceased tomorrow, the planet would not even warm by 1.5°C. Sure, some additional warming and ice melt is already locked into the system, but not much. The global carbon thermostat is still largely within our control. It is decisions that are yet to be made – airport runways yet to be built, coal boilers yet to be fired up, keys in petrol engines yet to be turned – that will determine how hot and how deadly our future becomes. I offer this book as a warning to illustrate the choices that we face, not as a doom-saying prediction of inevitable apocalypse. Anyone taking the evidence I have presented here as a reason to declare that 'it's too late' to change our future is wilfully misinterpreting my message.

Remember also that there are many pathways towards cleaner energy. Some countries are blessed with prodigious geothermal resources. Others – like the United Kingdom, where I live – can benefit from enormous quantities of offshore wind. Nations in the sub-tropical and tropical zones, including much of the developing world, can choose a future largely based around free and limitless solar power. Nations that are comfortable with next-generation nuclear, as I am personally, should have that option too – we must throw anything and everything at the carbon problem. At an individual level we can reduce our meat consumption in rich countries, fly less, devote more land to rewilding and other 'natural climate solutions', and switch rapidly to electric transport. We can declare climate emergencies and persuade our elected representatives to back legally binding plans to rapidly phase out fossil fuels. We can stand up to the carbon lobby and ensure that our own money is disinvested from fossil fuels, and deny climate-destroying companies economic resources and the social licence to operate.

I don't see much of a role for large-scale CO_2 removal using biomass and carbon sequestration, because it will use so much land that ecosystems would be devastated and food production further constrained. This means, in my view, that we should not set much store by 'overshoot' scenarios where we can emit more carbon into the atmosphere on a vague promise that it can be removed later by some technological means yet to be invented. These sorts of ideas have all the deluded logic of the drug addict promising themselves one last hit. We all know what is really required; we must kick the carbon habit, shut off the pumps and leave the remaining fossil fuels in the ground.

With apologies to some of my more techno-optimist friends, I don't see any role either – for the foreseeable future – for geo-engineering projects such as spreading sulphates in the stratosphere. Like most normal people, I simply do not want to see direct human manipulation of the world's climate and weather systems on a day-to-day basis. This seems to me like the ultimate Faustian bargain – we would gain some version of a future, but at the cost of our souls. The planet we would bring into being would not be the Earth I love and want to protect. I admit I cannot justify this position in scientific, rationalist terms. So I will instead state it truthfully – I find the prospect of an intentionally geoengineered planet morally and spiritually repellent. Yes, it's better than a dead planet, but only just.

Geoengineering proponents often talk about deploying their sunshade plan only as an 'emergency' option, when it is too late to stop warming by cutting carbon emissions. But the truth is we are now in an emergency: as I mentioned above, if current policies continue there is already as much as a 25% chance that we will push towards four degrees and thereby trigger the widespread collapse of human civilisation. We should not beguile ourselves with the prospect of quick fixes in future decades. We really do have to act now.

But let me repeat: it is not too late, and in fact it never will be too late. Just as 1.5°C is better than 2°C, so 2°C is better than 2.5°C, 3°C is better than 3.5°C and so on. We should never give up, and at no point should we hunker down and abandon any remaining hope of a better future. We still have several decades during which our choices will have a huge impact on how far global heating accelerates over the course of this century. My one insistence would be that sacrifices made must be fairly shared – we cannot demand carbon cuts at the expense of entrenching or worsening human poverty and inequality.

Pessimists sometimes gloomily ask me whether they should still have children, or whether the future is now so bad that they must remain childless and lonely. My response is unequivocal: of course you should have children! Bear children, love them, and then fight for their future with every fibre of your being. To my mind merchants of doom are no better than merchants of doubt. By all means grieve for what is lost, but focus that emotional pain into determination, resolution and renewed hope. Never despair, because there will always be someone whose life it is not yet too late to save. That person might even be your child.

So I invite you to join me in this pledge: I will fight on, even as the waters rise and the deserts advance. I will never give up, never be passive or defeatist, even as the beauty of this living world of ours is eroded and degraded. I reject survivalism and other self-centred approaches, and will always share what I have with others who are in need, as I would expect them to share with me. I will never surrender to despair and will always fight to save what still remains. If necessary I will fight on for years and decades, with endless determination and unbounded love, until the heat stops rising and our children have a future.

Acknowledgements

This book leans on the expert work of many people, first and foremost the climatologists and other scientific experts who have produced such a detailed, rigorous and voluminous literature about the past, present and future of our planet's climate. I am hugely in their debt, and am very aware that a small-print reference at the back of this book seems like small thanks for extensive use I have made of their work. I don't expect everyone to agree with the way I have compiled and presented this data, but I hope that at least some of those referred to feel like I have done their efforts justice.

I would not have felt prompted to write this book had it not been for the many people who have emailed and tweeted me over the years since the first *Six Degrees* was published, asking for an update. Obviously I can't mention individuals, except for Diletta Cateni from Pisa, Italy, who while corresponding on Facebook gave me the 'final warning' suggestion for the subtitle – which then became the title – of this new edition. This does in some ways feel like a community enterprise!

I am also very indebted to Cornell University, and all at the Cornell Alliance for Science – Dr Sarah Evanega, Joan Conrow, Vanessa Greenlee and the whole team – for support, academic facilities and access, and the daily reminder of how important it is to fight for science in all areas against those who would attack and undermine truth and evidence-based thinking in the service of their ideologies.

I'm also very grateful to everyone who has helped and supported me in Hay-on-Wye, where most of this book was written. That list includes everyone at the Hay Festival, the staff of Shepherds (purveyors of the best coffee anywhere on the Welsh borders), others in our small office – Finn Beales, Scott Wallace, Claire Purcell and Emma Beagle – as well as Andy Fryers, Mel Newton, Paul and Dundy from Cadwgan Farm, Corin and the Burgess family, Pat Stirling and our local rewilding group, our new Hay Ultimate frisbee team and everyone on Broadmeadow Lane. I'm especially grateful to George Monbiot and Rebecca Wrigley, not just for enduring friendship, but for their positive vision of rewilding even in an age of climate breakdown.

I have been fortunate enough to have a superb, knowledgeable and attentive editor in Nicholas Pearson, and am grateful to 4th Estate for taking on this second edition of *Six Degrees* after having made a success of the first. Thanks are also due to Iain Hunt, who worked tirelessly to improve the rather too meaty first drafts of this book and make it more readable, as well as Anthony Hippisley for proofreading. I have been with my agent Antony Harwood my whole career as a writer: there really is no one better.

I know it's a cliché, but I truthfully couldn't have written this book without daily support and love from my family. My children Tom and Rosa, who were small when the first edition was written, are now as engaged and opinionated on this subject as they should be as young people whose future is really on the line. My godsons Didier and Alex Delgorge have also been an inspiration. My parents Bry and Val Lynas and my siblings Jenny, Richard and Suzanne have always been enthused and engaged. Most of all my wonderful wife Maria, who urged me to take a step back from regular work and focus on writing this book, deserves my thanks and appreciation. In many ways this has been a joint endeavour.

Many moons ago I used to be a Cub Scout, and I recall that the Scouts had a phrase – 'Be Prepared' – that is in some ways an apt motto for this book. I hope this new *Six Degrees* helps its readers prepare for a hotter future, and also that it inspires people to take renewed action to cut emissions and thereby avoid the kind of devastation that is detailed in the later chapters. Love endures, and so does hope.

Notes

Foreword

xi 'extremely likely'. IPCC, 2014: *Climate Change 2014: Synthesis Report.*
Contribution of Working Groups I, II and III to the Fifth Assessment
Report of the Intergovernmental Panel on Climate Change, Core
writing team, R.K. Pachauri and L.A. Meyer (eds). IPCC, Geneva,
Switzerland. www.ipcc.ch/site/assets/uploads/2018/02/SYR_AR5_
FINAL_full.pdf

xi '1 in 3.5 million chance'. blogs.scientificamerican.com/observations/
five-sigmawhats-that/

One Degree

3 'atmospheric CO_2'. Dutton, A. et al., 2015: 'Sea-level rise due to polar
ice-sheet mass loss during past warm periods', *Science*, 349 (6244),
aaa4019

4 'increasing the heat content'. Cheng, L. et al., 2019: 'How fast are the
oceans warming?', *Science*, 363 (6423), 128–9

4 '6 zettajoules'. IPCC, 2019: 'Chapter 5: Changing Ocean, Marine
Ecosystems, and Dependent Communities'. In: *IPCC Special Report on
the Ocean and Cryosphere in a Changing Climate* [H.-O. Pörtner et al.
(eds)]. In press, pp. 5–14

4 'half a zettajoule'. Harvey, C., 2018: 'The Oceans Are Heating Up Faster
Than Expected', *E&E News*. www.scientificamerican.com/article/
the-oceans-are-heating-up-faster-than-expected/

4 'Hiroshima atomic bombs'. Cook, J., 2013: '4 Hiroshima bombs worth
of heat per second', Skeptical Science blog. www.skepticalscience.
com/4-Hiroshima-bombs-worth-of-heat-per-second.html. I have

downrated this estimate from 8 to 6 zettajoules/year in line with the latest estimates of ocean heat content.

4 '1.04°C above'. World Meteorological Organization, 2018: 'WMO climate statement: past 4 years warmest on record'. public.wmo.int/en/media/press-release/climate-change-signals-and-impacts-continue-2018

5 'Keeling first began'. Keeling, C., 1998: 'Rewards and Penalties of Monitoring the Earth', *Annual Review of Energy and the Environment*, 23, 25–82

5 'his son Ralph'. Keeling, R., 2008: 'Recording Earth's Vital Signs', *Science*, 319 (5871), 1771–2

6 'lava fields of Mauna Loa'. Keeling, C., 1998: 'Rewards and Penalties of Monitoring the Earth'. See Figure 3.

6 'rely on fossil fuels'. Scripps, 2013: 'Carbon dioxide at Mauna Loa Observatory reaches new milestone: Tops 400 ppm', press release. scripps.ucsd.edu/news/7992

7 'Global Carbon Project'. See www.globalcarbonproject.org/carbonbudget/index.htm

8 '80% of that increase'. Jackson, R. et al., 2017: 'Warning signs for stabilizing global CO2 emissions', *Environmental Research Letters*, 12 (11), 110202

8 '4% of global'. BP, 2019: *BP Statistical Review of World Energy*. https://www.bp.com/content/dam/bp/business-sites/en/global/corporate/pdfs/energy-economics/statistical-review/bp-stats-review-2019-full-report.pdf p. 11

8 'tenfold to arrest'. Pielke Jr, R., 2019: 'The world is not going to halve carbon emissions by 2030, so now what?', *Forbes*. www.forbes.com/sites/rogerpielke/2019/10/27/the-world-is-not-going-to-reduce-carbon-dioxide-emissions-by-50-by-2030-now-what/

8 'night frosts'. Malamud, B. et al., 2011: 'Temperature trends at the Mauna Loa observatory, Hawaii', *Climate of the Past*, 7, 975–83

9 'temperature fluctuations'. Neukom, R. et al., 2019: 'No evidence for globally coherent warm and cold periods over the preindustrial Common Era', *Nature*, 571 (7766), 550–4

9 'early Holocene'. Marcott, S. et al., 2013: 'A reconstruction of regional and global temperature for the past 11,300 years', *Science*, 339 (6124), 1198–201

10 'hippopotamuses'. Schreve, D., 2009: 'A new record of Pleistocene hippopotamus from River Severn terrace deposits, Gloucester, UK – palaeoenvironmental setting and stratigraphical significance', *Proceedings of the Geologists' Association*, 120 (1), 58–64

10 'cave dwelling'. Pedersen, R. et al., 2017: 'The last interglacial climate: comparing direct and indirect impacts of insolation changes', *Climate Dynamics*, 48 (9–10), 3391–407

10 '8°C higher'. McFarlin, J. et al., 2018: 'Pronounced summer warming in northwest Greenland during the Holocene and Last Interglacial', *PNAS*, 115 (25), 6357–62

10 'Arctic Ocean'. Stein, R. et al., 2017: 'Arctic Ocean sea ice cover during the penultimate glacial and the last interglacial', *Nature Communications*, 8 (373), 1–13

10 'six to ten metres'. Dutton, A. et al., 2015: 'Sea-level rise due to polar ice-sheet mass loss during past warm periods'

10 'a largish remnant'. Yau, A. et al., 2016: 'Reconstructing the last interglacial at Summit, Greenland: Insights from GISP2', *PNAS*, 113 (35), 9710–15

11 'creeping steadily'. Howat, I. et al., 2013: 'Brief Communication: "Expansion of meltwater lakes on the Greenland Ice Sheet"', *The Cryosphere*, 7 (1), 201–4

11 '50% higher'. van As, D. et al., 2018: 'Reconstructing Greenland Ice Sheet meltwater discharge through the Watson River (1949–2017)', *Arctic, Antarctic, and Alpine Research*, 50 (1), e1433799

12 'rebuild their camp'. Goldberg, S., 2012: 'Greenland ice sheet melted at unprecedented rate during July', *Guardian*. www. theguardian.com/environment/2012/jul/24/greenland-ice-sheet-thaw-nasa

12 'percolating down'. Nghiem, S. et al., 2012: 'The extreme melt across the Greenland ice sheet in 2012', *Geophysical Research Letters*, 39 (20), L20502

12 '2012 melt rates'. Trusel, L. et al., 2018: 'Nonlinear rise in Greenland runoff in response to post-industrial Arctic warming', *Nature*, 564 (7734), 104–8

12 'fastest-expanding melt zones'. Noël, B. et al., 2019: 'Rapid ablation zone expansion amplifies north Greenland mass loss', *Science Advances*, 5 (9), eaaw0123

12 'see more rain'. Oltmanns, M. et al., 2019: 'Increased Greenland melt triggered by large-scale, year-round cyclonic moisture intrusions', *The Cryosphere*, 13 (3), 815–25

12 'uncovered ice'. Noël, B. et al., 2019: 'Rapid ablation zone expansion amplifies north Greenland mass loss'

13 'by 15°C'. Saros, J. et al., 2019: 'Arctic climate shifts drive rapid ecosystem responses across the West Greenland landscape', *Environmental Research Letters*, 14 (7), 074027

13 'further 1.1°C'. Ibid.

13 'soared to 12°C'. Witze, A., 2019: 'Dramatic sea-ice melt caps tough Arctic summer', *Nature*, 573 (7744), 320–1

13 'until 2070'. Shankman, S., 2019: 'Greenland's melting: Heat waves are changing the landscape before their eyes', *InsideClimateNews* insideclimatenews.org/news/01082019/greenland-climate-change-ice-sheet-melt-heat-wave-sea-level-rise-fish-global-warming

13 'high as 1.5 mm'. Witze, A., 2019: 'Dramatic sea-ice melt caps tough Arctic summer', *Nature*, 573, 320–1

14 'global average'. Screen, J., 2017: 'Far-flung effects of Arctic warming', *Nature Geoscience*, 10 (4), 253–4

14 'system wafted'. Moore, G., 2016: 'The December 2015 North Pole warming event and the increasing occurrence of such events', *Scientific Reports*, 6, 39084

14 'above 66°N'. Overland, J. & Wang, M., 2016: 'Recent extreme Arctic temperatures are due to a split Polar Vortex', *Journal of Climate*, 29 (11), 5609–16

14 'super-extreme'. Kim, B.-M. et al., 2017: 'Major cause of unprecedented Arctic warming in January 2016: Critical role of an Atlantic windstorm', *Scientific Reports*, 7, 40051

14 'water skis'. Samenow, J., 2016: 'Weather buoy near North Pole hits melting point', *Washington Post*. www.washingtonpost.com/news/capital-weather-gang/wp/2016/12/22/weather-buoy-near-north-pole-hits-melting-point/

14 '20°C or more'. Hegyi, B. & Taylor, P., 2018: 'The unprecedented 2016–2017 Arctic sea ice growth season: the crucial role of atmospheric rivers and longwave fluxes', *Geophysical Research Letters*, 45 (10), 5204–12

14 'satellite period'. National Snow and Ice Data Center, 2016: 'Sea ice hits

record lows'. nsidc.org/arcticseaicenews/2016/12/arctic-and-antarctic-at-record-low-levels/

14 'off the charts'. Kahn, B., 2016: 'The Arctic is a seriously weird place right now', Climate Central. www.climatecentral.org/news/arctic-sea-ice-record-low-20903

14 'human carbon emissions'. World Weather Attribution, 2016: 'Unusually high temperatures at the North Pole, winter 2016'. www.worldweatherattribution.org/north-pole-nov-dec-2016/

15 '13% a decade'. Serreze, M. & Meier, W., 2018: 'The Arctic's sea ice cover: trends, variability, predictability, and comparisons to the Antarctic', *Annals of the New York Academy of Sciences*, 1436 (1), 36–53

15 '85% thinner'. Screen, J., 2017: 'Far-flung effects of Arctic warming'

15 'thinning trend'. McSweeney, R., 2018: 'Arctic sea ice summer minimum in 2018 is sixth lowest on record', Carbon Brief. www.carbonbrief.org/arctic-sea-ice-summer-minimum-in-2018-is-sixth-lowest-on-record

15 'right up to the pole'. Simpkins, G., 2017: 'Extreme Arctic heat', *Nature Climate Change*, 7 (2), 95

15 'Arctic sea ice'. Sun, L. et al., 2018: 'Drivers of 2016 record Arctic warmth assessed using climate simulations subjected to Factual and Counterfactual forcing', *Weather and Climate Extremes*, 19, 1–9

15 '82,300 km²'. National Snow and Ice Data Center, 2018: 'September Arctic sea ice extent at 6th lowest in the satellite record'. nsidc.org/news/newsroom/arctic-sea-ice-extent-6th-lowest-september

15 'contiguous United States'. Francis, J. & Vavrus, S., 2012: 'Evidence linking Arctic amplification to extreme weather in mid-latitudes', *Geophysical Research Letters*, 39 (6), L06801

15 '13 of the lowest'. *Nature*, 2019: 'Telescope windfall, genius grants and Arctic ice loss', The Week in Science: 27 September–3 October 2019

15 'once-frozen seas'. Timmermans, M.-L. et al., 2018: 'Warming of the interior Arctic Ocean linked to sea ice losses at the basin margins', *Science Advances*, 4 (8), eaat6773

16 'linear relationship'. Notz, D. & Stroeve, J., 2016: 'Observed Arctic sea-ice loss directly follows anthropogenic CO_2 emission', *Science*, 354 (6313), 747–50

16 'two metric tonnes'. Steig, E., 2019: 'How fast will the Antarctic ice sheet retreat?', *Science*, 364 (6444), 936–7

16 'skinny adult bears'. Pagano, A. et al., 2018: 'High-energy, high-fat lifestyle challenges an Arctic apex predator, the polar bear', *Science*, 359 (6375), 568–72

17 'ecosystem'. twitter.com/AEDerocher/status/1057390924517408769

17 '450 ppm'. Amstrup, S. et al., 2010: 'Greenhouse gas mitigation can reduce sea-ice loss and increase polar bear persistence', *Nature*, 468, 955–8

17 'Northern Passage'. Hauser, D. et al., 2018: 'Vulnerability of Arctic marine mammals to vessel traffic in the increasingly ice-free Northwest Passage and Northern Sea Route', *PNAS*, 115 (29), 7617–22

17 'migratory fish'. Fossheim, M. et al., 2015: 'Recent warming leads to a rapid borealization of fish communities in the Arctic', *Nature Climate Change*, 5, 673–7

17 'black guillemot'. Divoky, G. et al., 2015: 'Effects of recent decreases in Arctic sea ice on an ice-associated marine bird', *Progress in Oceanography*, 136, 151–61

17 'starve to death'. Waters, H., 2017: 'Can these seabirds adapt fast enough to survive a melting Arctic?', *Audubon*. www.audubon.org/ magazine/winter-2017/can-these-seabirds-adapt-fast-enough-survive

17 'Bering Sea'. Duffy-Anderson, J. et al., 2019: 'Responses of the Northern Bering Sea and Southeastern Bering Sea pelagic ecosystems following record-breaking low winter sea ice', *Geophysical Research Letters*, 46 (16), 9833–42

18 'terrestrial ecosystem'. Schmidt, M. et al., 2019: 'An ecosystem-wide reproductive failure with more snow in the Arctic', *PLOS Biology*, 17 (10), e3000392

18 'wildfire outbreaks'. Cvijanovic, I. et al., 2017: 'Future loss of Arctic sea-ice cover could drive a substantial decrease in California's rainfall', *Nature Communications*, 8, 1947

18 'declining yields'. Kim, J.-S. et al., 2017: 'Reduced North American terrestrial primary productivity linked to anomalous Arctic warming', *Nature Geoscience*, 10, 572–6

18 'southern Plains'. Budikova, D. et al., 2019: 'United States heat wave frequency and Arctic Ocean marginal sea ice variability', *Journal of Geophysical Research: Atmospheres*, 124 (12), 6247–64

18 'regime shift'. Len, Y.-D. et al., 2018: 'Extreme weather in Europe linked to less sea ice and warming in the Barents Sea', *The Conversation*

theconversation.com/extreme-weather-in-europe-linked-to-less-sea-ice-and-warming-in-the-barents-sea-100628

18 'assigning blame'. Screen, J. & Simmonds, I., 2013: 'Caution needed when linking weather extremes to amplified planetary waves', *PNAS*, 110 (26), E2327

18 'planetary waves'. Petoukhov, V. et al., 2013: 'Quasiresonant amplification of planetary waves and recent Northern Hemisphere weather extremes', *PNAS*, 110 (14), 5336–41

18 'events as diverse'. Mann, M. et al., 2017: 'Influence of anthropogenic climate change on planetary wave resonance and extreme weather events', *Scientific Reports*, 7, 45242

18 'climate models'. Ibid.

18 'helped weaken'. Kretschmer, M. et al., 2018: 'More-persistent weak stratospheric polar vortex states linked to cold extremes', *Bulletin of the American Meteorological Society*, January 2018, 49–60

19 'extreme winter conditions'. Zhang, J. et al., 2016: 'Persistent shift of the Arctic polar vortex towards the Eurasian continent in recent decades', *Nature Climate Change*, 6, 1094–9

19 'one study'. Kug, J.-S. et al., 2015: 'Two distinct influences of Arctic warming on cold winters over North America and East Asia', *Nature Geoscience*, 8, 759–62

19 'meteorologists'. Bellprat, O. et al., 2016: 'The role of Arctic sea ice and sea surface temperatures on the cold 2015 February over North America' [in *Explaining Extremes of 2015 from a Climate Perspective* supplement]. *Bulletin of the American Meteorological Society*, 97 (12), S36–S42

19 'What happens'. Watts, J., 2018: 'Summer weather is getting "stuck" due to Arctic warming', *Guardian*. www.theguardian.com/environment/2018/aug/20/summer-weather-is-getting-stuck-due-to-arctic-warming

19 'hundred wildfires'. Helmore, E., 2019: '"Unprecedented": more than 100 Arctic wildfires burn in worst ever season', *Guardian*. www.theguardian.com/world/2019/jul/26/unprecedented-more-than-100-wildfires-burning-in-the-arctic-in-worst-ever-season

19 'fenlands scorched'. Freedman, A., 2019: 'Greenland wildfire part of unusual spike in Arctic blazes this summer', *Washington Post*. www.washingtonpost.com/weather/2019/07/18/greenland-wildfire-part-unusual-spike-arctic-blazes-this-summer/

19 'emissions of Belgium'. Vaughan, A., 2019: 'Huge Arctic fires have now emitted a record-breaking amount of CO_2', *New Scientist*. www.newscientist.com/article/2211013-huge-arctic-fires-have-now-emitted-a-record-breaking-amount-of-co2/

20 'suddenly re-advanced'. Bromley, G., 2018: 'Interstadial rise and Younger Dryas demise of Scotland's last icefields', *Paleoceanography and Paleoclimatology*, 33, 412–29

20 'blamed on fluctuations'. Henry, L. et al., 2016: 'North Atlantic ocean circulation and abrupt climate change during the last glaciation', *Science*, 353 (6298), 470–4

20 'mighty current'. Weijer, W. et al., 2019: 'Stability of the Atlantic Meridional Overturning Circulation: A review and synthesis', *Journal of Geophysical Research: Oceans*, 124, 5336–75

20 '17 Sv'. Ibid.

21 'nuclear power stations'. Roughly 0.9 petawatts; 1 PW is 10^{15} W, while 1 GW is 10^9 W. Each nuclear power station might be 1.5–2 GW.

21 'warmer than'. Buckley, M. et al., 2016: 'Observations, inferences, and mechanisms of Atlantic Meridional Overturning Circulation variability: A review', *Reviews of Geophysics*, 54, 5–63

21 'slowed by 15%'. Caesar, L. et al., 2018: 'Observed fingerprint of a weakening Atlantic Ocean overturning circulation', *Nature*, 556, 191–6

21 '1,500 years'. Thornalley, D. et al., 2018: 'Anomalously weak Labrador Sea convection and Atlantic overturning during the past 150 years', *Nature*, 556, 227–30

21 'still persists'. Smeed, D.A. et al., 2018: 'The North Atlantic Ocean is in a state of reduced overturning', *Geophysical Research Letters*, 45, 1527–33

21 'one later study'. Jackson, L. et al., 2016: 'Recent slowing of Atlantic overturning circulation as a recovery from earlier strengthening', *Nature Geoscience*, 9, 518–22

22 'Less saline water'. Potsdam Institute for Climate Impact Research (PIK), 2018: 'Stronger evidence for a weaker Atlantic overturning', press release. www.pik-potsdam.de/news/press-releases/stronger-evidence-for-a-weaker-atlantic-overturning

22 'huge impacts'. Sgubin, G. et al., 2017: 'Abrupt cooling over the North Atlantic in modern climate models', *Nature Communications*, 8, 14375

22 'gigantic iceberg'. Geggel, L., 2018: 'Huge iceberg poised to break off

Antarctica's Pine Island Glacier', *Livescience*. www.livescience.
com/63782-pine-island-glacier-rift.html

22 'floated away'. Geggel, L., 2018: 'Iceberg 4.5 times the size of Manhattan
breaks off Antarctic glacier', *Livescience*. www.livescience.com/60530-
pine-island-glacier-calves-in-antarctica.html

22 'tenth of a millimetre'. Christianson, K. et al., 2016: 'Sensitivity of Pine
Island Glacier to observed ocean forcing', *Geophysical Research Letters*,
43, 10817–25

23 'process of unstoppable melt'. Feldman, J. & Levermann, A., 2015:
'Collapse of the West Antarctic Ice Sheet after local destabilization of
the Amundsen Basin', *PNAS*, 112 (46), 14191–6

23 'three metres'. Bamber, J. et al., 2009: 'Reassessment of the potential
sea-level rise from a collapse of the West Antarctic Ice Sheet', *Science*,
324 (5929), 901–3

23 'rate is increasing'. Jenkins, A. et al., 2018: 'West Antarctic Ice Sheet
retreat in the Amundsen Sea driven by decadal oceanic variability',
Nature Geoscience, 11, 733–73

23 'structural imbalance'. Shepherd, A. et al., 2019: 'Trends in Antarctic
Ice Sheet elevation and mass', *Geophysical Research Letters*, 46, 8174–83

23 'wave of thinning'. American Geophysical Union, 2019: 'Study finds 24
percent of West Antarctic ice is now unstable', press release. news.agu.
org/press-release/study-finds-24-percent-of-west-antarctic-ice-is-
now-unstable/

23 'early explorers'. Bell, R. et al., 2017: 'Antarctic ice shelf potentially
stabilized by export of meltwater in surface river', *Nature*, 544, 344–8

23 'melt regime'. Bell, R. et al., 2018: 'Antarctic surface hydrology and
impacts on ice-sheet mass balance', *Nature Climate Change*, 8, 1044–52

24 'meltwater pools'. Stokes, C. et al., 2019: 'Widespread distribution of
supraglacial lakes around the margin of the East Antarctic Ice Sheet',
Scientific Reports, 9, 13823

24 'In March 2015'. Rondanelli, R. et al., 2019: 'Strongest MJO on record
triggers extreme Atacama rainfall and warmth in Antarctica',
Geophysical Research Letters, 46, 3482–91

24 'Antarctic winter'. Kuipers Munneke, P. et al., 2018: 'Intense winter
surface melt on an Antarctic ice shelf', *Geophysical Research Letters*, 45,
7615–23

24 'rapid disintegration'. Massom, R. et al., 2018: 'Antarctic ice shelf

disintegration triggered by sea ice loss and ocean swell', *Nature*, 558, 383–9

24 'Rhode Island'. Hogg, A. & Hilmar Gudmundsson, G., 2017: 'Impacts of the Larsen-C Ice Shelf calving event', *Nature Climate Change*, 7, 540–2

24 'increased *sixfold*'. Rignot, E. et al., 2019: 'Four decades of Antarctic Ice Sheet mass balance from 1979–2017', *PNAS*, 116, 1095–103

24 'frigid continent'. Medley, B. & Thomas, E., 2018: 'Increased snowfall over the Antarctic Ice Sheet mitigated twentieth-century sea-level rise', *Nature Climate Change*, 9, 34–9

24 'reason for concern'. Mooney, C. & Dennis, B., 2019: 'Ice loss from Antarctica has sextupled since the 1970s, new research finds', *Washington Post*. www.washingtonpost.com/energy-environment/ 2019/01/14/ice-loss-antarctica-has-sextupled-since-s-new- research-finds/

25 'grounding lines'. Konrad, H. et al., 2018: 'Net retreat of Antarctic glacier grounding lines', *Nature Geoscience*, 11, 258–62

25 'orders of magnitude'. Sutherland, D. et al., 2019: 'Direct observations of submarine melt and subsurface geometry at a tidewater glacier', *Science*, 365, 6451, 369–74

26 'glacial runoff'. Buytaert, W. et al., 2017: 'Glacial melt content of water use in the tropical Andes', *Environmental Research Letters*, 12 (11), 114014

26 'similar losses'. Rabatel, A. et al., 2013: 'Current state of glaciers in the tropical Andes: a multi-century perspective on glacier evolution and climate change', *The Cryosphere*, 7, 81–102

27 'contributing more'. Dussaillant, I. et al., 2019: 'Two decades of glacier mass loss along the Andes', *Nature Geoscience*, 12, 802–8

27 '335 billion tonnes'. Zemp, M. et al., 2019: 'Global glacier mass changes and their contributions to sea-level rise from 1961 to 2016', *Nature*, 568, 382–6

27 'without precedent'. Zemp, M. et al., 2015: 'Historically unprecedented global glacier decline in the early 21st century', *Journal of Glaciology*, 61 (228), 745–62

27 'winter snowpack'. Belmecheri, S. et al., 2016: 'Multi-century evaluation of Sierra Nevada snowpack', *Nature Climate Change*, 6, 2–3

27 'only 5%'. Ibid.

27 'eastern Alps'. Colucci, R. et al., 2017: 'Unprecedented heat wave in December 2015 and potential for winter glacier ablation in the eastern Alps', *Scientific Reports*, 7, 7090

28 'heavy rain'. Stoffel, M. & Corona, C., 2018: 'Future winters glimpsed in the Alps', *Nature Geoscience*, 11, 458–60

28 'dramatically decreasing'. Fontrodona Bach, A. et al., 2018: 'Widespread and accelerated decrease of observed mean and extreme snow depth over Europe', *Geophysical Research Letters*, 45, 12312–19

28 'mid-February'. Mohdin, A., 2019: 'UK experiences hottest winter day ever as 21.2C is recorded in London', *Guardian*. www.theguardian. com/uk-news/2019/feb/26/uk-hottest-winter-day-ever

28 'Dent du Géant'. Evans, K., 2019: 'A hiker found this beautiful lake in the Alps. There's just one small problem', *IFL Science*. www.iflscience. com/environment/a-lake-popped-up-unexpectedly-in-the-alps-thanks-to-last-months-heatwave/

29 'in some regions'. Hoegh-Guldberg, O. et al., 2018: 'Impacts of 1.5°C global warming on natural and human systems'. In: *Global Warming of 1.5°C. An IPCC Special Report on the Impacts of Global Warming of 1.5°C above Pre-Industrial Levels and Related Global Greenhouse Gas Emission Pathways, in the Context of Strengthening the Global Response to the Threat of Climate Change, Sustainable Development, and Efforts to Eradicate Poverty*, Masson-Delmotte, V. et al. (eds). In press, p. 201

29 'largest 200 rivers'. Dai, A., 2016: 'Historical and future changes in streamflow and continental runoff'. In: *Terrestrial Water Cycle and Climate Change: Natural and Human-Induced Impacts*, Tang, Q. and Oki, T. (eds). American Geophysical Union (AGU), Washington DC, USA, pp. 17–37

29 'river-monitoring'. Do, H.-X. et al., 2017: 'A global-scale investigation of trends in annual maximum streamflow', *Journal of Hydrology*, 552, 28–43

30 'more vapour'. Fischer, E. & Knutti, R., 2016: 'Observed heavy precipitation increase confirms theory and early models', *Nature Climate Change*, 6, 986–91

30 'precipitation extremes'. Hoegh-Guldberg, O. et al., 2018: 'Impacts of 1.5°C Global Warming on Natural and Human Systems'. In: *Global Warming of 1.5°C. An IPCC Special Report on the Impacts of Global Warming of 1.5°C above Pre-Industrial Levels and Related Global*

Greenhouse Gas Emission Pathways, in the Context of Strengthening the Global Response to the Threat of Climate Change, Sustainable Development, and Efforts to Eradicate Poverty, Masson-Delmotte, V. et al. (eds). In press, p. 193

30 'definite increase'. Schleussner, C.-F. et al., 2017: 'In the observational record half a degree matters', *Nature Climate Change*, 7, 460–2

30 'increasing far faster'. Li, C. et al., 2019: 'Larger increases in more extreme local precipitation events as climate warms', *Geophysical Research Letters*, 46, 6885–91

30 'record-breaking'. Lehmann, J. et al., 2015: 'Increased record-breaking precipitation events under global warming', *Climatic Change*, 132, 501–15

30 'storm rainfall totals'. Demaria, E.M.C. et al., 2019: 'Intensification of the North American Monsoon rainfall as observed from a long-term high-density gauge network', *Geophysical Research Letters*, 46, 6839–47

30 'central India'. Roxy, M. et al., 2017: 'A threefold rise in widespread extreme rain events over central India', *Nature Communications*, 8, 708

30 'arid areas'. Donat, M. et al., 2016: 'More extreme precipitation in the world's dry and wet regions', *Nature Climate Change*, 6, 508–13

30 'Sahel region'. Taylor, C. et al., 2017: 'Frequency of extreme Sahelian storms tripled since 1982 in satellite observations', *Nature*, 544, 475–8

30 'tripled in incidence'. Yuan, X. et al., 2018: 'Anthropogenic intensification of Southern African flash droughts as exemplified by the 2015/16 season' [in *Explaining Extreme Events of 2016 from a Climate Perspective* supplement]. *Bulletin of the American Meteorological Society*, 99 (1), S86–S90

31 'China's history'. Zhou, C. et al., 2018: 'Attribution of the July 2016 extreme precipitation event over China's Wuhan' [in *Explaining Extreme Events of 2016 from a Climate Perspective* supplement]. *Bulletin of the American Meteorological Society*, 99 (1), S107–S112

31 'mesoscale convective systems'. Feng, Z. et al., 2016: 'More frequent intense and long-lived storms dominate the springtime trend in central US rainfall', *Nature Communications*, 7, 13429

31 'jury is no longer out'. Fischer, E. & Knutti, R., 2016: 'Observed heavy precipitation increase confirms theory and early models'

31 'clear dichotomy'. Sharma, A. et al., 2018: 'If precipitation extremes are increasing, why aren't floods?' *Water Resources Research*, 54, 8545–51

32 'permanent marker'. www.ksbw.com/article/east-texas-county-tells-residents-get-out-or-die/12142731

32 'Houston bridge'. www.ksbw.com/article/harvey-bodies-of-6-houston-family-members-recovered/12140867

32 'drowned mother'. www.ksbw.com/article/harvey-horror-shivering-girl-3-clinging-to-drowned-mom/12145338

32 'since 1919'. Blake, E. & Zelinsky, D., 2017: 'National Hurricane Center tropical cyclone report: Hurricane Harvey'. www.nhc.noaa.gov/data/tcr/AL092017_Harvey.pdf

32 'police officer'. www.chicagotribune.com/news/nationworld/ct-hurricane-harvey-flooding-houston-20170829-story.html

32 '90-minute'. whnt.com/2017/08/26/24-hours-after-making-landfall-harveys-rainfall-prompts-flash-flood-emergencies-in-houston/

33 'Niagara Falls'. The calculation is as follows: 22 km^3 of water (see reference below – this is for the initial landfall). Niagara Falls has 2,400 m^3/s, according to en.wikipedia.org/wiki/Niagara_Falls. So 2,400 × 3,600 × 24 = 207,360,000 m^3/day. That's about 0.2 km^3/day, so 22 km^3 takes 110 days.

33 'gradually rebound'. Milliner, C. et al., 2018: 'Tracking the weight of Hurricane Harvey's stormwater using GPS data', *Science Advances*, 4 (9), eaau2477

33 'shades of purple'. Schlanger, Z., 2017: 'Hurricane Harvey dropped so much rain the US National Weather Service added new colors to its maps', *Quartz*. qz.com/1063945/hurricane-harveys-rainfall-was-so-heavy-the-us-national-weather-service-added-new-colors-to-its-maps/

33 'urbanized islands'. www.chicagotribune.com/news/nationworld/ct-hurricane-harvey-flooding-houston-20170829-story.html

33 'water rescues'. Blake, E. & Zelinsky, D., 2017: 'National Hurricane Center Tropical Cyclone Report: Hurricane Harvey' (n. 153)

33 'world capital'. Hannam, P., 2017: 'Houston, you have a problem, and some of it of your own making', *Sydney Morning Herald*. www.smh.com.au/environment/climate-change/houston-you-have-a-problem-and-some-of-it-of-your-own-making-20170828-gy5cmy.html

35 'biblical'. Emanuel, K., 2017: 'Assessing the present and future probability of Hurricane Harvey's rainfall', *PNAS*, 114 (48), 12681–4

35 '15% more'. van Oldenborgh, G. et al., 2017: 'Attribution of extreme rainfall from Hurricane Harvey, August 2017', *Environmental Research Letters*, 12 (12), 124009. Although different analyses and approaches of all the research papers give varying estimates, their conclusions are remarkably similar. One found that climate change had increased the volume of Harvey's rainfall by about 38% and also made the storm three times more likely (Risser, M.D. et al., 2017: 'Attributable human-induced changes in the likelihood and magnitude of the observed extreme precipitation during Hurricane Harvey', *Geophysical Research Letters*, 44, 12457–64), while yet another study reported a 20% increase in extreme precipitation from Harvey that could be attributed to post-1980 climate warming (Wang, S.-Y. et al., 2018: 'Quantitative attribution of climate effects on Hurricane Harvey's extreme rainfall in Texas', *Environmental Research Letters*, 13, 054014).

35 'intense rain'. Trenberth, K.E. et al., 2018: 'Hurricane Harvey links to ocean heat content and climate change adaptation', *Earth's Future*, 6, 730–44

35 'by 10%'. Kossin, J., 2018: 'A global slowdown of tropical-cyclone translation speed', *Nature*, 558, 104–7

35 'prolonged battering'. Masters, J., 2019: 'Hurricane Dorian was worthy of a Category 6 rating', *Scientific American*. blogs.scientificamerican.com/eye-of-the-storm/hurricane-dorian-was-worthy-of-a-category-6-rating/

36 'Irma and Maria'. Klotzbach, P. et al., 2018: 'The extremely active 2017 North Atlantic hurricane season', *Monthly Weather Review*, 146, 3425–43

36 'investigated Maria'. Keellings, D. & Hernández Ayala, J., 2019: 'Extreme rainfall associated with Hurricane Maria over Puerto Rico and its connections to climate variability and change', *Geophysical Research Letters*, 46, 2964–73

36 'tropical North Atlantic'. Murakami, H. et al., 2018: 'Dominant effect of relative tropical Atlantic warming on major hurricane occurrence', *Science*, 362 (6416), 794–9

36 'infrastructure devastated'. IPCC, 2019: 'Chapter 6: Extremes, Abrupt Changes and Managing Risks'. In: *IPCC Special Report on the Ocean and Cryosphere in a Changing Climate*, H.-O. Pörtner et al. (eds). In press, pp. 6–56

36 'regime shift'. Paerl, H. et al., 2019: 'Recent increase in catastrophic tropical cyclone flooding in coastal North Carolina, USA: Long-term observations suggest a regime shift', *Scientific Reports*, 9, 10620

36 'Climate models do'. Patricola, C. & Wehner, M., 2018: 'Anthropogenic influences on major tropical cyclone events', *Nature*, 563, 339–46

37 'reliable records'. Rahmstorf, S., 2017: 'Rising hazard of storm-surge flooding', *PNAS*, 114 (45), 11806–8

37 'Atlantic at least'. Balaguru, K. et al., 2018: 'Increasing magnitude of hurricane rapid intensification in the central and eastern tropical Atlantic', *Geophysical Research Letters*, 45, 4238–47

37 'detectable increase'. Bhatia, K. et al., 2019: 'Recent increases in tropical cyclone intensification rates', *Nature Communications*, 10, 635

37 '185 knots'. Rogers, R. & Aberson, S., 2017: 'Rewriting the tropical record books: the extraordinary intensification of Hurricane Patricia (2015)', *Bulletin of the American Meteorological Society*, 2091–112

37 'western North Pacific'. Mei, W. & Xie, S.-P., 2016: 'Intensification of landfalling typhoons over the northwest Pacific since the late 1970s', *Nature Geoscience*, 9, 753–7

37 'overall numbers'. Kang, N.-Y. & Elsner, J., 2015: 'Trade-off between intensity and frequency of global tropical cyclones', *Nature Climate Change*, 5, 661–4

37 'coastal erosion'. IPCC, 2019: 'Chapter 6: Extremes, Abrupt Changes and Managing Risks'

38 'nearly 6 cm'. Nerem, R. et al., 2018: 'Climate-change-driven accelerated sea-level rise detected in the altimeter era', *PNAS*, 115 (9), 2022–5. Roughly 3mm/year × 18.

38 'global average'. Kench, P. et al., 2018: 'Patterns of island change and persistence offer alternate adaptation pathways for atoll nations', *Nature Communications*, 9, 605

39 'hotspot'. Sallenger Jr, A. et al., 2012: 'Hotspot of accelerated sea-level rise on the Atlantic coast of North America', *Nature Climate Change*, 2, 884–8

40 'intruding saltwater'. Kirwan, M. & Gedan, K., 2019: 'Sea-level driven land conversion and the formation of ghost forests', *Nature Climate Change*, 9, 450–7

40 'former marsh areas'. Upton, J., 2016: 'Ghost forests are eerie evidence

of rising seas', grist.org/article/ghost-forests-are-eerie-evidence-of-rising-seas (cross-posted from Climate Central)

40 'sixth-highest'. Sweet, W. et al., 2016: 'In tide's way: Southeast Florida's September 2015 sunny-day flood' [in *Explaining Extremes of 2015 from a Climate Perspective* supplement]. *Bulletin of the American Meteorological Society*, 97 (12), S25–S30

40 'last 30 years'. National Oceanic and Atmospheric Administration, 2018: *National Climate Report – May 2018. 2017 State of U.S. High Tide Flooding and a 2018 Outlook.* www.ncdc.noaa.gov/sotc/national/2018/05/supplemental/page-1

40 'shoreline erosion'. Albert, S. et al., 2016: 'Interactions between sea-level rise and wave exposure on reef island dynamics in the Solomon Islands', *Environmental Research Letters*, 11 (5), 054011

40 'numerous islets'. Garcin, M. et al., 2016: 'Lagoon islets as indicators of recent environmental changes in the South Pacific – The New Caledonian example', *Continental Shelf Research*, 122, 120–40

40 'remarkably resilient'. Duvat, V., 2018: 'A global assessment of atoll island planform changes over the past decades', *WIREs Climate Change*, 10 (1), e557

41 'blackout conditions'. Hughes, T., 2018: '"Like the gates of hell opened up": Thousands fled Paradise ahead of Camp Fire', *USA Today*. eu.usatoday.com/story/news/nation-now/2018/11/10/california-fires-thousands-fled-paradise-flames-roared/1962141002/

42 'face of the Earth'. Chavez, N., 2018: 'Paradise lost: How California's deadliest wildfire unfolded', *CNN*. edition.cnn.com/2018/11/17/us/california-fires-wrap/index.html

42 'DNA samples'. Lam, K., 2018: 'Camp Fire: At least 196 people still on missing list; death toll remains at 88', *USA Today*. eu.usatoday.com/story/news/2018/11/28/camp-fire-death-toll-holds-steady-88-california/2146081002/

42 'stunning tragedy'. twitter.com/Weather_West/status/1061316105308753920

42 'five-year drought'. Hay, A., 2018: 'Deadly "megafires" the new normal in California', *Reuters*. uk.reuters.com/article/us-california-wildfires-megafires/deadly-megafires-the-new-normal-in-california-idUKKCN1NI2OG

42 'drying trend'. Swain, D. et al., 2018: 'Increasing precipitation volatility

in twenty-first-century California', *Nature Climate Change*, 8, 427–33 (see Figure S7a in particular)

42 'fivefold increase'. Williams, A.P. et al., 2019: 'Observed impacts of anthropogenic climate change on wildfire in California', *Earth's Future*, 7 (8), 892–910

43 'by 1.4°C'. Ibid.

43 'forested areas'. Holden, Z., 2018: 'Decreasing fire season precipitation increased recent western US forest wildfire activity', *PNAS*, 115 (36) E8349–E8357

43 '355 km²'. Dennison, P. et al., 2014: 'Large wildfire trends in the western United States, 1984–2011', *Geophysical Research Letters*, 41 (8), 2928–33

43 '4.2 million'. Abatzoglou, J. & Williams, A.P., 2016: 'Impact of anthropogenic climate change on wildfire across western US forests', *PNAS*, 113 (42), 11770–5

43 '90,000 residents'. Petoukhov, V. et al., 2018: 'Alberta wildfire 2016: Apt contribution from anomalous planetary wave dynamics', *Scientific Reports*, 8, 12375

44 'two to four times'. Kirchmeier-Young, M. et al., 2019: 'Attribution of the influence of human-induced climate change on an extreme fire season', *Earth's Future*, 7, 2–10

44 'in the tundra'. Editorial, 2017: 'Spreading like wildfire', *Nature Climate Change*, 7, 755

44 'vegetated surface area'. Jolly, W.M. et al., 2015: 'Climate-induced variations in global wildfire danger from 1979 to 2013', *Nature Communications*, 6, 7357

44 'football field'. Jones, J., 2018: 'One of the California wildfires grew so fast it burned the equivalent of a football field every second', CNN. edition.cnn.com/2018/11/09/us/california-wildfires-superlatives-wcx/index.html

45 'twice a decade'. Christidis, N. et al., 2015: 'Dramatically increasing chance of extremely hot summers since the 2003 European heatwave', *Nature Climate Change*, 5, 46–50

45 'temperate England'. Chapman, S. et al., 2019: 'Warming trends in summer heatwaves', *Geophysical Research Letters*, 46 (3), 1634–40

45 '38.7°C'. BBC, 2019: 'UK heatwave: Met Office confirms record temperature in Cambridge'. www.bbc.co.uk/news/uk-49157898

45 '2019 French heatwave' Schiermeier, Q., 2019: 'Climate change made
Europe's mega-heatwave five times more likely', *Nature*, 571, 155

45 'Quriyat'. Samenow, J., 2018: 'A city in Oman just posted the world's
hottest low temperature ever recorded: 109 degrees', *Washington Post*.
www.washingtonpost.com/news/capital-weather-gang/
wp/2018/06/27/a-city-in-oman-just-set-the-worlds-hottest-low-
temperature-ever-recorded-109-degrees/

45 'Algerian Sahara'. BBC, 2018: 'Five places that have just broken heat
records'. www.bbc.co.uk/news/world-44779367

45 'northern mid-latitudes'. Vogel, M. et al., 2019: 'Concurrent 2018 hot
extremes across Northern Hemisphere due to human-induced climate
change', *Earth's Future*, 7, 692–703

46 'one modelling study'. Mann, M. et al., 2017: 'Record temperature
streak bears anthropogenic fingerprint', *Geophysical Research Letters*,
44 (15), 7936–44

46 '70,000 additional deaths'. Robine, J.-M. et al., 2008: 'Death toll
exceeded 70,000 in Europe during the summer of 2003', *Comptes
Rendus Biologies*, 331, 171–8

46 '157 million'. Watts, N. et al., 2018: 'The 2018 report of the *Lancet*
Countdown on health and climate change: shaping the health of
nations for centuries to come', *The Lancet*, dx.doi.org/10.1016/
S0140-6736(18)32594-7

46 'northerly Sweden'. Åström, C. et al., 2019: 'High mortality during the
2018 heatwave in Sweden', *Lakartidningen*, 116

46 'Japan'. Hayashida, K. et al., 2019: 'Severe heatwave in Japan', *Acute
Medicine & Surgery*, 6, 206–7

46 'tropical belt'. Staten, P. et al., 2018: 'Re-examining tropical expansion',
Nature Climate Change, 8, 768–75

46 'Sahara'. Thomas, N. & Nigam, S., 2017: 'Twentieth-century climate
change over Africa: Seasonal hydroclimate trends and Sahara Desert
expansion', *Journal of Climate*, 31, 3349–70

46 'Mediterranean'. Gudmundsson, L. & Seneviratne, S., 2016:
'Anthropogenic climate change affects meteorological drought risk in
Europe', *Environmental Research Letters*, 11 (4), 044005

47 '900 years'. Cook, B. et al., 2016: 'Spatiotemporal drought variability in
the Mediterranean over the last 900 years', *Journal of Geophysical
Research: Atmospheres*, 121 (5), 2060–74

47 'urban peripheries of Syria'. Kelley, C. et al., 2015: 'Climate change in the Fertile Crescent and implications of the recent Syrian drought', *PNAS*, 112 (11), 3241–6

47 'ethnically … fractionalized'. Schleussner, C.-F. et al., 2016: 'Armed-conflict risks enhanced by climate-related disasters in ethnically fractionalized countries', *PNAS*, 113 (33), 9216–9221

48 'geographical ranges'. Hoegh-Guldberg, O. et al., 2018: 'Impacts of 1.5°C Global Warming on Natural and Human Systems'. In: *Global Warming of 1.5°C. An IPCC Special Report on the Impacts of Global Warming of 1.5°C above Pre-Industrial Levels and Related Global Greenhouse Gas Emission Pathways, in the Context of Strengthening the Global Response to the Threat of Climate Change, Sustainable Development, and Efforts to Eradicate Poverty*, Masson-Delmotte, V. et al. (eds). In press, p. 218

49 'climatic debts'. Devictor, V. et al., 2012: 'Differences in the climatic debts of birds and butterflies at a continental scale', *Nature Climate Change*, 2, 121–4

49 'sandpiper chicks'. McKinnon, L. et al., 2012: 'Timing of breeding, peak food availability, and effects of mismatch on chick growth in birds nesting in the High Arctic', *Canadian Journal of Zoology*, 90 (8), 961–71

49 'supply of caterpillars'. Both, C. et al., 2006: 'Climate change and population declines in a long-distance migratory bird', *Nature*, 441, 81–3

49 'UK oak forests'. Burgess, M. et al., 2018: 'Tritrophic phenological match–mismatch in space and time', *Nature Ecology & Evolution*, 2, 970–5

50 'Cerro de Pantiacolla'. Freeman, B. et al., 2018: 'Climate change causes upslope shifts and mountaintop extirpations in a tropical bird community', *PNAS*, 115 (47), 11982–7

50 'Mojave Desert'. Iknayan, K. & Beissinger, S., 2018: 'Collapse of a desert bird community over the past century driven by climate change', *PNAS*, 115 (34), 8597–602

50 '976 species'. Wiens, J., 2016: 'Climate-related local extinctions are already widespread among plant and animal species', *PLOS Biology*, 14 (12), e2001104

50 '97% of its habitat'. Howard, B.C., 2019: 'First mammal species

recognized as extinct due to climate change', *National Geographic*. news.nationalgeographic.com/2016/06/first-mammal-extinct-climate-change-bramble-cay-melomys/

50 'officially extinct'. BBC, 2019: 'Bramble Cay melomys: Climate change-ravaged rodent listed as extinct'. www.bbc.co.uk/news/world-australia-47300992

51 'we failed'. Hannam, P., 2019: '"Our little brown rat": first climate change-caused mammal extinction', *Sydney Morning Herald*. www.smh.com.au/environment/climate-change/our-little-brown-rat-first-climate-change-caused-mammal-extinction-20190219-p50yry.html

51 'Australian vertebrates'. Woinarski, J. et al., 2016: 'The contribution of policy, law, management, research, and advocacy failings to the recent extinctions of three Australian vertebrate species', *Conservation Biology*, 31 (1), 13–23

51 '60% of the species'. Ripple, W. et al., 2015: 'Collapse of the world's largest herbivores', *Science Advances*, 1 (4), e1400103

51 'Sumatran rhinoceros'. Ibid.

52 'empty bays'. McCauley, D. et al., 2015: 'Marine defaunation: Animal loss in the global ocean', *Science*, 347 (6219), 1255641

52 'the Earth's history'. Ceballos, G. et al., 2017: 'Biological annihilation via the ongoing sixth mass extinction signaled by vertebrate population losses and declines', *PNAS*, 114 (30), E6089–E6096

52 'since 1970'. Rosenberg, K. et al., 2019: 'Decline of the North American avifauna', *Science*, 366 (6461), 120–4

52 'three billion'. Law, J., 2019: 'America's 3 billion missing birds: where did they go?', BirdLife. www.birdlife.org/worldwide/news/america%E2%80%99s-3-billion-missing-birds-where-did-they-go

52 '75% decline'. Hallmann, C. et al., 2017: 'More than 75 percent decline over 27 years in total flying insect biomass in protected areas', *PLOS One*, 12 (10), e0185809

52 'Puerto Rican rainforests'. Lister, B. & Garcia, A., 2018: 'Climate-driven declines in arthropod abundance restructure a rainforest food web', *PNAS*, 115 (44), E10397–E10406

52 'world's insect species'. Sánchez-Bayo, F. & Wyckhuys, C., 2019: 'Worldwide decline of the entomofauna: A review of its drivers', *Biological Conservation*, 232, 8–27

52 'US Midwest'. Wepprich, T. et al., 2019: 'Butterfly abundance declines

over 20 years of systematic monitoring in Ohio, USA', *PLOS One*, 14 (7), e0216270

53 'laboratory heatwaves'. Sales, K. et al., 2018: 'Experimental heatwaves compromise sperm function and cause transgenerational damage in a model insect', *Nature Communications*, 9, 4771

53 'chytridiomycosis disease'. Scheele, B. et al., 2019: 'Amphibian fungal panzootic causes catastrophic and ongoing loss of biodiversity', *Science*, 363 (6434), 1459–63

53 'global amphibian trade'. Greenberg, D. & Palen, W., 2019: 'A deadly amphibian disease goes global', *Science*, 363 (6434), 1386–8

53 'Panamanian golden frog'. Cohen, J. et al., 2018: 'An interaction between climate change and infectious disease drove widespread amphibian declines', *Global Change Biology*, 25 (3), 927–37

54 'expert on baobabs'. Patrut, A. et al., 2018: 'The demise of the largest and oldest African baobabs', *Nature Plants*, 4, 423–6

54 'Homasi tree'. Yong, E., 2018: 'Trees that have lived for millennia are suddenly dying', *The Atlantic*. www.theatlantic.com/science/archive/2018/06/baobab-trees-dying-climate-change/562499/

54 'Livingstone'. Clement-Davies, D., 2017: 'The enduring legacy of Chapman's Baobab', *Geographical*. geographical.co.uk/places/deserts/item/2137-the-enduring-legacy-of-the-fallen-baobab

55 'dangerous embolisms'. Vidal, J., 2018: 'From Africa's baobabs to America's pines: Our ancient trees are dying', *HuffPost US*. www.huffingtonpost.co.uk/entry/trees-dying-climate-change-baobabs_us_5b2395c4e4b07cb1712d8ea1

55 'large-scale forest die-offs'. Anderegg, W. et al., 2013: 'Consequences of widespread tree mortality triggered by drought and temperature stress', *Nature Climate Change*, 3, 30–6

55 'spruce … pine'. Allen, C. et al., 2010: 'A global overview of drought and heat-induced tree mortality reveals emerging climate change risks for forests', *Forest Ecology and Management*, 259 (4), 660–84

55 'iconic forests'. Davis, K. et al., 2019: 'Wildfires and climate change push low-elevation forests across a critical climate threshold for tree regeneration', *PNAS*, 116 (13), 6193–8

55 'amplified tree mortality'. Allen, C. et al., 2010: 'A global overview of drought and heat-induced tree mortality reveals emerging climate change risks for forests'

55 'California's epic'. Young, D. et al., 2016: 'Long-term climate and competition explain forest mortality patterns under extreme drought', *Ecology Letters*, 20 (1), 78–86

56 'moisture exhausted'. Goulden, M. & Bales, R., 2019: 'California forest die-off linked to multi-year deep soil drying in 2012–2015 drought', *Nature Geoscience*, 12, 632–7

56 'surface were greening'. Zhu, Z. et al., 2016: 'Greening of the Earth and its drivers', *Nature Climate Change*, 6, 791–5

56 'drying out forests'. Yuan, W. et al., 2019: 'Increased atmospheric vapor pressure deficit reduces global vegetation growth', *Science Advances*, 5 (8), eaax1396

57 'pH drop'. Hurd, C. et al., 2018: 'Current understanding and challenges for oceans in a higher-CO_2 world', *Nature Climate Change*, 8, 686–94

57 'chemical burndown'. Sulpis, O. et al., 2018: 'Current $CaCO_3$ dissolution at the seafloor caused by anthropogenic CO_2', *PNAS*, 115 (46), 11700–5

57 '77 billion'. Schmidtko, S. et al., 2017: 'Decline in global oceanic oxygen content during the past five decades', *Nature*, 542, 335–9

58 'fully anoxic water'. Breitburg, D. et al., 2018: 'Declining oxygen in the global ocean and coastal waters', *Science*, 359 (6371), eaam7240

58 'skin and bones'. Welch, C., 2015: 'Mass death of seabirds in Western U.S. is "unprecedented"', *National Geographic*. news.nationalgeographic.com/news/2015/01/150123-seabirds-mass-die-off-auklet-california-animals-environment/

58 'dubbed "The Blob"'. University of Washington, 2015: '"Warm blob" in Pacific Ocean linked to weird weather across the US', press release. www.sciencedaily.com/releases/2015/04/150409143041.htm

59 'since 1985'. Jones, T. et al., 2018: 'Massive mortality of a planktivorous seabird in response to a marine heatwave', *Geophysical Research Letters*, 45, 3193–202

59 'whale carcasses'. National Oceanic and Atmospheric Administration Fisheries, undated: '2015–2016 Large whale unusual mortality event in the Western Gulf of Alaska, United States and British Columbia'. www.fisheries.noaa.gov/national/marine-life-distress/2015-2016-large-whale-unusual-mortality-event-western-gulf-alaska

59 'California coast'. National Oceanic and Atmospheric Administration

Fisheries, undated: '2015–2019 Guadalupe fur seal unusual mortality event in California, Oregon and Washington'. www.fisheries.noaa.gov/national/marine-life-distress/2015-2018-guadalupe-fur-seal-unusual-mortality-event-california

59 'northeast Pacific warm anomaly'. Di Lorenzo, E. & Mantua, N., 2016: 'Multi-year persistence of the 2014/15 North Pacific marine heatwave', *Nature Climate Change*, 6, 1042–7

59 'Uruguay's capital'. Manta, G. et al., 2018: 'The 2017 record marine heatwave in the Southwestern Atlantic shelf', *Geophysical Research Letters*, 45, 12449–56

59 'Western Australia'. Arias-Ortiz, A. et al., 2018: 'A marine heatwave drives massive losses from the world's largest seagrass carbon stocks', *Nature Climate Change*, 8, 338–44

59 'bottlenose dolphins'. Wild, S. et al., 2019: 'Long-term decline in survival and reproduction of dolphins following a marine heatwave', *Current Biology*, 29 (7), R239–R240

59 '1982 and 2016'. Frölicher, T. et al., 2018: 'Marine heatwaves under global warming', *Nature*, 560, 360–4

60 '50% in recent'. Smale, D. et al., 2019: 'Marine heatwaves threaten global biodiversity and the provision of ecosystem services', *Nature Climate Change*, 9, 306–12

60 'seagrasses dying'. Carrington, D., 2019: 'Heatwaves sweeping oceans "like wildfires", scientists reveal', *Guardian*. www.theguardian.com/environment/2019/mar/04/heatwaves-sweeping-oceans-like-wildfires-scientists-reveal

61 '3,863 reefs'. Hughes, T. et al., 2018: 'Global warming transforms coral reef assemblages', *Nature*, 556, 492–6

61 'passing tropical storm'. Ibid.

61 'virtually unknown'. Hughes, T. et al., 2018: 'Spatial and temporal patterns of mass bleaching of corals in the Anthropocene', *Science*, 359 (6371), 80–3

61 'Orpheus Island'. Hughes, T. et al., 2017: 'Global warming and recurrent mass bleaching of corals', *Nature*, 543, 373–7

61 'skip the bleaching'. Leggat, W. et al., 2019: 'Rapid coral decay is associated with marine heatwave mortality events on reefs', *Current Biology*, 29 (16), P2723–P2730

61 'catastrophic impacts'. Stuart-Smith, R. et al., 2018: 'Ecosystem

restructuring along the Great Barrier Reef following mass coral bleaching', *Nature*, 560, 92–6

61 '90 metres'. Schramek, T. et al., 2018: 'Depth-dependent thermal stress around corals in the tropical Pacific Ocean', *Geophysical Research Letters*, 45, 9739–47

62 'resistant to bleaching'. Burt, J. et al., 2019: 'Causes and consequences of the 2017 coral bleaching event in the southern Persian/Arabian Gulf', *Coral Reefs*, 38 (4), 567–89

62 'few tough species'. EurekAlert, 2018: 'Global warming is transforming the Great Barrier Reef'. www.eurekalert.org/pub_releases/2018-04/acoe-gwi041718.php

62 'ecological grief'. Conroy, G., 2019: '"Ecological grief" grips scientists witnessing Great Barrier Reef's decline', *Nature*, 573, 318–19

62 'juvenile corals'. Hughes, T. et al., 2018: 'Ecological memory modifies the cumulative impact of recurrent climate extremes', *Nature Climate Change*, 9, 40–3

62 '80% reduction'. Price, N. et al., 2019: 'Global biogeography of coral recruitment: tropical decline and subtropical increase', *Marine Ecology Progress Series*, 621, 1–17

62 'reproductive capacity'. Hughes, T. et al., 2019: 'Global warming impairs stock–recruitment dynamics of corals', *Nature*, 568, 387–90

63 'Red Sea'. Shlesinger, T. & Loya, Y., 2019: 'Breakdown in spawning synchrony: A silent threat to coral persistence', *Science*, 365 (6457), 1002–17

Two Degrees

67 'Arctic sea ice'. Fischer, H. et al., 2018: 'Palaeoclimate constraints on the impact of 2°C anthropogenic warming and beyond', *Nature Geoscience*, 11, 474–85

68 'limited to two degrees'. Screen, J. & Williamson, D., 2017: 'Ice-free Arctic at 1.5°C?', *Nature Climate Change*, 7, 230–3

68 '2018 study'. Jahn, A., 2018: 'Reduced probability of ice-free summers for 1.5°C compared to 2°C warming', *Nature Climate Change*, 8, 409–13

68 'final threshold'. Niederdrenk, A.L. & Notz, D., 2018: 'Arctic sea ice in a 1.5°C warmer world', *Geophysical Research Letters*, 45, 1963–71. This is for monthly means, so not directly comparable to the instantaneous

view of the earlier reference. Hence I use the more sensitive model estimate from the paper.

68 '1-in-40-year'. Sanderson, B. et al., 2017: 'Community climate simulations to assess avoided impacts in 1.5 and 2°C futures', *Earth System Dynamics*, 8, 827–47

68 'dramatic rate'. Notz, D. & Stroeve, J., 2016: 'Observed Arctic sea-ice loss directly follows anthropogenic CO_2 emission', *Science*, 354 (6313), 747–50

68 'underestimate how quickly'. Massonnet, F. et al., 2012: 'Constraining projections of summer Arctic sea ice', *The Cryosphere*, 6, 1383–94

68 'late 2020s'. Wang, M. & Overland, J., 2009: 'A sea ice free summer Arctic within 30 years?', *Geophysical Research Letters*, 36 (7), L07502

69 'the 2030s'. Wang, M. & Overland, J., 2012: 'A sea ice free summer Arctic within 30 years: An update from CMIP5 models', *Geophysical Research Letters*, 39, L18501

69 'atmospheric CO_2'. Stein, R. et al., 2016: 'Evidence for ice-free summers in the late Miocene central Arctic Ocean', *Nature Communications*, 7, 11148

69 'tropical rain band'. Sun, L., 2018: 'Evolution of the global coupled climate response to Arctic sea ice loss during 1990–2090 and its contribution to climate change', *Journal of Climate*, 7823–43

70 '"blocked" weather'. Chemke, R. et al., 2019: 'The effect of Arctic sea ice loss on the Hadley circulation', *Geophysical Research Letters*, 46, 963–72

70 'hydrological cycle'. Deser, C. et al., 2015: 'The role of ocean-atmosphere coupling in the zonal-mean atmospheric response to Arctic sea ice loss', *Journal of Climate*, 28, 2168–86

70 'impacts ricochet'. Sun, L., 2018: 'Evolution of the global coupled climate response to Arctic sea ice loss during 1990–2090 and its contribution to climate change'

70 'snow-dominated system'. Bintanja, R. & Andry O., 2017: 'Towards a rain-dominated Arctic', *Nature Climate Change*, 7, 263–7

70 'Rain on snow'. Tyler, N., 2010: 'Climate, snow, ice, crashes, and declines in populations of reindeer and caribou (*Rangifer tarandus* L.)', *Ecological Monographs*, 80 (2), 197–219

70 'Nunavut'. Van Dusen, J., 2017: 'Starvation after weather event killed caribou on remote Arctic island', *CBC News*. www.cbc.ca/news/canada/north/mystery-caribou-deaths-arctic-island-1.3962747

70 'humungous'. Joyce, C., 2009: 'When rain falls on snow, arctic animals may starve', National Public Radio. www.npr.org/templates/story/story.php?storyId=111109436

70 'Svalbard'. Hansen, B. et al., 2013: 'Climate events synchronize the dynamics of a resident vertebrate community in the High Arctic', *Science*, 339 (6117), 313–15

71 'plankton blooms'. Trainer, V. et al., 2019: 'Where the sea ice recedes, so does an Alaska way of life', *New York Times*. www.nytimes.com/2019/09/25/opinion/climate-change-ocean-Arctic.html

71 'emaciated polar bears'. Mittermeier, C., 2018: 'Starving-polar-bear photographer recalls what went wrong', *National Geographic*. www.nationalgeographic.com/magazine/2018/08/explore-through-the-lens-starving-polar-bear-photo/

71 '180 days'. Pilfold, N. et al., 2016: 'Mass loss rates of fasting polar bears', *Physiological and Biochemical Zoology*, 89, 5

71 'northern Alaska'. Rode, K. et al., 2010: 'Reduced body size and cub recruitment in polar bears associated with sea ice decline', *Ecological Applications*, 20 (3), 768–82

71 'bears' frozen'. Regehr, E. et al., 2016: 'Conservation status of polar bears (*Ursus maritimus*) in relation to projected sea-ice declines', *Biology Letters*, 12, 12

72 '70%'. Hjort, J. et al., 2018: 'Degrading permafrost puts Arctic infrastructure at risk by mid-century', *Nature Communications*, 9, 5147

72 'all in Russia'. Chadburn, S. et al., 2017: 'An observation-based constraint on permafrost loss as a function of global warming', *Nature Climate Change*, 7, 340–4

72 '60–70 billion'. Comyn-Platt, E. et al., 2018: 'Carbon budgets for 1.5 and 2°C targets lowered by natural wetland and permafrost feedbacks', *Nature Geoscience*, 11, 568–73

72 'by 2100'. Burke, E. et al., 2018: 'CO_2 loss by permafrost thawing implies additional emissions reductions to limit warming to 1.5 or 2°C', *Environmental Research Letters*, 13, 2, 024024

72 'come as methane'. Knoblauch, C. et al., 2018: 'Methane production as key to the greenhouse gas budget of thawing permafrost', *Nature Climate Change*, 8, 309–12

72 '6.6 million km²'. Chadburn, S. et al., 2017: 'An observation-based constraint on permafrost loss as a function of global warming'

73 '30–50 billion'. Comyn-Platt, E. et al., 2018: 'Carbon budgets for 1.5 and 2°C targets lowered by natural wetland and permafrost feedbacks'

73 '345 billion'. Burke, E. et al., 2018: 'CO_2 loss by permafrost thawing implies additional emissions reductions to limit warming to 1.5 or 2°C'

73 'rates far exceeding'. Parkinson, C., 2019: 'A 40-year record reveals gradual Antarctic sea ice increases followed by decreases at rates far exceeding the rates seen in the Arctic', *PNAS*, 116 (29), 14414–23

73 '1.5°C and 2°C'. Hoegh-Guldberg, O. et al., 2018: 'Impacts of 1.5°C Global Warming on Natural and Human Systems'. In: *Global Warming of 1.5°C. An IPCC Special Report on the Impacts of Global Warming of 1.5°C above Pre-Industrial Levels and Related Global Greenhouse Gas Emission Pathways, in the Context of Strengthening the Global Response to the Threat of Climate Change, Sustainable Development, and Efforts to Eradicate Poverty*, Masson-Delmotte, V. et al. (eds). In press, p. 257

74 '20 metres of additional sea level rise'. DeConto, R. & Pollard, D., 2016: 'Contribution of Antarctica to past and future sea-level rise', *Nature*, 531, 591–7

74 'retreated and thinned'. Nick, F. et al., 2013: 'Future sea-level rise from Greenland's main outlet glaciers in a warming climate', *Nature*, 497, 235–8

74 'irreversible mass loss'. Pattyn, F. et al., 2018: 'The Greenland and Antarctic ice sheets under 1.5°C global warming', *Nature Climate Change*, 8, 1053–61

75 'very moderate warmth'. Hoffman, J. et al., 2017: 'Regional and global sea-surface temperatures during the last interglaciation', *Science*, 355 (6322), 276–9

76 '700%'. IPCC, 2019: 'Summary for Policymakers'. In: *IPCC Special Report on the Ocean and Cryosphere in a Changing Climate*, H.-O. Pörtner et al. (eds). In press

76 '79 million people'. Hoegh-Guldberg, O. et al., 2018: 'Impacts of 1.5°C Global Warming on Natural and Human Systems'. In: *Global Warming of 1.5°C. An IPCC Special Report on the Impacts of Global Warming of 1.5°C above Pre-Industrial Levels and Related Global Greenhouse Gas Emission Pathways, in the Context of Strengthening the Global Response to the Threat of Climate Change, Sustainable Development, and Efforts to Eradicate Poverty*, Masson-Delmotte, V. et al. (eds). In press, p. 231

76 'invading oceans'. Davies, K.F. et al., 2018: 'A universal model for predicting human migration under climate change: examining future sea level rise in Bangladesh', *Environmental Research Letters*, 13 (6), 064030

76 'world's coastlines'. Vousdoukas, M. et al., 2018: 'Global probabilistic projections of extreme sea levels show intensification of coastal flood hazard', *Nature Communications*, 9, 2360

76 '50 million people'. Hoegh-Guldberg, O. et al., 2018: 'Impacts of 1.5°C Global Warming on Natural and Human Systems'. In: *Global Warming of 1.5°C. An IPCC Special Report on the Impacts of Global Warming of 1.5°C above Pre-Industrial Levels and Related Global Greenhouse Gas Emission Pathways, in the Context of Strengthening the Global Response to the Threat of Climate Change, Sustainable Development, and Efforts to Eradicate Poverty*, Masson-Delmotte, V. et al. (eds). In press, p. 231

76 '$1.4 trillion'. Jevrejeva, S. et al., 2018: 'Flood damage costs under the sea level rise with warming of 1.5°C and 2°C', *Environmental Research Letters*, 13 (7), 074014

76 '$1 million'. The Center for Climate Integrity, 2019: *High Tide Tax – The Price to Protect Coastal Communities from Rising Seas*. www. climatecosts2040.org/files/ClimateCosts2040_Report.pdf

77 'atoll islands'. Storlazzi, C. et al., 2018: 'Most atolls will be uninhabitable by the mid-21st century because of sea-level rise exacerbating wave-driven flooding', *Science Advances*, 4 (4), eaap9741

78 '200% increase'. Maldives Independent, 2019: 'Maldives records sharp rise in dengue cases'. reliefweb.int/report/maldives/maldives-records-sharp-rise-dengue-cases

78 'hundred nations'. World Health Organization, 2019: 'Dengue and severe dengue – key facts'. www.who.int/news-room/fact-sheets/detail/dengue-and-severe-dengue

78 '390 million'. Bhatt, S. et al., 2013: 'The global distribution and burden of dengue', *Nature*, 496, 504–7

78 'risks increase'. Hoegh-Guldberg, O. et al., 2018: 'Impacts of 1.5°C Global Warming on Natural and Human Systems'. In: *Global Warming of 1.5°C. An IPCC Special Report on the Impacts of Global Warming of 1.5°C above Pre-Industrial Levels and Related Global Greenhouse Gas Emission Pathways, in the Context of Strengthening the Global Response*

to the Threat of Climate Change, Sustainable Development, and Efforts to Eradicate Poverty, Masson-Delmotte, V. et al. (eds). In press, p. 241

78 '1,000 kilometres'. Ogden, N. et al., 2014: 'Recent and projected future climatic suitability of North America for the Asian tiger mosquito *Aedes albopictus*', *Parasites and Vectors*, 7, 532

78 '40%'. Colón-González, F. et al., 2013: 'The effects of weather and climate change on dengue', *PLOS Neglected Tropical Diseases*, 7 (11), e2503

78 'new hotspots'. Bouzid, M. et al., 2014: 'Climate change and the emergence of vector-borne diseases in Europe: case study of dengue fever', *BMC Public Health*, 14, 781

78 'Parts of Africa'. Mweya, C. et al., 2016: 'Climate change influences potential distribution of infected *Aedes aegypti* co-occurrence with dengue epidemics risk areas in Tanzania', *PLOS One*, 11 (9), e0162649

78 'half a million dengue cases'. Colón-González, F. et al., 2018: 'Limiting global-mean temperature increase to 1.5–2°C could reduce the incidence and spatial spread of dengue fever in Latin America', *PNAS*, 115 (24), 6243–8

79 'US–Mexican border'. Reiter, P. et al., 2003: 'Texas lifestyle limits transmission of dengue virus', *Emerging Infectious Diseases*, 9 (1), 86–9

79 'US citizens'. Centers for Disease Control and Prevention, undated: Dengue and Dengue Hemorrhagic Fever. www.cdc.gov/dengue/resources/denguedhf-information-for-health-care-practitioners_2009.pdf

79 'genetic engineering'. Lynas, M., 2016: 'Alert! There's a dangerous new viral outbreak: Zika conspiracy theories', *Guardian.* www.theguardian.com/world/2016/feb/04/alert-theres-a-dangerous-new-viral-outbreak-zika-conspiracy-theories

80 'kills a child'. Target Malaria, undated: 'Why malaria matters'. targetmalaria.org/why-malaria-matters/

80 'caloric availability'. Ray, D. et al., 2019: 'Climate change has likely already affected global food production', *PLOS ONE*, 14 (5), e0217148

81 '99kcal'. Springmann, M. et al., 2016: 'Global and regional health effects of future food production under climate change: a modelling study', *The Lancet*, 387 (10031), 1937–46

82 'yield by 1%'. Lobell, D. et al., 2011: 'Nonlinear heat effects on African maize as evidenced by historical yield trials', *Nature Climate Change*, 1, 42–5

82 'drought-tolerant maize'. Lynas, M., 2017: 'Tanzania is burning GM corn while people go hungry', *Little Atoms*. littleatoms.com/science-world/tanzania-burning-GM-corn-while-people-go-hungry

82 'the new normal'. Zampieri, M. et al., 2019: 'When will current climate extremes affecting maize production become the norm?' *Earth's Future*, 7, 113–22

83 '10% loss'. Zhao, C. et al., 2017: 'Temperature increase reduces global yields of major crops in four independent estimates', *PNAS*, 114 (35), 9326–31

83 '6% fall'. Asseng, S. et al., 2014: 'Rising temperatures reduce global wheat production', *Nature Climate Change*, 5, 143–7; Liu, B. et al., 2016: 'Similar estimates of temperature impacts on global wheat yield by three independent methods', *Nature Climate Change*, 6, 1130–6

83 '25% per degree'. Deutsch, C. et al., 2018: 'Increase in crop losses to insect pests in a warming climate', *Science*, 361, 916–19

83 'protein, zinc and iron'. Smith, M. & Myers, S., 2018: 'Impact of anthropogenic CO_2 emissions on global human nutrition', *Nature Climate Change*, 8, 834–9

85 '2050 climates'. Bastin, J.-F. et al., 2019: 'Understanding climate change from a global analysis of city analogues', *PLOS ONE* 14 (7), e0217592

86 'hotter environments'. Matthews, T. et al., 2017: 'Communicating the deadly consequences of global warming for human heat stress', *PNAS*, 114 (15), 3861–6

86 '98-page guidebook'. Sengupta, S., 2019: 'Red Cross to world's cities: Here's how to prevent heat wave deaths', *New York Times*. www.nytimes.com/2019/07/16/climate/red-cross-heat-waves.html

87 'Moscow in smog'. *BBC News*, 2012: 'Death rate doubles in Moscow as heatwave continues'. www.bbc.co.uk/news/world-europe-10912658

87 'roads melting'. Wingfield-Hayes, R., 2010: 'Russian deaths mount as heatwave and vodka mix', *BBC News*. www.bbc.co.uk/news/world-europe-10646106

87 'unique phenomenon'. Hermant, N., 2010: 'Morgues fill as deaths double in sweltering Moscow', *ABC News*. www.abc.net.au/news/2010-08-10/morgues-fill-as-deaths-double-in-sweltering-moscow/938856

87 'wheat exports'. Kramer, A., 2010: 'Russia, crippled by drought, bans grain exports', *New York Times*. www.nytimes.com/2010/08/06/world/europe/06russia.html

87 'human death toll'. Barriopedro, D. et al., 2011: 'The hot summer of 2010: redrawing the temperature record map of europe', *Science*, 332 (6026), 220–4

87 '38.2°C'. Ibid.

87 'Yashkul'. Met Office, undated: 'The Russian heatwave of summer 2010'. www.metoffice.gov.uk/weather/learn-about/weather/case-studies/russian-heatwave

87 'US National Weather Service'. National Weather Service, undated: 'Heat'. www.weather.gov/bgm/heat

87 'call 911'. National Weather Service, undated: 'Heat cramps, exhaustion, stroke'. www.weather.gov/safety/heat-illness

88 '"mega-heatwave" of 2003'. Mitchell, D. et al., 2018: 'Extreme heat-related mortality avoided under Paris Agreement goals', *Nature Climate Change*, 8, 551–3

88 '500 years'. Barriopedro, D. et al., 2011: 'The Hot Summer of 2010: Redrawing the Temperature Record Map of Europe'

88 '2017 also saw'. Sánchez-Benítez, A. et al., 2018: 'June 2017: The earliest European summer mega-heatwave of reanalysis period', *Geophysical Research Letters*, 45, 1955–62

88 'average European summer'. Suarez-Gutierrez, L. et al., 2018: 'Internal variability in European summer temperatures at 1.5°C and 2°C of global warming', *Environmental Research Letters*, 13, 064026

88 '163 million'. King, A., 2018: 'Reduced heat exposure by limiting global warming to 1.5°C', *Nature Climate Change*, 8, 549–51

88 'deadly summer of 2003'. King, A. & Karoly, D., 2017: 'Climate extremes in Europe at 1.5 and 2 degrees of global warming', *Environmental Research Letters*, 12, 114031

88 'experiencing 30,000'. The Lancet & CPME, 2018: *Lancet Countdown 2018 Report: Briefing for EU Policymakers*. www.lancetcountdown.org/media/1420/2018-lancet-countdown-policy-brief-eu.pdf

88 '49°C'. Australian Government Bureau of Meteorology, 2013: *Special Climate Statement 43 – Extreme Heat in January 2013*. www.bom.gov.au/climate/current/statements/scs43e.pdf

88 'five times more likely'. Lewis, S. & Karoly, D., 2013: 'Anthropogenic contributions to Australia's record summer temperatures of 2013', *Geophysical Research Letters*, 40 (14), 3705–9

88 'Australia of the future'. King, A. et al., 2017: 'Australian climate

extremes at 1.5°C and 2°C of global warming', *Nature Climate Change*, 7, 412–16

89 'double the average rise'. Lewis, S. et al., 2017: 'Australia's unprecedented future temperature extremes under Paris limits to warming', *Geophysical Research Letters*, 44, 9947–56

89 '2013 summer in China'. Sun, Y. et al., 2018: 'Substantial increase in heat wave risks in China in a future warmer world', *Earth's Future*, 6, 1528–38; Lin, L. et al., 2018: 'Additional intensification of seasonal heat and flooding extreme over China in a 2°C warmer world compared to 1.5°C', *Earth's Future*, 6, 968–78

89 '25–50%'. Zhan, M. et al., 2018: 'Changes in extreme maximum temperature events and population exposure in China under global warming scenarios of 1.5 and 2.0°C: analysis using the regional climate model COSMO-CLM', *Journal of Meteorological Research*, 32 (1), 99–112

89 'natural disaster'. *BBC News*, 2018: 'Japan heatwave declared natural disaster as death toll mounts'. www.bbc.co.uk/news/world-asia-44935152

89 '1.5 or 2°C'. Imada, Y. et al., 2019: 'The July 2018 high temperature event in Japan could not have happened without human-induced global warming', *Scientific Online Letters on the Atmosphere*, 15A, 8–11

89 'two billion people'. Dosio, A. et al., 2018: 'Extreme heat waves under 1.5°C and 2°C global warming', *Environmental Research Letters*, 13, 054006

90 '"exceptional" heat waves'. Ibid.

90 'exposed coastlines'. Matthews, T. et al., 2019: 'An emerging tropical cyclone–deadly heat compound hazard', *Nature Climate Change*, 9, 602–6

90 'Rajasthan'. Agarwal, V., 2016: 'Indian heat wave breaks record for highest temperature', *Wall Street Journal*. blogs.wsj.com/indiarealtime/2016/05/20/indian-heat-wave-breaks-record-for-highest-temperature/

90 '92 times increase'. Mishra, V. et al., 2017: 'Heat wave exposure in India in current, 1.5°C, and 2.0°C worlds', *Environmental Research Letters*, 12, 124012

90 'developing countries in Africa'. Parkes, B. et al., 2019: 'Climate change in Africa: costs of mitigating heat stress', *Climatic Change*, 154 (3–4), 461–76

90 'additional electricity supply'. International Energy Agency, 2018: 'Air conditioning use emerges as one of the key drivers of global electricity-demand growth', press release. www.iea.org/newsroom/news/2018/may/air-conditioning-use-emerges-as-one-of-the-key-drivers-of-global-electricity-dema.html

91 '0.8 tonnes'. World Bank, undated. CO_2 Emissions per Capita. data.worldbank.org/indicator/EN.ATM.CO2E.PC?locations=EU

91 '2017 paper'. Lehner, F. et al., 2017: 'Projected drought risk in 1.5°C and 2°C warmer climates', Geophysical Research Letters, 44, 7419–28. See Figure 1.

92 'daily newspaper Mmegi'. Mguni, M., 2014: 'A requiem as Gaborone Dam gives up the ghost', Mmegi Online. www.mmegi.bw/index.php?aid=46594&dir=2014/october/10

93 'loss of 10–20%'. Maúre, G. et al., 2018: 'The southern African climate under 1.5°C and 2°C of global warming as simulated by CORDEX regional climate models', Environmental Research Letters, 13, 065002

93 'Dikgatlhong Dam'. Monitor dam levels and water supplies to different Botswanan towns and cities here: www.wuc.bw/wuc-content/id/471/dam-levels/

93 'Botswana Daily News'. Batlotleng, B., 2017: 'Gaborone Dam overflows after 10 years', Botswana Daily News. www.dailynews.gov.bw/news-details.php?nid=34266

93 'remaining ice fields'. Cullen, N. et al., 2013: 'A century of ice retreat on Kilimanjaro: the mapping reloaded', The Cryosphere, 7, 419–31

95 'Lewis Glacier'. Prinz, R. et al., 2018: 'Mapping the loss of Mt. Kenya's glaciers: an example of the challenges of satellite monitoring of very small glaciers', Geosciences, 8 (5), 174

95 'Colombian Andes'. Poveda, G. & Pineda, K., 2009: 'Reassessment of Colombia's tropical glaciers retreat rates: are they bound to disappear during the 2010–2020 decade?' Advances in Geosciences, 22, 107–16; Instituto de Hidrología, Meteorología y Estudios Ambientales, undated: Informe del Estado de los Glaciares Colombianos. www.ideam.gov.co/documents/24277/72621342/Informe+del+Estado+de+los+glaciares+colombianos.pdf/26773334-c132-4672-91db-f620e8a989f9

95 'Peruvian Andes'. Schauwecker, S. et al., 2017: 'The freezing level in the tropical Andes, Peru: An indicator for present and future glacier extents', Journal of Geophysical Research: Atmospheres, 122, 5172–89

96 'Under current rates'. Zemp, M., 2019: 'Global glacier mass changes and their contributions to sea-level rise from 1961 to 2016', *Nature*, 568, 382–6

96 'High Mountain Asia'. Kraaijenbrink, P. et al., 2017: 'Impact of a global temperature rise of 1.5 degrees Celsius on Asia's glaciers', *Nature*, 549, 257–60

96 'during the 21st century'. Marzeion, B. et al., 2018: 'Limited influence of climate change mitigation on short-term glacier mass loss', *Nature Climate Change*, 8, 305–8

96 'hard-hit'. Huss, M. & Hock, R., 2018: 'Global-scale hydrological response to future glacier mass loss', *Nature Climate Change*, 8, 135–40

97 'July 2019'. Biemans, H. et al., 2019: 'Importance of snow and glacier meltwater for agriculture on the Indo-Gangetic Plain', *Nature Sustainability*, 2, 594–601

97 '221 million people'. Pritchard, H., 2019: 'Asia's shrinking glaciers protect large populations from drought stress', *Nature*, 569, 649–54

97 'days of plenty'. Sorg, A. et al., 2014: 'The days of plenty might soon be over in glacierized Central Asian catchments', *Environmental Research Letters*, 9, 104018

98 'in danger'. Bosson, J.-B. et al., 2019: 'Disappearing World Heritage glaciers as a keystone of nature conservation in a changing climate', *Earth's Future*, 7, 469–79

98 'arid Indus'. Wang, S.-Y. et al., 2011: 'Pakistan's two-stage monsoon and links with the recent climate change', *Journal of Geophysical Research: Atmospheres*, 116, D16

98 'Ban Ki-moon'. Houze Jr, R. et al., 2011: 'Anomalous atmospheric events leading to the summer 2010 floods in Pakistan', *Bulletin of the American Meteorological Society*, 291–8

98 '$500 million'. Webster, P. et al., 2011: 'Were the 2010 Pakistan floods predictable?', *Geophysical Research Letters*, 38 (4), L04806

99 'moral dilemma'. McGivering, J., 2010: '"Elation and unease" at helping Pakistan flood child', *BBC News*. news.bbc.co.uk/1/hi/programmes/from_our_own_correspondent/8965711.stm

99 '10% increase'. Zhang, W. et al., 2018: 'Reduced exposure to extreme precipitation from 0.5°C less warming in global land monsoon regions', *Nature Communications*, 9, 3153

99 '2017 flood'. Uhe, P. et al., 2019: 'Enhanced flood risk with 1.5°C global

warming in the Ganges–Brahmaputra–Meghna basin', *Environmental Research Letters*, 14, 074031

99   'flow of the Ganges'. Betts, R.A. et al., 2018: 'Changes in climate extremes, fresh water availability and vulnerability to food insecurity projected at 1.5°C and 2°C global warming with a higher-resolution global climate model', *Philosophical Transactions of the Royal Society*, A376, 20160452

100 '25% increase'. Ali, H. & Mishra, V., 2018: 'Increase in subdaily precipitation extremes in India under 1.5 and 2.0°C warming worlds', *Geophysical Research Letters*, 45, 6972–82

100 'significant increase'. Mohammed, K. et al., 2017: 'Extreme flows and water availability of the Brahmaputra River under 1.5 and 2°C global warming scenarios', *Climatic Change*, 145 (1–2), 159–75

100 'Asian monsoon'. Lee, D. et al., 2018: 'Impacts of half a degree additional warming on the Asian summer monsoon rainfall characteristics', *Environmental Research Letters*, 13, 044033

100 '1,600 people'. Reuters, 2019: 'More than 1,600 die in India's heaviest monsoon season for 25 years'. uk.reuters.com/article/us-india-floods/more-than-1600-die-in-indias-heaviest-monsoon-season-for-25-years-idUKKBN1WG3N5

100 '2018 study'. Li, W. et al., 2018: 'Additional risk in extreme precipitation in China from 1.5°C to 2.0°C global warming levels', *Science Bulletin*, 63 (4), 228–34

100 'about 2040'. Alfieri, L. et al., 2015: 'Global warming increases the frequency of river floods in Europe', *Hydrology and Earth System Sciences*, 19, 2247–60

100 'dams in California'. Mallakpour, I. et al., 2019: 'Climate-induced changes in the risk of hydrological failure of major dams in California', *Geophysical Research Letters*, 46, 2130–9

100 'week-long flooding'. Döll, P. et al., 2018: 'Risks for the global freshwater system at 1.5°C and 2°C global warming', *Environmental Research Letters*, 13, 044038

100 'as much as 50%'. Betts, R.A. et al., 2018: 'Changes in climate extremes, fresh water availability and vulnerability to food insecurity projected at 1.5°C and 2°C global warming with a higher-resolution global climate model'

100 'IPCC's 2018'. Hoegh-Guldberg, O. et al., 2018: 'Impacts of 1.5°C

Global Warming on Natural and Human Systems'. In: *Global Warming of 1.5°C. An IPCC Special Report on the Impacts of Global Warming of 1.5°C above Pre-Industrial Levels and Related Global Greenhouse Gas Emission Pathways, in the Context of Strengthening the Global Response to the Threat of Climate Change, Sustainable Development, and Efforts to Eradicate Poverty*, Masson-Delmotte, V. et al. (eds). In press, p. 203

101 '70,000 people'. United Nations Office for the Coordination of Humanitarian Affairs, 2019: 'Mozambique: Cyclone Idai & Floods Situation Report No. 14 (as of 15 April 2019)', *ReliefWeb*. reliefweb.int/ report/mozambique/mozambique-cyclone-idai-floods-situation-report-no-14-15-april-2019

102 'Botswanans celebrated'. Batlotleng, B., 2017: 'Gaborone Dam overflows after 10 years'

102 'already arid areas'. Muthige, M. et al., 2018: 'Projected changes in tropical cyclones over the South West Indian Ocean under different extents of global warming', *Environmental Research Letters*, 13, 065019

102 'IPCC states'. Hoegh-Guldberg, O. et al., 2018: 'Impacts of 1.5°C Global Warming on Natural and Human Systems'. In: *Global Warming of 1.5°C. An IPCC Special Report on the Impacts of Global Warming of 1.5°C above Pre-Industrial Levels and Related Global Greenhouse Gas Emission Pathways, in the Context of Strengthening the Global Response to the Threat of Climate Change, Sustainable Development, and Efforts to Eradicate Poverty*, Masson-Delmotte, V. et al. (eds). In press, p. 204

103 'extra-intense hurricanes'. Wehner, M. et al., 2018: 'Changes in tropical cyclones under stabilized 1.5 and 2.0°C global warming scenarios as simulated by the Community Atmospheric Model under the HAPPI protocols', *Earth Systems Dynamics*, 9, 187–95

103 '$1.4 billion'. Burgess, C.P. et al., 2018: 'Estimating damages from climate-related natural disasters for the Caribbean at 1.5°C and 2°C global warming above preindustrial levels', *Regional Environmental Change*, 18 (8), 2297–312

103 'sevenfold increase'. Wen, S. et al., 2019: 'Estimation of economic losses from tropical cyclones in China at 1.5C and 2.0C warming using the regional climate model COSMO-CLM', *International Journal of Climatology*, 39, 724–37

103 'jet streams'. Li, C. et al., 2018: 'Midlatitude atmospheric circulation

responses under 1.5 and 2.0C warming and implications for regional impacts', *Earth Systems Dynamics*, 9, 359–82

103 'shifts east'. Barcikowska, M. et al., 2018: 'Euro-Atlantic winter storminess and precipitation extremes under 1.5C vs. 2C warming scenarios', *Earth Systems Dynamics*, 9, 679–99

103 'doldrums'. Li, C. et al., 2018: 'Midlatitude atmospheric circulation responses under 1.5 and 2.0C warming and implications for regional impacts'

104 '2019 paper'. Pfleiderer, P. et al., 2019: 'Summer weather becomes more persistent in a 2°C world', *Nature Climate Change*, 9, 666–71

104 'extreme El Niños'. Wang, G. et al., 2017: 'Continued increase of extreme El Niño frequency long after 1.5°C warming stabilization', *Nature Climate Change*, 7, 568–72

104 '2014–15 El Niño'. World Meteorological Organization, 2017: *WMO Statement on the State of the Global Climate in 2016*. library.wmo.int/ doc_num.php?explnum_id=3414

104 'every seven years'. Cai, W. et al., 2018: 'Stabilised frequency of extreme positive Indian Ocean Dipole under 1.5°C warming', *Nature Communications*, 9, 1419

105 '20% global'. Xu, L. et al., 2019: 'Global drought trends under 1.5 and 2C warming', *International Journal of Climatology*, 39, 2375–85

105 '410 million'. Liu, W. et al., 2018: 'Global drought and severe drought-affected populations in 1.5 and 2C warmer worlds', *Earth Systems Dynamics*, 9, 267–83

105 'about 15%'. Marengo, J. et al., 2018: 'Changes in climate and land use over the Amazon region: current and future variability and trends', *Frontiers in Earth Science*, 6, 228

105 '11 different'. Liu, W. et al., 2018: 'Global drought and severe drought-affected populations in 1.5 and 2C warmer worlds'

106 '2017 paper'. Lehner, F. et al., 2017: 'Projected drought risk in 1.5°C and 2°C warmer climates'

106 '150–200 billion'. Brienen, R. et al., 2015: 'Long-term decline of the Amazon carbon sink', *Nature*, 519, 344–8

106 'species of tree'. Esquivel-Muelbert, A. et al., 2019: 'Compositional response of Amazon forests to climate change', *Global Change Biology*, 25, 39–56

106 'Hadley Centre'. Cox, P. et al., 2000: 'Acceleration of global warming

due to carbon-cycle feedbacks in a coupled climate model', *Nature*, 408, 184–7

106 'dieback by 2100'. Settele, J. et al., 2014: 'Terrestrial and inland water systems'. In: *Climate Change 2014: Impacts, Adaptation, and Vulnerability. Part A: Global and Sectoral Aspects. Contribution of Working Group II to the Fifth Assessment Report of the Intergovernmental Panel on Climate Change*, Field, C. et al. (eds). Cambridge University Press, Cambridge, UK, p. 309, Box 4.3

107 'region's climate'. Gloor, M. et al., 2015: 'Recent Amazon climate as background for possible ongoing and future changes of Amazon humid forests', *Global Biogeochemical Cycles*, 29, 1384–99

107 'quick succession'. Marengo, J. & Espinoza, J., 2016: 'Extreme seasonal droughts and floods in Amazonia: causes, trends and impacts', *International Journal of Climatology*, 36, 1033–50

107 'last few decades'. Gloor, M. et al., 2015: 'Recent Amazon climate as background for possible ongoing and future changes of Amazon humid forests'

107 'fell to its lowest'. University of Leeds, 2011: 'Two severe Amazon droughts in five years alarms scientists', news release. www.leeds.ac.uk/news/article/1466/

107 'tributaries dried'. Black, R., 2011: 'Amazon drought "severe" in 2010, raising warming fears', *BBC News*. www.bbc.co.uk/news/science-environment-12356835

107 'in 2009'. Marengo, J. et al., 2013: 'Two contrasting severe seasonal extremes in tropical South America in 2012: Flood in Amazonia and drought in Northeast Brazil', *Journal of Climate*, 26, 9137–54

107 'water shortage'. Yang, J. et al., 2018: 'Amazon drought and forest response: Largely reduced forest photosynthesis but slightly increased canopy greenness during the extreme drought of 2015/2016', *Global Change Biology*, 24, 1919–34

107 'well-watered'. Feldpausch, T. et al., 2016: 'Amazon forest response to repeated droughts', *Global Biogeochemical Cycles*, 30, 964–82

107 'dry-affiliated'. Esquivel-Muelbert, A. et al., 2019: 'Compositional response of Amazon forests to climate change'

107 'tropical evergreen'. Hilker, T. et al., 2014: 'Vegetation dynamics and rainfall sensitivity of the Amazon', *PNAS*, 111 (45), 16041–6

107 'shift to savannah'. Brando, P.M. et al., 2014: 'Abrupt increases in

Amazonian tree mortality due to drought–fire interactions', *PNAS*, 111 (17), 6347–52

107 '300 plots'. Brienen, R. et al., 2015: 'Long-term decline of the Amazon carbon sink'

108 '*Guardian*'. Phillips, T., 2019: '"Chaos, chaos, chaos": a journey through Bolsonaro's Amazon inferno', *Guardian*. www.theguardian.com/environment/2019/sep/09/amazon-fires-brazil-rainforest

108 'unceremoniously'. *BBC News*, 2019: 'Amazon fires increase by 84% in one year – space agency'. www.bbc.co.uk/news/world-latin-america-49415973

108 'perilously close'. Wernick, A., 2019: 'Amazon fires push the forest closer to a dangerous tipping point', Public Radio International. www.pri.org/stories/2019-09-17/amazon-fires-push-forest-closer-dangerous-tipping-point

109 'three free-flowing'. Castello, L. & Macedo, M., 2016: 'Large-scale degradation of Amazonian freshwater ecosystems', *Global Change Biology*, 22, 990–1007

109 '55 billion'. Steffen, W. et al., 2018: 'Trajectories of the Earth System in the Anthropocene', *PNAS*, 115 (33), 8252–9. Supplementary info.

109 'quantities of peat'. Wang, S. et al., 2018: 'Potential shift from a carbon sink to a source in Amazonian peatlands under a changing climate', *PNAS*, 115 (49), 12407–12

110 '305 tribes'. Survival International, undated: 'Brazilian Indians'. www.survivalinternational.org/tribes/brazilian

110 'species of wildlife'. Pavid, K., 2019: 'Experts explain the effect of the Amazon wildfires on people, animals and plants', Natural History Museum. www.nhm.ac.uk/discover/news/2019/august/experts-explain-the-effect-of-the-amazon-wildfires.html

110 'adapted to fire'. Daly, N., 2019: 'What the Amazon fires mean for wild animals', *National Geographic*. www.nationalgeographic.com/animals/2019/08/how-the-amazon-rainforest-wildfires-will-affect-wild-animals/

111 'by 2100'. Warren, R. et al., 2018: 'The projected effect on insects, vertebrates, and plants of limiting global warming to 1.5°C rather than 2°C', *Science*, 360 (6390), 791–5. Supplementary info.

112 'using BECCS'. Boysen, L. et al., 2017: 'The limits to global-warming mitigation by terrestrial carbon removal', *Earth's Future*, 5, 463–74

112 'above two degrees'. Griscom, B. et al., 2017: 'Natural Climate Solutions', *PNAS*, 114 (44), 11645-11650

113 'Monbiot'. See www.naturalclimate.solutions/the-letter

113 'can only happen'. Smith, P. et al., 2018: 'Impacts on terrestrial biodiversity of moving from a 2°C to a 1.5°C target', *Philosophical Transactions of the Royal Society*, A376, 20160456

114 'made in 2014'. Hoegh-Guldberg, O. et al., 2018: 'Impacts of 1.5°C Global Warming on Natural and Human Systems'. In: *Global Warming of 1.5°C. An IPCC Special Report on the Impacts of Global Warming of 1.5°C above Pre-Industrial Levels and Related Global Greenhouse Gas Emission Pathways, in the Context of Strengthening the Global Response to the Threat of Climate Change, Sustainable Development, and Efforts to Eradicate Poverty*, Masson-Delmotte, V. et al. (eds). In press, p. 226 and Box 3.4

114 'world's reefs'. Schleussner, C.-F. et al., 2016: 'Differential climate impacts for policy-relevant limits to global warming: the case of 1.5°C and 2°C', *Earth Systems Dynamics*, 7, 327–51

115 'acidification'. Eyre, B. et al., 2018: 'Coral reefs will transition to net dissolving before end of century', *Science*, 359 (6378), 908–11

115 'emaciated refugees'. Kersting, D. & Linares, C., 2019: 'Living evidence of a fossil survival strategy raises hope for warming-affected corals', *Science Advances*, 5 (10), eaax2950

116 'IPCC now warns'. Hoegh-Guldberg, O. et al., 2018: 'Impacts of 1.5°C Global Warming on Natural and Human Systems'. In: *Global Warming of 1.5°C. An IPCC Special Report on the Impacts of Global Warming of 1.5°C above Pre-Industrial Levels and Related Global Greenhouse Gas Emission Pathways, in the Context of Strengthening the Global Response to the Threat of Climate Change, Sustainable Development, and Efforts to Eradicate Poverty*, Masson-Delmotte, V. et al. (eds). In press, p. 226 and Box 3.4

116 'brown swathe'. Duke, N. et al., 2017: 'Large-scale dieback of mangroves in Australia's Gulf of Carpentaria: a severe ecosystem response, coincidental with an unusually extreme weather event', *Marine & Freshwater Research*, 68 (10), 1816–29

116 'existing meadow'. Valle, M. et al., 2014: 'Projecting future distribution of the seagrass *Zostera noltii* under global warming and sea level rise', *Biological Conservation*, 170, 74–85

Three Degrees

121 'discovered in 1994'. Leakey, M. et al., 1995: 'New four-million-year-old hominid species from Kanapoi and Allia Bay, Kenya', *Nature*, 376, 565–71

121 'ate leaves'. Cerling, T. et al., 2013: 'Stable isotope-based diet reconstructions of Turkana Basin hominins', *PNAS*, 110 (26), 10501–6

122 'missing link'. Villmoare, B. et al., 2015: 'Early Homo at 2.8 Ma from Ledi-Geraru, Afar, Ethiopia', *Science*, 347 (6228), 1352–5

122 'Zanclean flood'. Garcia-Castellanos, D. et al., 2009: 'Catastrophic flood of the Mediterranean after the Messinian salinity crisis', *Nature*, 462, 778–81

122 'Pliocene beaver'. Tedford, R. & Harington, R., 2003: 'An Arctic mammal fauna from the Early Pliocene of North America', *Nature*, 425, 388–90

123 '19°C higher'. Ballantyne, A. et al., 2010: 'Significantly warmer Arctic surface temperatures during the Pliocene indicated by multiple independent proxies', *Geology*, 38 (7), 603–6

123 'temperate 14°C'. Csank, A. et al., 2011: 'Estimates of Arctic land surface temperatures during the early Pliocene from two novel proxies', *Earth and Planetary Science Letters*, 304 (3–4), 291–9

123 'Arctic Ocean'. Feng, R. et al., 2019: 'Contributions of aerosol-cloud interactions to mid-Piacenzian seasonally sea ice-free Arctic Ocean', *Geophysical Research Letters*, 46, 9920–9

123 'Oliver Bluffs'. Rees-Owen, R. et al., 2018: 'The last forests on Antarctica: Reconstructing flora and temperature from the Neogene Sirius Group, Transantarctic Mountains', *Organic Geochemistry*, 118, 4–14

123 'Pliocene remains'. Chaloner, B. & Kenrick, P., 2015: 'Did Captain Scott's *Terra Nova* expedition discover fossil *Nothofagus* in Antarctica?' *The Linnean*, 31 (2), 11–17

124 'monumental change'. Cook, C. et al., 2013: 'Dynamic behaviour of the East Antarctic ice sheet during Pliocene warmth', *Nature Geoscience*, 6, 765–9

124 'more sensitive'. Bertram, R. et al., 2018: 'Pliocene deglacial event timelines and the biogeochemical response offshore Wilkes Subglacial Basin, East Antarctica', *Earth and Planetary Science Letters*, 494, 109–16

124   '2009 *Nature*'. Naish, T. et al., 2009: 'Obliquity-paced Pliocene West
      Antarctic ice sheet oscillations', *Nature*, 458, 322–8

124   'waxed and waned'. Dolan, A. et al., 2015: 'Using results from the
      PlioMIP ensemble to investigate the Greenland Ice Sheet during the
      mid-Pliocene Warm Period', *Climate of the Past*, 11, 403–24; Koenig,
      S., 2015: 'Ice sheet model dependency of the simulated Greenland Ice
      Sheet in the mid-Pliocene', *Climate of the Past*, 11, 369–81

125   'ancient landscape'. Bierman, P. et al., 2014: 'Preservation of a preglacial
      landscape under the center of the Greenland Ice Sheet', *Science*, 344
      (6182), 402–5

125   '22 metres'. Miller, K. et al., 2012: 'High tide of the warm Pliocene:
      Implications of global sea level for Antarctic deglaciation', *Geology*, 40
      (5), 407–10

125   'higher Pliocene'. Rovere, A. et al., 2014: 'The Mid-Pliocene sea-level
      conundrum: Glacial isostasy, eustasy and dynamic topography', *Earth
      and Planetary Science Letters*, 387, 27–33

125   'latest calculations'. Berends, C. et al., 2019: 'Modelling ice sheet
      evolution and atmospheric CO_2 during the Late Pliocene', *Climate of
      the Past*, 15, 1603–19

125   '400 ppm'. Willeit, M. et al., 2019: 'Mid-Pleistocene transition in glacial
      cycles explained by declining CO_2 and regolith removal', *Science
      Advances*, 5 (4), eaav7337

125   'melt of Greenland'. Koenig, S. et al., 2014: 'Impact of reduced Arctic
      sea ice on Greenland ice sheet variability in a warmer than present
      climate', *Geophysical Research Letters*, 41, 3934–43

125   'CO_2 concentrations'. Tan, N. et al., 2018: 'Dynamic Greenland ice
      sheet driven by pCO_2 variations across the Pliocene Pleistocene
      transition', *Nature Communications*, 9, 4755

125   'current emissions trends'. Burke, K. et al., 2018: 'Pliocene and Eocene
      provide best analogs for near-future climates', *PNAS*, 115 (52),
      13288–93

126   'nibbling away'. Shepherd, A. et al., 2004: 'Warm ocean is eroding West
      Antarctic Ice Sheet', *Geophysical Research Letters*, 31, 23

126   'final breakup'. van den Broeke, M., 2005: 'Strong surface melting
      preceded collapse of Antarctic Peninsula ice shelf', *Geophysical
      Research Letters*, 32, 12

126   'fracturing process'. Banwell, A. et al., 2013: 'Breakup of the Larsen B

Ice Shelf triggered by chain reaction drainage of supraglacial lakes', *Geophysical Research Letters*, 40, 22, 5872–6

127 'minor tsunamis'. MacAyeal, D. et al., 2003: 'Catastrophic ice-shelf break-up by an ice-shelf-fragment-capsize mechanism', *Journal of Glaciology*, 49 (164), 22–36

127 'in 2016'. DeConto, R. & Pollard, D., 2016: 'Contribution of Antarctica to past and future sea-level rise', *Nature*, 531, 591–7

127 'year 5000'. Golledge, N. et al., 2015: 'The multi-millennial Antarctic commitment to future sea-level rise', *Nature*, 526, 421–5

127 '2018 in *Nature*'. Shakun, J. et al., 2018: 'Minimal East Antarctic Ice Sheet retreat onto land during the past eight million years', *Nature*, 558, 284–7

128 'next millennium'. Aschwanden, A. et al., 2019: 'Contribution of the Greenland Ice Sheet to sea level over the next millennium', *Science Advances*, 5, eaav9396

129 '177 cm'. Le Bars, D. et al., 2017: 'A high-end sea level rise probabilistic projection including rapid Antarctic ice sheet mass loss', *Environmental Research Letters*, 12, 044013

129 '50 million'. Rasmussen, D. et al., 2018: 'Extreme sea level implications of 1.5°C, 2.0°C, and 2.5°C temperature stabilization targets in the 21st and 22nd centuries', *Environmental Research Letters*, 13, 034040

129 '2018 study'. Ibid.

129 '43 New Yorkers'. City of New York, 2013: *Plan NYC – A Stronger, More Resilient New York*. s-media.nyc.gov/agencies/sirr/SIRR_singles_Lo_res.pdf

129 'In California'. Barnard, P. et al., 2019: 'Dynamic flood modeling essential to assess the coastal impacts of climate change', *Scientific Reports*, 9, 4309

129 '2,500 km²'. Brown, S. et al., 2018: 'What are the implications of sea-level rise for a 1.5, 2 and 3°C rise in global mean temperatures in the Ganges-Brahmaputra-Meghna and other vulnerable deltas?', *Regional Environmental Change*, 18, 1829–42

129 '320 new'. Karim, M.F. & Mimura, N., 2008: 'Impacts of climate change and sea-level rise on cyclonic storm surge floods in Bangladesh', *Global Environmental Change*, 18 (3), 490–500

130 'Billions of dollars'. Dasgupta, S. et al., 2011: 'Climate proofing infrastructure in Bangladesh: The incremental cost of limiting future

flood damage', *The Journal of Environment & Development*, 20 (2), 167–90

130 '*Scientific American*'. Frank, T., 2019: 'After a $14-billion upgrade, New Orleans' levees are sinking', *E&E News*. www.scientificamerican.com/article/after-a-14-billion-upgrade-new-orleans-levees-are-sinking/

130 '$400 billion'. The Center for Climate Integrity, 2019: *High Tide Tax – The Price to Protect Coastal Communities from Rising Seas*. www.climatecosts2040.org/files/ClimateCosts2040_Report.pdf

131 'Center for Climate Integrity'. Ibid.

131 'UNESCO'. Marzeion, B. & Levermann, A., 2014: 'Loss of cultural world heritage and currently inhabited places to sea-level rise', *Environmental Research Letters*, 9, 034001

131 'list also includes'. Ibid.

132 'Cosquer Cave'. Cazenave, A., 2014: 'Anthropogenic global warming threatens world cultural heritage', *Environmental Research Letters*, 9, 051001

132 'By 2100'. Jevrejeva, S. et al., 2016: 'Coastal sea level rise with warming above 2°C', *PNAS*, 113 (47), 13342–7

132 'Delhi is burning'. twitter.com/edking_I/status/1138159252323864576

132 'rare red warning'. *Business Today*, 2019: 'Delhi heat wave: IMD issues red warning, temp expected to cross 45 degrees in the next 2 days'. www.businesstoday.in/current/economy-politics/delhi-heat-wave-imd-issues-red-warning-temp-expected-to-cross-45-degrees-in-the-next-2-days/story/354800.html

133 'warned Delhi'. Sharma, P., 2019: 'Delhi simmers: Amid scorching heat, doctors say heat stroke cases are rising in city', *India Today*. www.indiatoday.in/mail-today/story/delhi-simmers-doctors-say-heat-stroke-cases-rising-city-1542015-2019-06-04

133 'Kerala Express'. *India Today*, 2019: '4 passengers on board Kerala Express die due to extreme heat in Uttar Pradesh's Jhansi'. www.indiatoday.in/india/story/kerala-express-passengers-dead-heatwave-uttar-pradesh-jhansi-1546733-2019-06-11

133 '51.1°C'. Accuweather, 2019: 'India: Monsoon reaches the south while dangerous heat wave continues in the north'. www.accuweather.com/en/weather-news/dangerous-india-heat-wave-to-worsen-with-temperatures-to-approach-all-time-record-in-new-delhi-this-weekend/70008472

133 'killed 3,500'. Im, E.-S. et al., 2017: 'Deadly heat waves projected in the densely populated agricultural regions of South Asia', *Science Advances*, 3 (8), e1603322

133 'Ahmedabad'. Azhar, G. et al., 2014: 'Heat-related mortality in India: excess all-cause mortality associated with the 2010 Ahmedabad heat wave', *PLOS ONE*, 9 (3), e91831

133 '2.25°C warmer'. Im, E.-S. et al., 2017: 'Deadly heat waves projected in the densely populated agricultural regions of South Asia'

134 '100 and 300'. Weber, T. et al., 2018: 'Analyzing regional climate change in Africa in a 1.5, 2, and 3°C global warming world', *Earth's Future*, 6, 643–55

134 '145 days'. Rohat, G. et al., 2019: 'Projections of human exposure to dangerous heat in African cities under multiple socioeconomic and climate scenarios', *Earth's Future*, 7, 528–46

134 'central South America'. Tebaldi, C. & Wehner, M., 2018: 'Benefits of mitigation for future heat extremes under RCP4.5 compared to RCP8.5', *Climatic Change*, 146, 349

134 '2,700 more'. Lo, Y.T.E. et al., 2019: 'Increasing mitigation ambition to meet the Paris Agreement's temperature goal avoids substantial heat-related mortality in U.S. cities', *Science Advances*, 5 (6), eaau4373

135 '2017 study'. Mora, C. et al., 2017: 'Global risk of deadly heat', *Nature Climate Change*, 7, 501–6

135 '2018 study'. Rasmijn, L. et al., 2018: 'Future equivalent of 2010 Russian heatwave intensified by weakening soil moisture constraints', *Nature Climate Change*, 8, 381–5

135 '*The Lancet*'. Andrews, O. et al., 2018: 'Implications for workability and survivability in populations exposed to extreme heat under climate change: a modelling study', *The Lancet Planetary Health*, 2, e540–7

137 '187%'. Turco, M. et al., 2018: 'Exacerbated fires in Mediterranean Europe due to anthropogenic warming projected with non-stationary climate-fire models', *Nature Communications*, 9, 3821

137 'all climate models'. Prudhomme, C. et al., 2014: 'Hydrological droughts in the 21st century, hotspots and uncertainties from a global multimodel ensemble experiment', *PNAS*, 111 (9), 3262–7

137 'Mediterranean region'. Guiot, J. & Cramer, W., 2016: 'Climate change: The 2015 Paris Agreement thresholds and Mediterranean basin ecosystems', *Science*, 354 (6311), 465–8

137 'Mediterranean drought'. Samaniego, L. et al., 2018: 'Anthropogenic warming exacerbates European soil moisture droughts', *Nature Climate Change*, 8, 421–6

137 'today's Mediterranean'. Orth, R. et al., 2016: 'Record dry summer in 2015 challenges precipitation projections in Central Europe', *Scientific Reports*, 6, 28334

137 '*Nature Climate Change*'. Huang, J. et al., 2016: 'Accelerated dryland expansion under climate change', *Nature Climate Change*, 6, 166–71

138 'additional billion'. Schewe, J. et al., 2014: 'Multimodel assessment of water scarcity under climate change', *PNAS*, 111 (9), 3245–50

138 'three-degree map'. Naumann, G. et al., 2018: 'Global changes in drought conditions under different levels of warming', *Geophysical Research Letters*, 45, 3285–96

139 'large belts'. Cairns, J. et al., 2013: 'Adapting maize production to climate change in sub-Saharan Africa', *Food Security*, 5, 345

139 'sub-Saharan Africa'. Rippke, U. et al., 2016: 'Timescales of transformational climate change adaptation in sub-Saharan African agriculture', *Nature Climate Change*, 6, 605–609

140 'wheat yield'. Lobell, D. et al., 2012: 'Extreme heat effects on wheat senescence in India', *Nature Climate Change*, 2, 186–9

140 'Russia and Alaska'. Schlenker, W. & Roberts, M., 2009: 'Nonlinear temperature effects indicate severe damages to U.S. crop yields under climate change', *PNAS*, 106 (37), 15594–8

140 'outside the tropics'. Teixeira, E. et al., 2013: 'Global hot-spots of heat stress on agricultural crops due to climate change', *Agricultural and Forest Meteorology*, 170, 206–15

140 'IPCC wrote'. Easterling, W. et al., 2007: 'Food, fibre and forest products'. In: *Climate Change 2007: Impacts, Adaptation and Vulnerability. Contribution of Working Group II to the Fourth Assessment Report of the Intergovernmental Panel on Climate Change*, M.L. Parry et al. (eds). Cambridge University Press, Cambridge, UK, 273–313

141 'even Canada'. Qian, B. et al., 2019: 'Climate change impacts on Canadian yields of spring wheat, canola and maize for global warming levels of 1.5°C, 2.0°C, 2.5°C and 3.0°C', *Environmental Research Letters*, 14 (7), 074005

141 'analysis'. Battisti, D. & Naylor, R., 2009: 'Historical warnings of future

food insecurity with unprecedented seasonal heat', *Science*, 323 (5911), 240–4

142 'riots swept Africa'. Berazneva, J. & Lee, D., 2013: 'Explaining the African food riots of 2007–2008: An empirical analysis', *Food Policy*, 39, 28–39

144 'picnic blanket'. Thomas, K., 2018: 'Hexagon KH-9: Meeting the challenge', *SPIE magazine*. spie.org/news/spie-professional-magazine/2018-october/hexagon-kh-9-meeting-the-challenge?SSO=1

144 'how much ice'. Maurer, J. et al., 2019: 'Acceleration of ice loss across the Himalayas over the past 40 years', *Science Advances*, 5 (6), eaav7266

144 'Himalayan glaciers'. Marzeion, B. et al., 2018: 'Limited influence of climate change mitigation on short-term glacier mass loss', *Nature Climate Change*, 8, 305–8

144 'at least 50%'. Kraaijenbrink, P. et al., 2017: 'Impact of a global temperature rise of 1.5 degrees Celsius on Asia's glaciers', *Nature*, 549, 257–60

145 '*Nature* in 2019'. Zemp, M. et al., 2019: 'Global glacier mass changes and their contributions to sea-level rise from 1961 to 2016', *Nature*, 568, 382–6

145 'quantified precisely'. Huss, M. & Hock, R., 2015: 'A new model for global glacier change and sea-level rise', *Frontiers in Earth Science*, 3, 54

145 'loss of 43%'. Bosson, J.-B. et al., 2019: 'Disappearing World Heritage glaciers as a keystone of nature conservation in a changing climate', *Earth's Future*, 7, 469–79

146 '200 million'. Dottori, F. et al., 2018: 'Increased human and economic losses from river flooding with anthropogenic warming', *Nature Climate Change*, 8, 781–6

147 'floods expected'. Guerreiro, S. et al., 2018: 'Future heat-waves, droughts and floods in 571 European cities', *Environmental Research Letters*, 13, 034009

147 '€17 billion'. Alfieri, L. et al., 2018: 'Multi-model projections of river flood risk in Europe under global warming', *Climate*, 6 (1), 6

147 'north–south divide'. Thober, S. et al., 2018: 'Multi-model ensemble projections of European river floods and high flows at 1.5, 2, and 3 degrees global warming', *Environmental Research Letters*, 13, 014003

148 '2019 study'. Wobus, C. et al., 2019: 'Projecting changes in expected annual damages from riverine flooding in the United States', *Earth's Future*, 7, 516–27

148 'Mississippi'. Huang, S. et al., 2018: 'Multimodel assessment of flood characteristics in four large river basins at global warming of 1.5, 2.0 and 3.0 K above the pre-industrial level', *Environmental Research Letters*, 13, 124005

148 '100-year flood'. Arnell, N. & Gosling, S., 2014: 'The impacts of climate change on river flood risk at the global scale', *Climatic Change*, 134 (3), 387–401

149 '2018 *Science*'. Warren, R. et al., 2018: 'The projected effect on insects, vertebrates, and plants of limiting global warming to 1.5°C rather than 2°C', *Science*, 360 (6390), 791–5

150 'by 2100'. Ibid. Supplementary info.

150 'increase fivefold'. Wiens, J., 2016: 'Climate-related local extinctions are already widespread among plant and animal species', *PLOS Biology*, 14 (12), e2001104

150 'nearly 500'. Schloss, C., 2012: 'Dispersal will limit ability of mammals to track climate change in the Western Hemisphere', *PNAS*, 109 (22), 8606–11

150 'two-thirds of North American'. Bateman, B. et al., 2019: 'North American birds require mitigation and adaptation to reduce vulnerability to climate change', in preparation. *Audubon*, 2019: 'Five climate-threatened birds and how you can help them'. www.audubon. org/magazine/fall-2019/five-climate-threatened-birds-and-how-you-can-help

151 'bird emergency'. *Audubon*, 2019: 'New Audubon science: two-thirds of North American birds at risk of extinction due to climate change', news release. www.audubon.org/news/new-audubon-science-two-thirds-north-american-birds-risk-extinction-due-climate

151 '*Science* magazine'. Ash, C., 2019: 'Thermal intolerance', *Science*, 365 (6450), 246–7

151 'IUCN Red List'. Foden, W., 2013: 'Identifying the world's most climate change vulnerable species: a systematic trait-based assessment of all birds, amphibians and corals', *PLOS One*, 8 (6), e65427

151 'emperor penguins'. Trathan, P. et al., 2019: 'The emperor penguin – Vulnerable to projected rates of warming and sea ice loss', *Biological Conservation*. In press

151 'silversword example'. Krushelnycky, P. et al., 2012: 'Climate-

associated population declines reverse recovery and threaten future of an iconic high-elevation plant', *Global Change Biology*, 19 (3), 911–22

152 '100 kilometres'. Zarco-Perello, S. et al., 2017: 'Tropicalization strengthens consumer pressure on habitat-forming seaweeds', *Scientific Reports*, 7, 820

152 'One study'. Wernberg, T. et al., 2016: 'Climate-driven regime shift of a temperate marine ecosystem', *Science*, 353 (6295), 169–72

152 'multiple ecosystem collapses'. Lotze, H. et al., 2019: 'Global ensemble projections reveal trophic amplification of ocean biomass declines with climate change', *PNAS*, 116 (26), 12907–12

153 'US Midwest'. Till, A. et al., 2019: 'Fish die-offs are concurrent with thermal extremes in north temperate lakes', *Nature Climate Change*, 9, 637–41

153 'primate groups'. Zhang, L. et al., 2019: 'Global assessment of primate vulnerability to extreme climatic events', *Nature Climate Change*, 9, 554–61

153 'novel ecosystems'. García Molinos, J. et al., 2015: 'Climate velocity and the future global redistribution of marine biodiversity', *Nature Climate Change*, 6, 83–8

154 'Gondwana on fire'. Marris, E., 2016: 'Tasmanian bushfires threaten iconic ancient forests', *Nature*, 530, 137–8

155 'Amazonia'. Fu, R. et al., 2013: 'Increased dry-season length over southern Amazonia in recent decades and its implication for future climate projection', *PNAS*, 110 (45), 18110–15

155 'scorched large areas'. Erfanian, A. et al., 2017: 'Unprecedented drought over tropical South America in 2016: significantly under-predicted by tropical SST', *Scientific Reports*, 7, 5811

155 'long-term decline'. Brienen, R., 2015: 'Long-term decline of the Amazon carbon sink', *Nature*, 519, 344–8

155 'conspiracy theory'. Watts, J., 2019: 'Jair Bolsonaro claims NGOs behind Amazon forest fire surge – but provides no evidence', *Guardian*. www.theguardian.com/world/2019/aug/21/jair-bolsonaro-accuses-ngos-setting-fire-amazon-rainforest

155 'Hadley Centre'. Jones, C., 2009: 'Committed terrestrial ecosystem changes due to climate change', *Nature Geoscience*, 2, 484–7

155 'even up to 4°C'. Huntingford, C. et al., 2013: 'Simulated resilience of

tropical rainforests to CO_2-induced climate change', *Nature Geoscience*, 6, 268–273

156   'higher number'. Salazar, L.F. & Nobre, C., 2010: 'Climate change and thresholds of biome shifts in Amazonia', *Geophysical Research Letters*, 37, L17706

156   'trees are lost'. Baker, J. & Spracklen, D., 2019: 'Climate Benefits of Intact Amazon Forests and the Biophysical Consequences of Disturbance', *Frontiers in Forests and Global Change*, 2, 47

156   'unstoppable collapse'. Zemp, D.C. et al., 2017: 'Self-amplified Amazon forest loss due to vegetation-atmosphere feedbacks', *Nature Communications*, 8, 14681

156   'savannah-style'. Boisier, J. et al., 2015: 'Projected strengthening of Amazonian dry season by constrained climate model simulations', *Nature Climate Change*, 5, 656–60

156   'temperature analog'. Feeley, K. & Rehm, E., 2012: 'Amazon's vulnerability to climate change heightened by deforestation and man-made dispersal barriers', *Global Change Biology*, 18, 3606–14

156   'IUCN Red List'. Gomes, V. et al., 2019: 'Amazonian tree species threatened by deforestation and climate change', *Nature Climate Change*, 9, 547–53

156   'Bangladeshi'. Rahman, M. et al., 2018: 'Tree radial growth is projected to decline in South Asian moist forest trees under climate change', *Global and Planetary Change*, 170, 106–19

157   'Costa Rica'. Clark, D. et al., 2013: 'Field-quantified responses of tropical rainforest above ground productivity to increasing CO2 and climatic stress, 1997–2009', *Journal of Geophysical Research: Biogeosciences*, 118, 783–94

157   'more arid ecosystems'. Lyra, A. et al., 2016: 'Projections of climate change impacts on central America tropical rainforest', *Climatic Change*, 141, 93

157   'arid savannah'. Brando, P.M. et al., 2014: 'Abrupt increases in Amazonian tree mortality due to drought–fire interactions', *PNAS*, 111 (17), 6347–52

157   'entire Amazon'. Le Page, Y. et al., 2017: 'Synergy between land use and climate change increases future fire risk in Amazon forests', *Earth System Dynamics*, 8, 1237–46

157   'small fraction'. Rappaport, D. et al., 2018: 'Quantifying long-term

changes in carbon stocks and forest structure from Amazon forest degradation', *Environmental Research Letters*, 13, 065013

157 '150–200 billion'. Brienen, R. et al., 2015: 'Long-term decline of the Amazon carbon sink'

158 'endured on Earth'. Le Page, Y. et al., 2017: 'Synergy between land use and climate change increases future fire risk in Amazon forests'

159 'trillion tonnes'. Schuur, E. et al., 2015: 'Climate change and the permafrost carbon feedback', *Nature*, 520, 171–9

159 '2017 paper'. Chadburn, S. et al., 2017: 'An observation-based constraint on permafrost loss as a function of global warming', *Nature Climate Change*, 7, 340–4

159 '100 billion'. Schneider von Deimling, T. et al., 2015: 'Observation-based modelling of permafrost carbon fluxes with accounting for deep carbon deposits and thermokarst activity', *Biogeosciences*, 12, 3469–88

159 'by 2100'. Schuur, E. et al., 2015: 'Climate change and the permafrost carbon feedback'

160 'off Siberia'. Dmitrenko, I. et al., 2011: 'Recent changes in shelf hydrography in the Siberian Arctic: Potential for subsea permafrost instability', *Journal of Geophysical Research*, 116, C10027

160 '50-gigatonne'. Whiteman, G. et al., 2013: 'Vast costs of Arctic change', *Nature*, 499, 401–3

160 'north of Siberia'. Connor, S., 2011: 'Vast methane "plumes" seen in Arctic ocean as sea ice retreats', *Independent*. www.independent.co.uk/news/science/vast-methane-plumes-seen-in-arctic-ocean-as-sea-ice-retreats-6276278.html

160 'runaway … feedback'. Shakhova, N. et al., 2010: 'Extensive methane venting to the atmosphere from sediments of the East Siberian Arctic Shelf', *Science*, 327 (5970), 1246–50

160 'thaws out'. Anthony, K.W. et al., 2018: '21st-century modeled permafrost carbon emissions accelerated by abrupt thaw beneath lakes', *Nature Communications*, 9, 3262

160 'vast underestimate'. Turetsky, M. et al., 2019: 'Permafrost collapse is accelerating carbon release', *Nature*, 569, 32–4

160 'additional greenhouse gas'. Turetsky, M. et al., 2019: 'Permafrost collapse is accelerating carbon release'

161 'troughs and ponds'. Farquharson, L. et al., 2019: 'Climate change drives widespread and rapid thermokarst development in very cold

permafrost in the Canadian High Arctic', *Geophysical Research Letters*, 46, 6681–9

161 'back in 2015'. Schuur, E. et al., 2015: 'Climate change and the permafrost carbon feedback'

161 'northern forests'. Hayes, D. et al., 2011: 'Is the northern high-latitude land-based CO_2 sink weakening?', *Global Biogeochemical Cycles*, 25, GB3018

161 'summertime ice-free'. Sigmond, M. et al., 2018: 'Ice-free Arctic projections under the Paris Agreement', *Nature Climate Change*, 8, 404–8

161 'about 2070'. Laliberté, F. et al., 2016: 'Regional variability of a projected sea ice-free Arctic during the summer months', *Geophysical Research Letters*, 43, 256–63

162 'slushy ice floes'. Meier, W. et al., 2014: 'Arctic sea ice in transformation: A review of recent observed changes and impacts on biology and human activity', *Reviews of Geophysics*, 51, 185–217

162 'ricochet around'. Cohen, J. et al., 2014: 'Recent Arctic amplification and extreme mid-latitude weather', *Nature Geoscience*, 7, 627–37

162 'warmth and moisture'. Moore, G. et al., 2018: 'Collapse of the 2017 winter Beaufort High: A response to thinning sea ice?' *Geophysical Research Letters*, 45, 2860–9

162 'jet stream'. Screen, J. et al., 2018: 'Consistency and discrepancy in the atmospheric response to Arctic sea-ice loss across climate models', *Nature Geoscience*, 11, 155–63

163 '0.7 watts'. Pistone, K. et al., 2019: 'Radiative heating of an ice-free arctic ocean', *Geophysical Research Letters*, 46, 7474–80

Four Degrees

168 'great megacities'. Matthews, T. et al., 2017: 'Communicating the deadly consequences of global warming for human heat stress', *PNAS*, 114 (15), 3861–6

169 '40–80 days'. Liu, Z. et al., 2017: 'Global and regional changes in exposure to extreme heat and the relative contributions of climate and population change', *Scientific Reports*, 7, 43909

169 'Extreme hotspots'. Zhao, Y. et al., 2015: 'Estimating heat stress from climate-based indicators: present-day biases and future spreads in the CMIP5 global climate model ensemble', *Environmental Research Letters*, 10, 084013

169 'where a city'. Fitzpatrick, M. & Dunn, R., 2019: 'Contemporary climatic analogs for 540 North American urban areas in the late 21st century', *Nature Communications*, 10, 614

169 '20-fold increase'. Dahl, K. et al., 2019: 'Increased frequency of and population exposure to extreme heat index days in the United States during the 21st century', *Environmental Research Communications*, 1, 075002

169 'Death Valley conditions'. Wobus, C. et al., 2018: 'Reframing future risks of extreme heat in the United States', *Earth's Future*, 6, 1323–35

170 'half the Earth's'. Mora, C. et al., 2017: 'Global risk of deadly heat', *Nature Climate Change*, 7, 501–6

170 'Jakarta … Borneo'. Im, E.-S. et al., 2018: 'Projections of rising heat stress over the western Maritime Continent from dynamically downscaled climate simulations', *Global and Planetary Change*, 165, 160–72

170 'heatwave conditions'. Coffel, E. et al., 2017: 'Temperature and humidity based projections of a rapid rise in global heat stress exposure during the 21st century', *Environmental Research Letters*, 13, 014001

170 'as 20-fold'. Ahmadalipour, A. et al., 2019: 'Mortality risk from heat stress expected to hit poorest nations the hardest', *Climatic Change*, 152, 569

170 '2,000%'. Coffel, E. et al., 2017: 'Temperature and humidity based projections of a rapid rise in global heat stress exposure during the 21st century'

170 'transmit pathogens'. Ryan, S. et al., 2019: 'Global expansion and redistribution of *Aedes*-borne virus transmission risk with climate change', *PLOS Neglected Tropical Diseases*, 13 (3), e0007213

171 '2010 study'. Sherwood, S. & Huber, M., 2010: 'An adaptability limit to climate change due to heat stress', *PNAS*, 107 (21), 9552–5

172 '34.6°C'. Schär, C., 2016: 'The worst heat waves to come', *Nature Climate Change*, 6, 128–9

172 'liveability threshold'. Pal, J. & Eltahir, E., 2015: 'Future temperature in southwest Asia projected to exceed a threshold for human adaptability', *Nature Climate Change*, 6, 197–200

172 'record is 54°C'. Burt, C., 2016: 'Hottest reliably measured air temperatures on Earth', *Weather Underground*. www.wunderground.com/blog/weatherhistorian/hottest-reliably-measured-air-temperatures-on-earth.html

172 'Hajj'. Kang, S. et al., 2019: 'Future heat stress during Muslim pilgrimage (Hajj) projected to exceed "extreme danger" levels', *Geophysical Research Letters*, 46, 10094–100

172 'most intense hazard'. Im, E.-S. et al., 2017: 'Deadly heat waves projected in the densely populated agricultural regions of South Asia', *Science Advances*, 3 (8), e1603322

173 'limit habitability'. Kang, S. & Eltahir, E., 2018: 'North China Plain threatened by deadly heatwaves due to climate change and irrigation', *Nature Communications*, 9, 2894

174 '2019 study'. Matthews, T. et al., 2019: 'An emerging tropical cyclone–deadly heat compound hazard', *Nature Climate Change*, 9, 602–6

175 'Brian Allen'. Crenshaw, Z., 2018: 'Father contracts Valley Fever, dies weeks after moving to Arizona', *ABC 15*. www.abc15.com/news/region-southeast-valley/mesa/father-contracts-valley-fever-dies-weeks-after-moving-to-arizona

176 'strong correlation'. Tong, D. et al., 2017: 'Intensified dust storm activity and Valley fever infection in the southwestern United States', *Geophysical Research Letters*, 44, 4304–12

176 '17 states'. Gorris, M. et al., 2019: 'Expansion of coccidioidomycosis endemic regions in the United States in response to climate change', *GeoHealth*, 3 (10), 308–27

176 'probability of megadrought'. Ault, T. et al., 2016: 'Relative impacts of mitigation, temperature, and precipitation on 21st-century megadrought risk in the American Southwest', *Science Advances*, 2 (10), e1600873

177 'pine and fir forests'. Williams, A.P. et al., 2013: 'Temperature as a potent driver of regional forest drought stress and tree mortality', *Nature Climate Change*, 3, 292–7

177 '2018 paper'. Park, C.-E. et al., 2018: 'Keeping global warming within 1.5°C constrains emergence of aridification', *Nature Climate Change*, 8, 70–4

177 '5.8 million'. Feng, S. & Fu, Q., 2013: 'Expansion of global drylands under a warming climate', *Atmospheric Chemistry and Physics*, 13, 10081–94

177 'drylands dominate'. Huang, J. et al., 2015: 'Accelerated dryland expansion under climate change', *Nature Climate Change*, 6, 166–71

177 '1.9 billion'. Koutroulis, A., 2019: 'Dryland changes under different levels of global warming', *Science of the Total Environment*, 655, 482–511

177 'whole European continent'. Spinoni, J. et al., 2017: 'Will drought events become more frequent and severe in Europe?', *International Journal of Climatology*, 38 (4), 1718–36

178 '2019 paper'. Koutroulis, A., 2019: 'Global water availability under high-end climate change: A vulnerability based assessment', *Global and Planetary Change*, 175, 52–63

178 'less water will flow'. Wanders, N. et al., 2015: 'Global hydrological droughts in the 21st century under a changing hydrological regime', *Earth Systems Dynamics*, 6, 1–15

178 'West Africa'. Sylla, M.B. et al., 2018: 'Projected increased risk of water deficit over major West African river basins under future climates', *Climatic Change*, 151 (2), 247–58

178 '600 million'. Sandeep, S. et al., 2018: 'Decline and poleward shift in Indian summer monsoon synoptic activity in a warming climate', *PNAS*, 115 (11), 2681–6

178 'dry sub-tropical'. Schlaepfer, D. et al., 2017: 'Climate change reduces extent of temperate drylands and intensifies drought in deep soils', *Nature Communications*, 8, 14196

178 'Ebola outbreaks'. Redding, W. et al., 2019: 'Impacts of environmental and socio-economic factors on emergence and epidemic potential of Ebola in Africa', *Nature Communications*, 10, 4531

178 'fire-related particulate'. Ford, B. et al., 2018: 'Future fire impacts on smoke concentrations, visibility, and health in the contiguous United States', *GeoHealth*, 2, 229–47

179 '100 and 600%'. Barbero, R. et al., 2015: 'Climate change presents increased potential for very large fires in the contiguous United States', *International Journal of Wildland Fire*, 24 (7), 892–9

179 'sharp increases projected'. Bowman, D. et al., 2017 'Human exposure and sensitivity to globally extreme wildfire events', *Nature Ecology & Evolution*, 1, 0058

179 'Mediterranean region'. Turco, M. et al., 2018: 'Exacerbated fires in Mediterranean Europe due to anthropogenic warming projected with non-stationary climate-fire models', *Nature Communications*, 9, 3821

179 'frequent lightning'. Lang, T. & Rutledge, S., 2006: 'Cloud-to-ground

lightning downwind of the 2002 Hayman forest fire in Colorado', *Geophysical Research Letters*, 33 (3), L03804

179 'fire tornados'. Cunningham, P. & Reeder, M., 2009: 'Severe convective storms initiated by intense wildfires: Numerical simulations of pyro-convection and pyro-tornadogenesis', *Geophysical Research Letters*, 36 (12), L12812; McRae, R. et al., 2012: 'An Australian pyro-tornadogenesis event', *Natural Hazards*, 65 (3), 1801–11

179 'black hail'. Fromm, M. et al., 2006: 'Violent pyro-convective storm devastates Australia's capital and pollutes the stratosphere', *Geophysical Research Letters*, 33, L05815

179 'into the stratosphere'. McRae, R. et al., 2015: 'Linking local wildfire dynamics to pyroCb development', *Natural Hazards and Earth System Sciences*, 15, 417–28

179 'Kasatochi volcano'. Peterson, D. et al., 2018: 'Wildfire-driven thunderstorms cause a volcano-like stratospheric injection of smoke', *npj Climate and Atmospheric Science*, 1, 30

179 'nuclear war'. Yu, P. et al., 2019: 'Black carbon lofts wildfire smoke high into the stratosphere to form a persistent plume', *Science*, 365 (6453), 587–90

179 'soot particles'. Christian, K. et al., 2019: 'Radiative forcing and stratospheric warming of pyrocumulonimbus smoke aerosols: First modeling results with multisensor (EPIC, CALIPSO, and CATS) views from space', *Geophysical Research Letters*, 46, 10061–71

179 'much larger areas'. Carrão, H. et al., 2018: 'Global projections of drought hazard in a warming climate: a prime for disaster risk management', *Climate Dynamics*, 50 (5–6), 2137–55

180 '80–90%'. Berg, N. & Hall, A., 2017: 'Anthropogenic warming impacts on California snowpack during drought', *Geophysical Research Letters*, 44 (5), 2511–18

181 'very highest peaks'. Schauwecker, S. et al., 2017: 'The freezing level in the tropical Andes, Peru: An indicator for present and future glacier extents', *Journal of Geophysical Research: Atmospheres*, 122 (10), 5172–89

181 'Peru would lose'. Drenkhan, F. et al., 2018: 'Current and future glacier and lake assessment in the deglaciating Vilcanota-Urubamba basin, Peruvian Andes', *Global and Planetary Change*, 169, 105–18

181 'Quelccaya Ice Cap'. Yarleque, C. et al., 2018: 'Projections of the future

disappearance of the Quelccaya Ice Cap in the Central Andes',
Scientific Reports, 8, 15564

181 '90% of the ice'. Kraaijenbrink, P. et al., 2017: 'Impact of a global
temperature rise of 1.5 degrees Celsius on Asia's glaciers', *Nature*, 549,
257–60

183 '1998 event'. del Ninno, C. et al., 2001: 'The 1998 floods in Bangladesh:
Disaster impacts, household coping strategies, and response', *Research
Reports: No. 122*, The International Food Policy Research Institute
(IFPRI)

184 'flood disaster of 1998'. Monirul Qader Mirza, M., 2002: 'Global
warming and changes in the probability of occurrence of floods in
Bangladesh and implications', *Global Environmental Change*, 12 (2),
127–38

184 'colossal quantities of rainfall'. Mohammed, K. et al., 2018: 'Future
floods in Bangladesh under 1.5°C, 2°C, and 4°C global warming
scenarios', *Journal of Hydrologic Engineering*, 23 (12), 04018050

184 'Bay of Bengal'. Rahman, S. et al., 2019: 'Projected changes of
inundation of cyclonic storms in the Ganges–Brahmaputra–Meghna
delta of Bangladesh due to SLR by 2100', *Journal of Earth System
Science*, 128, 145

184 '62 million'. Hirabayashi, Y. et al., 2013: 'Global flood risk under
climate change', *Nature Climate Change*, 3, 816–21

185 '20-fold increase'. Alfieri, L. et al., 2017: 'Global projections of river
flood risk in a warmer world', *Earth's Future*, 5, 171–82

185 '€100 billion'. Alfieri, L. et al., 2015: 'Ensemble flood risk assessment in
Europe under high end climate scenarios', *Global Environmental
Change*, 35, 199–212

185 'up to 200%'. Musselman, K. et al., 2018: 'Projected increases and shifts
in rain-on-snow flood risk over western North America', *Nature
Climate Change*, 8, 808–12

185 'Atmospheric rivers'. Espinoza, V. et al., 2018: 'Global analysis of
climate change projection effects on atmospheric rivers', *Geophysical
Research Letters*, 45, 4299–308

186 '2019 paper'. Bevacqua, E. et al., 2019: 'Higher probability of
compound flooding from precipitation and storm surge in Europe
under anthropogenic climate change', *Science Advances*, 5 (9),
eaaw5531

186 'as 400%'. Prein, A. et al., 2017: 'The future intensification of hourly precipitation extremes', *Nature Climate Change*, 7, 48–52

187 'most powerful MCSs'. Prein, A. et al., 2017: 'Increased rainfall volume from future convective storms in the US', *Nature Climate Change*, 7, 880–4

188 'Cray XC40'. Met Office, undated: 'The Cray XC40 supercomputer'. www.metoffice.gov.uk/about-us/what/technology/supercomputer

188 '(HiFLOR)'. Murakami, H. et al., 2015: 'Simulation and prediction of Category 4 and 5 hurricanes in the high-resolution GFDL HiFLOR coupled climate model', *Journal of Climate*, 28, 9058–79

189 'high-CO_2 world'. Bhatia, K. et al., 2018: 'Projected response of tropical cyclone intensity and intensification in a global climate model', *Journal of Climate*, 31, 8281–303

189 'Category 4 and 5'. Yoshida, K. et al., 2017: 'Future changes in tropical cyclone activity in high-resolution large-ensemble simulations', *Geophysical Research Letters*, 44, 9910–17

190 'tried this in 2017'. Sugi, M. et al., 2016: 'Projection of future changes in the frequency of intense tropical cyclones', *Climate Dynamics*, 49 (1–2), 619–32

190 '500 mm'. Emanuel, K., 2017: 'Assessing the present and future probability of Hurricane Harvey's rainfall', *PNAS*, 114 (48), 12681–4

190 'about 26°C'. Tory, K. & Dare, R., 2015: 'Sea surface temperature thresholds for tropical cyclone formation', *Journal of Climate*, 28, 8171–83

190 'Arabian Sea'. Murakami, H. et al., 2017: 'Increasing frequency of extremely severe cyclonic storms over the Arabian Sea', *Nature Climate Change*, 7, 885–9

190 'occurrence of medicanes'. González-Alemán, J. et al., 2019: 'Potential increase in hazard from Mediterranean hurricane activity with global warming', *Geophysical Research Letters*, 46, 1754–64

191 'hurricane-free regions'. Jung, C. & Lackmann, G., 2019: 'Extratropical transition of Hurricane Irene (2011) in a changing climate', *Journal of Climate*, 32, 4847–71

191 'fewer rain-bearing storms'. Muthige, M. et al., 2018: 'Projected changes in tropical cyclones over the South West Indian Ocean under different extents of global warming', *Environmental Research Letters*, 13, 065019

191 '2015 paper'. Lin, N. & Emanuel, K., 2015: 'Grey swan tropical cyclones', *Nature Climate Change*, 6, 106–11

192 'lethal thresholds'. Schauberger, B. et al., 2017: 'Consistent negative response of US crops to high temperatures in observations and crop models', *Nature Communications*, 8, 13931

192 'US maize crop'. Ibid.

192 'US Dust Bowl'. Glotter, M. & Elliott, J., 2016: 'Simulating US agriculture in a modern Dust Bowl drought', *Nature Plants*, 3, 16193

193 '2018 paper'. Tigchelaar, M. et al., 2018: 'Future warming increases probability of globally synchronized maize production shocks', *PNAS*, 115 (26), 6644–9

194 '2019 paper'. Trnka, M. et al., 2019: 'Mitigation efforts will not fully alleviate the increase in water scarcity occurrence probability in wheat-producing areas', *Science Advances*, 5, eaau2406

195 'horticultural production'. Scheelbeek, P. et al., 2018: 'Effect of environmental changes on vegetable and legume yields and nutritional quality', *PNAS*, 115 (26), 6804–9

195 'animal production'. Rojas-Downing, M. et al., 2017: 'Climate change and livestock: Impacts, adaptation, and mitigation', *Climate Risk Management*, 16, 145–63

195 'crop-suitable'. King, M. et al., 2018: 'Northward shift of the agricultural climate zone under 21st-century global climate change', *Scientific Reports*, 8, 7904

197 'four degrees lower'. Annan, J. & Hargreaves, J., 2013: 'A new global reconstruction of temperature changes at the Last Glacial Maximum', *Climate of the Past*, 9, 367–76

197 'Oligocene and Miocene'. Burke, K. et al., 2018: 'Pliocene and Eocene provide best analogs for near-future climates', *PNAS*, 115 (52), 13288–93

198 '65 times'. Nolan, C. et al., 2018: 'Past and future global transformation of terrestrial ecosystems under climate change', *Science*, 361 (6405), 920–3

198 'sixth of all species'. Urban, M., 2015: 'Accelerating extinction risk from climate change', *Science*, 348 (6234), 571–3

198 'lot of overlap'. Warszawski, L., 2013: 'A multi-model analysis of risk of ecosystem shifts under climate change', *Environmental Research Letters*, 8, 044018

199 'no suitable habitat'. Williams, J. et al., 2007: 'Projected distributions of novel and disappearing climates by 2100 AD', *PNAS*, 104 (14), 5738–42

199 '98% chance'. Muñoz, N. et al., 2015: 'Adaptive potential of a Pacific salmon challenged by climate change', *Nature Climate Change*, 5, 163–6

199 'Mediterranean ecosystem'. Guiot, J. & Cramer, W., 2016: 'Climate change: The 2015 Paris Agreement thresholds and Mediterranean basin ecosystems', *Science*, 354 (6311), 465–8

199 'climate envelopes'. Gonzalez, P. et al., 2018: 'Disproportionate magnitude of climate change in United States national parks', *Environmental Research Letters*, 13, 104001

199 'current local habitats'. Newbold, T., 2018: 'Future effects of climate and land-use change on terrestrial vertebrate community diversity under different scenarios', *Proceedings of the Royal Society B: Biological Sciences*, 285, 1881

199 'on a gigantic scale'. Heyder, U. et al., 2011: 'Risk of severe climate change impact on the terrestrial biosphere', *Environmental Research Letters*, 6, 034036

199 'Brazilian Amazon'. Sampaio, G. et al., 2019: 'Assessing the possible impacts of a 4°C or higher warming in Amazonia'. In: Nobre C. et al. (eds), *Climate Change Risks in Brazil*. Springer International Publishing, Cham

200 'future mass extinction'. Cardoso da Silva, J.-M. et al., 2005: 'The fate of the Amazonian areas of endemism', *Conservation Biology*, 19 (3), 689–94

200 '41-fold … 21 times'. Frölicher, T. et al., 2018: 'Marine heatwaves under global warming', *Nature*, 560, 360–4

200 '100% of species'. Stuart-Smith, R. et al., 2015: 'Thermal biases and vulnerability to warming in the world's marine fauna', *Nature*, 528, 88–92

200 'marine protected areas'. Bruno, J. et al., 2018: 'Climate change threatens the world's marine protected areas', *Nature Climate Change*, 8, 499–503

200 'considerable overlap'. Ramírez, F. et al., 2017: 'Climate impacts on global hot spots of marine biodiversity', *Science Advances*, 3 (2), e1601198

200 'declining krill'. Tulloch, V. et al., 2019: 'Future recovery of baleen whales is imperiled by climate change', *Global Change Biology*, 25 (4), 1263–81

200 'Southern Ocean'. Negrete-García, G. et al., 2019: 'Sudden emergence of a shallow aragonite saturation horizon in the Southern Ocean', *Nature Climate Change*, 9, 313–17

201 'Toxic algae'. Riebesell, U. et al., 2018: 'Toxic algal bloom induced by ocean acidification disrupts the pelagic food web', *Nature Climate Change*, 8, 1082–6

201 'voracious algae'. Segschneider, J. & Bendtsen, J., 2013: 'Temperature-dependent remineralization in a warming ocean increases surface pCO_2 through changes in marine ecosystem composition', *Global Biogeochemical Cycles*, 27, 1214–25

202 'advance by 20 days'. Cassou, C. & Cattiaux, J., 2016: 'Disruption of the European climate seasonal clock in a warming world', *Nature Climate Change*, 6, 589–94

202 'winds reversing direction'. Manzini, E. et al., 2018: 'Nonlinear response of the stratosphere and the North Atlantic-European climate to global warming', *Geophysical Research Letters*, 45, 4255–63

202 '2014 paper'. Cai, W. et al., 2014: 'Increasing frequency of extreme El Niño events due to greenhouse warming', *Nature Climate Change*, 4, 111–16

203 'Hurricane Mitch'. Ibid.

203 'collapse in AMOC'. Jackson, L. et al., 2015: 'Global and European climate impacts of a slowdown of the AMOC in a high resolution GCM', *Climate Dynamics*, 45 (11–12), 3299–316

203 'large cooling hole'. Liu, W. et al., 2017: 'Overlooked possibility of a collapsed Atlantic Meridional Overturning Circulation in warming climate', *Science Advances*, 3 (1), e1601666

204 'impacts ricochet'. Weijer, W. et al., 2019: 'Stability of the Atlantic Meridional Overturning Circulation: A review and synthesis', *Journal of Geophysical Research: Oceans*, 124, 5336–75

204 'without weather processes'. Goddard, P. et al., 2015: 'An extreme event of sea-level rise along the Northeast coast of North America in 2009–2010', *Nature Communications*, 6, 6346

205 'glaciers are surging'. Rintoul, S. et al., 2018: 'Choosing the future of Antarctica', *Nature*, 558, 233–41

205 'dark-blue … gigantic waterfalls'. Trusel, L. et al., 2015: 'Divergent trajectories of Antarctic surface melt under two twenty-first-century climate scenarios', *Nature Geoscience*, 8, 927–32

205 'unseen dark depths'. Bell, R. et al., 2018: 'Antarctic surface hydrology and impacts on ice-sheet mass balance', *Nature Climate Change*, 8, 1044–52

206 'shade of green'. Rintoul, S. et al., 2018: 'Choosing the future of Antarctica'

206 'residual smaller ice cap'. Clark, P. et al., 2016: 'Consequences of twenty-first-century policy for multi-millennial climate and sea-level change', *Nature Climate Change*, 6, 360–9

206 'just the US'. Strauss, B. et al., 2015: 'Carbon choices determine US cities committed to futures below sea level', *PNAS*, 112 (44), 13508–13

206 '2017 paper'. Hauer, M., 2017: 'Migration induced by sea-level rise could reshape the US population landscape', *Nature Climate Change*, 7 (5), 321–5

207 '$130 billion … trillions'. Neumann, J. et al., 2014: 'Joint effects of storm surge and sea-level rise on US Coasts: new economic estimates of impacts, adaptation, and benefits of mitigation policy', *Climatic Change*, 129, 337

207 'risk of cataclysmic losses'. Vousdoukas, M. et al., 2018: 'Climatic and socioeconomic controls of future coastal flood risk in Europe', *Nature Climate Change*, 8, 776–80

208 'Bronze Age'. Jevrejeva, S. et al., 2016: 'Coastal sea level rise with warming above 2°C', *PNAS*, 113 (47), 13342–7

208 'New York … Lagos'. Ibid.

208 '5% chance'. Jevrejeva, S. et al., 2014: 'Upper limit for sea level projections by 2100', *Environmental Research Letters*, 9, 104008

208 '292 cm'. Le Bars, D. et al., 2017: 'A high-end sea level rise probabilistic projection including rapid Antarctic ice sheet mass loss', *Environmental Research Letters*, 12, 044013

208 'land lost from the world's coasts'. Nicholls, R. et al., 2011: 'Sea-level rise and its possible impacts given a "beyond 4°C world" in the twenty-first century', *Philosophical Transactions of the Royal Society A: Mathematical, Physical and Engineering Sciences*, 369, 161–81

208 'October 2019'. Kulp, S. & Strauss, B., 2019: 'New elevation data triple estimates of global vulnerability to sea-level rise and coastal flooding', *Nature Communications*, 10, 4844

209 '2.8% of global GDP'. Jevrejeva, S. et al., 2018: 'Flood damage costs

under the sea level rise with warming of 1.5°C and 2°C', *Environmental Research Letters*, 9, 104008

210 'circumpolar permafrost'. Kleinen, T. & Brovkin, V., 2018: 'Pathway-dependent fate of permafrost region carbon', *Environmental Research Letters*, 13, 094001

210 'another couple of tenths'. Gedney, N. et al., 2019: 'Significant feedbacks of wetland methane release on climate change and the causes of their uncertainty', *Environmental Research Letters*, 14, 084027

210 'globe-girdling forest'. Walker, X. et al., 2019: 'Increasing wildfires threaten historic carbon sink of boreal forest soils', *Nature*, 572, 520–3

210 '1.5 trillion tonnes'. Koven, C. et al., 2015: 'A simplified, data-constrained approach to estimate the permafrost carbon–climate feedback', *Philosophical Transactions of the Royal Society A: Mathematical, Physical and Engineering Sciences*, 373, 20140423

210 'may be occurring faster'. Plaza, P. et al., 2019: 'Direct observation of permafrost degradation and rapid soil carbon loss in tundra', *Nature Geoscience*, 12, 627–31

211 '100 billion tonnes'. McGuire, A. et al., 2018: 'Dependence of the evolution of carbon dynamics in the northern permafrost region on the trajectory of climate change', *PNAS*, 115 (15), 3882–7

211 'decade of current'. Global Carbon Project, 2018: *Global Carbon budget.* www.globalcarbonproject.org/carbonbudget/18/highlights.htm

211 'less than 0.2°C'. Schaefer, K. et al., 2014: 'The impact of the permafrost carbon feedback on global climate', *Environmental Research Letters*, 9, 085003

Five Degrees

215 'deadly heat'. Mora, C. et al., 2017: 'Global risk of deadly heat', *Nature Climate Change*, 7, 501–6

216 '200 days'. Rohat, G. et al., 2019: 'Projections of human exposure to dangerous heat in African cities under multiple socioeconomic and climate scenarios', *Earth's Future*, 7, 528–46

216 'Synchronous harvest failures'. Tigchelaar, M. et al., 2018: 'Future warming increases probability of globally synchronized maize production shocks', *PNAS*, 115 (26), 6644–9

218 'eight billionaires'. Oxfam, 2017: 'Just 8 men own same wealth as half

the world', press release. www.oxfam.org/en/pressroom/
pressreleases/2017-01-16/just-8-men-own-same-wealth-half-world

218   'Right-wing populist parties'. Gardiner, B., 2019: 'For Europe's far-right
      parties, climate is a new battleground', *Yale Environment 360*. e360.
      yale.edu/features/for-europes-far-right-parties-climate-is-a-
      new-battleground

223   'massive ongoing melt'. Le Bars, D. et al., 2017: 'A high-end sea level
      rise probabilistic projection including rapid Antarctic ice sheet mass
      loss', *Environmental Research Letters*, 12, 044013

223   '800 million … inundated'. Brown, S. et al., 2018: 'Quantifying land
      and people exposed to sea-level rise with no mitigation and 1.5C and
      2.0C rise in global temperatures to year 2300', *Earth's Future*, 6,
      583–600

223   'crust rebounds'. Jevrejeva, S. et al., 2016: 'Coastal sea level rise with
      warming above 2°C', *PNAS*, 113 (47), 13342–7

224   '5% … GDP'. Hinkel, J. et al., 2014: 'Coastal flood damage and
      adaptation costs under 21st century sea-level rise', *PNAS*, 111 (9), 3292–7

224   '2–4 centimetres'. DeConto, R. & Pollard, D., 2016: 'Contribution of
      Antarctica to past and future sea-level rise', *Nature*, 531, 591–7

224   'tenfold acceleration'. Nicholls, R. et al., 2018: 'Stabilization of global
      temperature at 1.5°C and 2.0°C: implications for coastal areas',
      *Philosophical Transactions of the Royal Society A: Mathematical,
      Physical and Engineering Sciences*, 376 (2119), 20160448

224   'Greenland ice sheet'. Aschwanden, A. et al., 2019: 'Contribution of the
      Greenland Ice Sheet to sea level over the next millennium', *Science
      Advances*, 5 (6), eaav9396

224   'within 250 years'. DeConto, R. & Pollard, D., 2016: 'Contribution of
      Antarctica to past and future sea-level rise'

224   'by 7.5 metres'. Bamber, J. et al., 2019: 'Ice sheet contributions to future
      sea-level rise from structured expert judgment', *PNAS*, 116 (23),
      11195–200

224   '10,000 years'. Winkelmann, R. et al., 2015: 'Combustion of available
      fossil fuel resources sufficient to eliminate the Antarctic Ice Sheet',
      Science Advances, 1 (8), e1500589

224   '0.63 trillion'. Keep tabs here: trillionthtonne.org/

225   'new land appears'. Lee, J. et al., 2017: 'Climate change drives expansion
      of Antarctic ice-free habitat', *Nature*, 547, 49–54

225 'iconic animals'. Jenouvrier, S. et al., 2019: 'The Paris Agreement objectives will likely halt future declines of emperor penguins', *Global Change Biology*. In press

226 '56 million years'. Zhu, J. et al., 2019: 'Simulation of Eocene extreme warmth and high climate sensitivity through cloud feedbacks', *Science Advances*, 5 (9), eaax1874

227 'support hypotheses'. Chen, C. et al., 2018: 'Estimating regional flood discharge during Palaeocene-Eocene global warming', *Scientific Reports*, 8, 13391

228 'mixture of debris'. Pujalte, V., 2019: 'Microcodium-rich turbidites in hemipelagic sediments during the T Paleocene–Eocene Thermal Maximum: Evidence for extreme precipitation events in a Mediterranean climate (Río Gor section, southern Spain)', *Global and Planetary Change*, 178, 153–67

228 'Bighorn Basin'. Kraus, M. et al., 2013: 'Paleohydrologic response to continental warming during the Paleocene–Eocene Thermal Maximum, Bighorn Basin, Wyoming', *Palaeogeography, Palaeoclimatology, Palaeoecology*, 370, 196–208

228 'resurgent monsoon'. Foreman, B. et al., 2012: 'Fluvial response to abrupt global warming at the Palaeocene/Eocene boundary', *Nature*, 491, 92–5

229 'pollen from the PETM'. Suan, G. et al., 2017: 'Subtropical climate conditions and mangrove growth in Arctic Siberia during the early Eocene', *Geology*, 45 (6), 539–42

230 'southeastern United States'. Eberle, J. & Greenwood, D., 2012: 'Life at the top of the greenhouse Eocene world – A review of the Eocene flora and vertebrate fauna from Canada's High Arctic', *GSA Bulletin*, 124 (1–2), 3–23

230 '20°C or above'. Denis, E. et al., 2017: 'Fire and ecosystem change in the Arctic across the Paleocene–Eocene Thermal Maximum', *Earth and Planetary Science Letters*, 467, 149–56

230 'across the North Pole'. Eberle, J. & Greenwood, D., 2012: 'Life at the top of the greenhouse Eocene world'

230 '55-million-year-old'. Willard, D. et al., 2019: 'Arctic vegetation, temperature, and hydrology during Early Eocene transient global warming events', *Global and Planetary Change*, 178, 139–52

230 'Arctic rainforests'. Harrington, G. et al., 2012: 'Arctic plant diversity in

the Early Eocene greenhouse', *Proceedings of the Royal Society B: Biological Sciences*, 279, 1515–21

231   'drastic polar amplification'. Pross, J. et al., 2012: 'Persistent near-tropical warmth on the Antarctic continent during the early Eocene epoch', *Nature*, 488 (7409), 73–7

231   'oceanic plankton'. Aze, T. et al., 2014: 'Extreme warming of tropical waters during the Paleocene–Eocene Thermal Maximum' *Geology*, 42 (9), 739–42

231   'Nigerian core'. Frieling, J. et al., 2017: 'Extreme warmth and heat-stressed plankton in the tropics during the Paleocene-Eocene Thermal Maximum', *Science Advances*, 3 (3), e1600891

231   'reef crises'. Kiessling, W. et al., 2011: 'On the potential for ocean acidification to be a general cause of ancient reef crises', *Global Change Biology*, 17 (1), 56–67

231   'coral reefs later disappeared'. Speijer, R. et al., 2012: 'Response of marine ecosystems to deep-time global warming: A synthesis of biotic patterns across the Paleocene-Eocene thermal maximum (PETM)', *Austrian Journal of Earth Sciences*, 105 (1), 6–16

232   'zooxanthellate algae'. Weiss, A. & Martindale, R., 2019: 'Paleobiological traits that determined Scleractinian coral survival and proliferation during the Late Paleocene and Early Eocene hyperthermals', *Paleoceanography and Paleoclimatology*, 34 (2), 252–74

232   'muddy algal mats'. Zamagni, J. et al., 2012: 'The evolution of mid Paleocene-early Eocene coral communities: How to survive during rapid global warming', *Palaeogeography, Palaeoclimatology, Palaeoecology*, 317, 48–65

232   'PETM rock samples'. Bralower, T. et al., 2018: 'Evidence for shelf acidification during the onset of the Paleocene-Eocene Thermal Maximum', *Paleoceanography and Paleoclimatology*, 33 (12), 1408–26

232   'due to human emissions'. Babila, T. et al., 2018: 'Capturing the global signature of surface ocean acidification during the Palaeocene–Eocene Thermal Maximum', *Philosophical Transactions of the Royal Society A: Mathematical, Physical and Engineering Sciences*, 376 (2130), 20170072

232   'outright extreme heat'. Gibbs, S. et al., 2016: 'Ocean warming, not acidification, controlled coccolithophore response during past greenhouse climate change', *Geology*, 44 (1), 59–62

233   'hydrogen sulphide'. Yao, W. et al., 2018: 'Large-scale ocean

deoxygenation during the Paleocene-Eocene Thermal Maximum', *Science*, 361 (6404), 804–6

233 'neurotoxins'. Cramwinckel, M. et al., 2019: 'Harmful algae and export production collapse in the equatorial Atlantic during the zenith of Middle Eocene Climatic Optimum warmth', *Geology*, 47 (3), 247–50

233 'marine food chain'. Winguth, A. et al., 2012: 'Global decline in ocean ventilation, oxygenation, and productivity during the Paleocene-Eocene Thermal Maximum: Implications for the benthic extinction', *Geology*, 40 (3), 263–6

233 'vast volcanic episode'. Troll, V. et al., 2019: 'A large explosive silicic eruption in the British Palaeogene Igneous Province', *Scientific Reports*, 9 (1), 494

234 '57 million years'. Saunders, A., 2016: 'Two LIPs and two Earth-system crises: the impact of the North Atlantic Igneous Province and the Siberian Traps on the Earth-surface carbon cycle', *Geological Magazine*, 153 (2), 201–22

234 'North Atlantic Igneous Province'. Gutjahr, M. et al., 2017: 'Very large release of mostly volcanic carbon during the Palaeocene–Eocene Thermal Maximum', *Nature*, 548 (7669), 573

234 '18 and 40 trillion'. Saunders, A., 2016: 'Two LIPs and two Earth-system crises'

234 'PETM temperature spike'. Frieling, J. et al., 2019: 'Widespread warming before and elevated barium burial during the Paleocene-Eocene thermal maximum: Evidence for methane hydrate release?' *Paleoceanography and Paleoclimatology*, 34 (4), 546–566

234 '2012 paper'. DeConto, R. et al., 2012: 'Past extreme warming events linked to massive carbon release from thawing permafrost', *Nature*, 484 (7392), 87

235 'statistical signatures'. Armstrong McKay, D. & Lenton, T., 2018: 'Reduced carbon cycle resilience across the Palaeocene-Eocene Thermal Maximum', *Climate of the Past*, 14, 1515–1527

235 'political assignment of 2°C'. Frieling, J. et al., 2019: 'Widespread Warming Before and Elevated Barium Burial During the Paleocene-Eocene Thermal Maximum'

235 'later hyperthermal events'. Westerhold, T. et al., 2018: 'Late Lutetian Thermal Maximum – Crossing a thermal threshold in Earth's climate system?' *Geochemistry, Geophysics, Geosystems*, 19 (1), 73–82

235 'Eocene Thermal Maximum 2'. Harper, D. et al., 2018: 'Subtropical sea-surface warming and increased salinity during Eocene Thermal Maximum 2', *Geology*, 46 (2), 187–90

236 '4,000 years'. Zeebe, R. et al., 2016: 'Anthropogenic carbon release rate unprecedented during the past 66 million years', *Nature Geoscience*, 9 (4), 325

236 'ten billion tonnes'. Ibid.

236. 'worsen ocean acidification'. Ridgwell, A. & Schmidt, D., 2010: 'Past constraints on the vulnerability of marine calcifiers to massive carbon dioxide release', *Nature Geoscience*, 3 (3), 196

236 '140 years'. Gingerich, P., 2019: 'Temporal scaling of carbon emission and accumulation rates: Modern anthropogenic emissions compared to estimates of PETM onset accumulation', *Paleoceanography and Paleoclimatology*, 34 (3), 329–35

237 'wholesale unravelling'. Warren, R. et al., 2018: 'The projected effect on insects, vertebrates, and plants of limiting global warming to 1.5°C rather than 2°C', *Science*, 360 (6390), 791–5

237 '4.5°C warming'. Ibid. Supplementary info.

238 'thresholds of catastrophe'. Rothman, D., 2017: 'Thresholds of catastrophe in the Earth System', *Science Advances*, 3, e1700906

Six Degrees

242 'very high greenhouse gas'. Sanderson, B. et al., 2011: 'The response of the climate system to very high greenhouse gas emission scenarios', *Environmental Research Letters*, 6 (3), 034005

245 '5 trillion tonnes'. Tokarska, K. et al., 2016: 'The climate response to five trillion tonnes of carbon', *Nature Climate Change*, 6 (9), 851

245 '500 years'. Winkelmann, R. et al., 2015: 'Combustion of available fossil fuel resources sufficient to eliminate the Antarctic Ice Sheet', *Science Advances*, 1 (8), e1500589

245 'human survivability'. Sherwood, S. & Huber, M., 2010: 'An adaptability limit to climate change due to heat stress', *PNAS*, 107 (21), 9552–5

246 'Arctic Ocean'. Korty, R. et al., 2017: 'Tropical cyclones downscaled from simulations with very high carbon dioxide levels', *Journal of Climate*, 30 (2), 649–67

247 '15°C higher'. Cramwinckel, M. et al., 2018: 'Synchronous tropical and polar temperature evolution in the Eocene', *Nature*, 559 (7714), 382

247 'than the PETM'. Huber, B. et al., 2018: 'The rise and fall of the Cretaceous Hot Greenhouse climate', *Global and Planetary Change*, 167, 1–23

247 'Ocean Anoxic Event 2'. Fischer, V. et al., 2016: 'Extinction of fish-shaped marine reptiles associated with reduced evolutionary rates and global environmental volatility', *Nature Communications*, 7, 10825

248 'layer of black shale'. Clarkson, M. et al., 2018: 'Uranium isotope evidence for two episodes of deoxygenation during Oceanic Anoxic Event 2', *PNAS*, 115 (12), 2918–23

248 'Atlantic and Pacific'. Jenkyns, H., 2018: 'Transient cooling episodes during Cretaceous Oceanic Anoxic Events with special reference to OAE 1a (Early Aptian)', *Philosophical Transactions of the Royal Society A: Mathematical, Physical and Engineering Sciences*, 376 (2130), 20170073

248 'carbonate plankton fossils'. Erba, E. et al., 2010: 'Calcareous nannoplankton response to surface-water acidification around Oceanic Anoxic Event 1a', *Science*, 329 (5990), 428–32

248 'wadi-type channels'. Wu, C. et al., 2017: 'Mid-Cretaceous desert system in the Simao Basin, southwestern China, and its implications for sea-level change during a greenhouse climate', *Palaeogeography, Palaeoclimatology, Palaeoecology*, 468, 529–44

248 'coniferous trees'. Mays, C. et al., 2017: 'Polar wildfires and conifer serotiny during the Cretaceous global hothouse', *Geology*, 45 (12), 1119–22

248 'ice-free super-greenhouse'. Hay, W. et al., 2019: 'Possible solutions to several enigmas of Cretaceous climate', *International Journal of Earth Sciences*, 108 (2), 587–620

248 'triggering OAE 1a'. Erba, E. et al., 2010: 'Calcareous nannoplankton response to surface-water acidification around Oceanic Anoxic Event 1a'

249 '100,000 years'. Clarkson, M. et al., 2018: 'Uranium isotope evidence for two episodes of deoxygenation during Oceanic Anoxic Event 2'

249 'Deccan Traps'. Barnet, J. et al., 2018: 'A new high-resolution chronology for the late Maastrichtian warming event: Establishing robust temporal links with the onset of Deccan volcanism', *Geology*, 46 (2), 147–50

249 '400–500 ppm'. Zhang, L. et al., 2018: 'Deccan volcanism caused

coupled pCO_2 and terrestrial temperature rises, and pre-impact extinctions in northern China', *Geology*, 46 (3), 271–4

249 '425 billion'. Artemieva, N. et al., 2017: 'Quantifying the release of climate-active gases by large meteorite impacts with a case study of Chicxulub', *Geophysical Research Letters*, 44 (20), 10–180

249 'considerably higher'. Vellekoop, J. et al., 2018: 'Shelf hypoxia in response to global warming after the Cretaceous-Paleogene boundary impact', *Geology*, 46 (8), 683–6

249 '30-year recovery'. Brugger, J. et al., 2017: 'Baby, it's cold outside: climate model simulations of the effects of the asteroid impact at the end of the Cretaceous', *Geophysical Research Letters*, 44 (1), 419–27

250 'oceans anoxic'. Vellekoop, J. et al., 2018: 'Shelf hypoxia in response to global warming after the Cretaceous-Paleogene boundary impact'

250 'extreme ocean acidification'. Henehan, M. et al., 2019: 'Rapid ocean acidification and protracted Earth system recovery followed the end-Cretaceous Chicxulub impact', *PNAS*, 116 (45), 22500–4

251 'lush tropical forests'. Bernardi, M. et al., 2017: 'Late Permian (Lopingian) terrestrial ecosystems: a global comparison with new data from the low-latitude Bletterbach Biota', *Earth-Science Reviews*, 175, 18–43

253 'boreholes confirm'. Svensen, H. et al., 2009: 'Siberian gas venting and the end-Permian environmental crisis', *Earth and Planetary Science Letters*, 277 (3–4), 490–500

253 '(approximately 500°C)'. Ogden, D. & Sleep, N., 2012: 'Explosive eruption of coal and basalt and the end-Permian mass extinction', *PNAS*, 109(1), 59–62

253 '100,000–200,000 years'. Shen, S. et al., 2011: 'Calibrating the end-Permian mass extinction', *Science*, 334 (6061), 1367–72

254 'interhemispheric ash clouds'. Grasby, S. et al., 2011: 'Catastrophic dispersion of coal fly ash into oceans during the latest Permian extinction', *Nature Geoscience*, 4 (2), 104

254 'toxic mercury'. Grasby, S. et al., 2017: 'Isotopic signatures of mercury contamination in latest Permian oceans', *Geology*, 45 (1), 55–8

254 'malformed pollen'. Hochuli, P. et al., 2017: 'Evidence for atmospheric pollution across the Permian-Triassic transition', *Geology*, 45 (12), 1123–6

254 'averaged acidity'. Black, B. et al., 2014: 'Acid rain and ozone depletion from pulsed Siberian Traps magmatism', *Geology*, 42 (1), 67–70

255 'killer cause'. Brand, U. et al., 2016: 'Methane hydrate: killer cause of earth's greatest mass extinction', *Palaeoworld*, 25 (4), 496–507

255 'gas hydrate release'. Majorowicz, J. et al., 2014: 'Gas hydrate contribution to Late Permian global warming', *Earth and Planetary Science Letters*, 393, 243–53

256 'mutation-causing'. Black, B. et al., 2014: 'Acid rain and ozone depletion from pulsed Siberian Traps magmatism'

256 'modern conifers'. Benca, J. et al., 2018: 'UV-B–induced forest sterility: Implications of ozone shield failure in Earth's largest extinction', *Science Advances*, 4 (2), e1700618

256 'devegetated'. Smith, R. & Botha-Brink, J., 2014: 'Anatomy of a mass extinction: sedimentological and taphonomic evidence for drought-induced die-offs at the Permo-Triassic boundary in the main Karoo Basin, South Africa', *Palaeogeography, Palaeoclimatology, Palaeoecology*, 396, 99–118

257 'coal gap'. Retallack, G. et al., 1996: 'Global coal gap between Permian–Triassic extinction and Middle Triassic recovery of peat-forming plants', *Geological Society of America Bulletin*, 108 (2), 195–207

257 '30°N to 40°S'. Sun, Y. et al., 2012: 'Lethally hot temperatures during the Early Triassic greenhouse', *Science*, 338 (6105), 366–70

257 'fire-derived products'. Shen, S. et al., 2011: 'Calibrating the end-Permian mass extinction'

258 'organic debris'. Sun, Y. et al., 2012: 'Lethally hot temperatures during the Early Triassic greenhouse'

258 'Great Dying'. Penn, J. et al., 2018: 'Temperature-dependent hypoxia explains biogeography and severity of end-Permian marine mass extinction', *Science*, 362 (6419), eaat1327. Song, H. et al., 2014: 'Anoxia/high temperature double whammy during the Permian-Triassic marine crisis and its aftermath', *Scientific Reports*, 4, 4132

258 'Panthalassic and Tethys'. Zhang, F. et al., 2018: 'Congruent Permian-Triassic $\delta238U$ records at Panthalassic and Tethyan sites: Confirmation of global-oceanic anoxia and validation of the U-isotope paleoredox proxy', *Geology*, 46 (4), 327–30

258 'by 4–6°C'. MacLeod, K. et al., 2017: 'Warming and increased aridity during the earliest Triassic in the Karoo Basin, South Africa', *Geology*, 45 (6), 483–6

258 'of 4–8°C'. Joachimski, M. et al., 2012: 'Climate warming in the latest Permian and the Permian–Triassic mass extinction', *Geology*, 40 (3), 195–198

258 '40 kilometres'. Schobben, M. et al., 2014: 'Palaeotethys seawater temperature rise and an intensified hydrological cycle following the end-Permian mass extinction', *Gondwana Research*, 26 (2), 675–83

259 'two billion tonnes'. Svensen, H. et al., 2009: 'Siberian gas venting and the end-Permian environmental crisis'

259 'extreme greenhouse event'. Kump, L., 2018: 'Prolonged Late Permian–Early Triassic hyperthermal: failure of climate regulation?' *Philosophical Transactions of the Royal Society A: Mathematical, Physical and Engineering Sciences*, 376 (2130), 20170078

263 '96% CO_2'. Kane, S. et al., 2019: 'Venus as a laboratory for exoplanetary science', *Journal of Geophysical Research: Planets*, 124 (8), 2015–28

263 '0.97 to 0.99 AUs'. Wolf, E. & Toon, O., 2014: 'Delayed onset of runaway and moist greenhouse climates for Earth', *Geophysical Research Letters*, 41 (1), 167–72

263 'magnetic field'. Driscoll, P. & Bercovici, D., 2013: 'Divergent evolution of Earth and Venus: influence of degassing, tectonics, and magnetic fields', *Icarus*, 226 (2), 1447–64

265 '100 ppm'. Feulner, G., 2017: 'Formation of most of our coal brought Earth close to global glaciation', *PNAS*, 114 (43), 11333–7

265 'habitability zone'. Popp, M. et al., 2016: 'Transition to a moist greenhouse with CO_2 and solar forcing', *Nature Communications*, 7, 10627

266 '6% … ~650 million'. Wolf, E. & Toon, O., 2014: 'Delayed onset of runaway and moist greenhouse climates for Earth'

266 'doubling CO_2'. Ibid.

266 '15.5% increase'. Ibid.

266 'transition to Venus'. Goldblatt, C. et al., 2013: 'Low simulated radiation limit for runaway greenhouse climates', *Nature Geoscience*, 6 (8), 661

266 'hotter climatic regime'. Wolf, E. & Toon, O., 2015: 'The evolution of habitable climates under the brightening Sun', *Journal of Geophysical Research: Atmospheres*, 120 (12), 5775–94

266 '>500K'. Ramirez, R. et al., 2014: 'Can increased atmospheric CO_2 levels trigger a runaway greenhouse?' *Astrobiology*, 14 (8), 714–31

267 'total fossil fuel resource'. Tokarska, K. et al., 2016: 'The climate response to five trillion tonnes of carbon'

267 'stratocumulus decks'. Schneider, T. et al., 2019: 'Possible climate transitions from breakup of stratocumulus decks under greenhouse warming', *Nature Geoscience*, 12 (3), 163

7: The Endgame

270 'committed emissions'. Tong, D. et al., 2019: 'Committed emissions from existing energy infrastructure jeopardize 1.5 C climate target', *Nature*, 572 (7769), 373–377

271 'net-zero emissions'Rogelj, J. et al., 2018: 'Mitigation pathways compatible with 1.5°C in the context of sustainable development'. In: *Global warming of 1.5°C. An IPCC Special Report on the impacts of global warming of 1.5°C above pre-industrial levels and related global greenhouse gas emission pathways, in the context of strengthening the global response to the threat of climate change, sustainable development, and efforts to eradicate poverty*, Masson-Delmotte, V. et al. (eds). In press, p. 96

278 'a brief summary'. See earlier chapters for references for all the facts and figures in this summary.

281 '10–25% chance'. Climate Action Tracker, 2019: 'Warming projections global update, September 2019'. climateactiontracker.org/documents/644/CAT_2019-09-19_BriefingUNSG_WarmingProjections GlobalUpdate_Sept2019.pdf

Index